Evolutionary Anthropology
A READER IN HUMAN BIOLOGY

Hermann K. Bleibtreu
UNIVERSITY OF ARIZONA

ALLYN and BACON, INC.
BOSTON

To Arthur G. Steinberg

Second Printing . . . August, 1969

Preface

THIS READER consists of theoretical statements and research reports dealing with human evolution and human variation, the study of which is physical anthropology. The articles were chosen with the aim of invoking in the student a questioning and problem-oriented approach to material generally presented in college-level courses. Fortunately, many of today's scholars occasionally write for the nonspecialist. Without popularizing, they write to communicate with students and with their colleagues in other fields. The Reader draws from such writings those that best present the major directions of current research in human evolution. The fact that many of the authors of articles in the Reader are professionals in fields other than anthropology is characteristic of physical anthropology, for rather than being a separate discipline, it is a study with an eclectic approach to any information about human evolution and variation.

This volume has two primary objectives. The first is to introduce the beginning student to the study of physical anthropology without protecting him from some of the complexities and problems which are the very elements that give it intellectual life. It is assumed that any student required to be familiar with the data of human biology must be provided with a theoretical framework in which the data are relevant. The second important objective of the Reader is to encourage the more advanced student to become thoroughly familiar with the synthetic theory of evolution, particularly the population concept, and use it as the basic framework for his study and research in human biology and paleontology.

The Reader is organized in two parts. The first five sections deal with processes and events pertinent to the establishment of the species *Homo sapiens*; the remaining five are concerned with the forces of evolution that have acted and still are acting on that species.

If an article were originally published with a bibliography, it has been retained in the Reader. No effort has been made to cover all areas that might be considered physical anthropology; instead, the articles were chosen because of their pertinency to a specific issue or problem which I have tried to emphasize in the introduction to each selection. In most of the articles the authors have been explicit in their use of new or specialized terminology, thus the index to the Reader is also calculated to serve as a glossary.

HERMANN K. BLEIBTREU
UNIVERSITY OF ARIZONA

Contents

1

The Study of Evolution

The Study of Evolution:
Methods and Present Status of Theory*

GEORGE GAYLORD SIMPSON

(*Editor's Note*) Evolution, as it is understood today, is a synthesis of theories of which the first may be labeled transformism. Transformism was accepted by many leading students of nature prior to Darwin and stated that living organisms had developed out of previously existing different organisms. Along with this idea went an acceptance that relative to recorded history, the world was exceedingly old, that fossils represented extinct ancestral animals, and that change was one of the chief characteristics of nature. Then came Darwin's theory of natural selection, which explained how environmental factors promote the retention and proliferation of some hereditary characteristics at the expense of others. Such an interaction explained why forms change—why one species could evolve into a new species. Up to that time, about 1859, scientists had emphasized "hen evolution," focusing their attention on the changing organism. Next came a period of "egg evolution," during which discoveries were made about the cytologic and genetic aspects of the evolutionary process, namely the theory of the chromosomes (especially the demonstration of meiosis) and the corresponding statistical theory of Mendel concerning the behavior of genes (their segregation and independent assortment). The nature of the hereditary material was further investigated, yielding a theory of mutation, and finally, with the Watson-Crick model in 1953, a theory of the nature of the gene itself. Along a somewhat different tack, dating back to the 1920's, the concept of the population as the evolutionary unit, rather than the hen or the egg, began to assume great theoretical im-

*From *Behavior and Evolution*, Anne Roe and George Gaylord Simpson, editors, pages 7–26. Copyright 1958 by Yale University Press, Inc. By permission of the publisher.

port. Migration and genetic drift were added to natural selection and mutation as evolutionary "forces." Such is the history of the theory of evolution, for all these elements comprise a synthesis called the modern theory of evolution.

In this brilliant article Simpson summarizes what evolution is and how it is studied. He points out that inferences about evolution are based on the study of events and processes. The study of the fossil record (paleontology) provides evidence of events interpreted as the product of evolutionary processes which can be studied in living populations (neontology). Populations change over time and vary from one geographical area to the next because they have responded genetically to changing and different environmental pressures. This process is called adaptation. It occurs when differential reproduction (i.e., members of a population with different genetic constitutions contribute unequally to the next generation) inhibits the full expression of the genetic variation of which the gene pool is capable. Instead, those individuals that survive the reproduction period and are most fertile establish themselves at the expense of the variants. Heritable variation, constantly generated by mutation and recombination, is always under varying degrees of selective pressure. Sometimes this results in gene frequency changes, sometimes in the maintenance of equilibria. Of course, not all changes in a population's genetic repertory (its gene pool) need be adaptive. For example, gene frequencies can change in a fortuitous way, with respect to adaptation, by the action of genetic drift and migration. All these processes, while theoretically understood, have only begun to be applied in research on human evolution. It is not only that man is a special case in the animal kingdom, but that the students of man have had a particularly difficult struggle to overcome a heritage of typological thinking.

S AMUEL Butler said that a hen is an egg's way of producing another egg. Thus in the Darwinian epoch he foreshadowed a reorientation of evolutionary studies that did later occur. Without expressing it in that way, the evolutionary scientists of Butler's and earlier times held the common-sense view that an egg is a hen's way of producing another hen. They were trying to explain the evolution of the hen, not of the egg. It was the geneticists, after 1900, who came around to Butler's view that the essence of the matter is in the egg, not in the hen.[1]

Those contrasting points of view reflect different ideas as to the involvement of behavior in evolution. The 19th-century evolutionary theories of the naturalists were largely, if not primarily, behavioral. The behavioral element tended at first to be minimized in the 20th-century evolutionary theories of the geneticists, who might in some cases be accused of leaving the hen out of the picture altogether except as a means of learning what the egg "knows."

The first great issue in naturalistic evolutionary theory was between the neo-Lamarckians and the Darwinians. (There were and are non-naturalistic alternative schools, such as those of vitalism or of finalism, but their metaphysics can legitimately be omitted from this brief account.) Lamarck, himself, stressed behavior almost to the point of considering it the sole effective cause of evolution. It is, he taught, the habitual actions of organisms—in other words, their behavior—that modify their morphology, and these modifications accumulated through the generations *are* evolution. It is true that Lamarck also believed in a perfecting principle that somehow has driven organisms up the *scala naturae*, but the neo-Lamarckians discarded that essentially nonnaturalistic element in his theory. The neo-Lamarckians also incorporated into their views the accumulation of direct results of the action of the environment on organisms, a hypothesis that is non-Lamarckian and nonbehavioral.

Darwin's theory of evolution was hardly less behavioral than Lamarck's. Darwin saw no reason to question the Lamarckian belief in the direct influence of behavior on evolution, through the

[1]Without, indeed, any real debt to Butler. That an egg somehow "knows" how to produce a hen and thus produces another egg that "knows" just a little more seems brilliantly apt in retrospect. But, like other flashes of Butler's peculiar genius, this bit of insight was so embedded in nonsense that it was not really helpful at the time and had no useful outcome.

induction of heritable modifications. Darwin's own main contribution, the theory of natural selection, also involved essential relationships between behavior and evolution. He saw and illustrated with many examples that the behavior of animals is often determined and always circumscribed by their heredity, although he knew even less than we do about the mechanisms involved. The behavior of animals is also obviously and crucially involved in their survival and success in reproduction. Thus natural selection provides another way, less direct but truer than the supposed Lamarckian way, in which behavior is bound in with the changes in heredity that constitute evolution.

Few now doubt that the Lamarckian and neo-Lamarckian views are essentially false, and we need pay no further attention to them here. The point is that Lamarck, Darwin, and their many colleagues and followers were all primarily interested in the behaving animal, the hen, rather than in the egg, which has no behavior in usual senses of the word, and that one of the things they sought and stressed was a relationship between behavior and evolution. It is a pity, in a way, that we cannot accept a direct and simple relationship, but Darwin pointed out a relationship that is surely present, in some degree, and that is all the more effective for being indirect and subtle.

Then came the shift of emphasis to the egg by the geneticists from about 1900 onward. In extreme form, their views practically eliminated behavior as an essential element in evolution. What a hen is and does depends on the egg, that is, on the mechanism of heredity complete within the fertilized egg. Evolutionary changes in the hen, so some of the early geneticists submitted and a dwindling few still hold, arise without any prior relationship to the hen and its behavior. Evolution is reduced to processes in the precursor cells of the gametes and in the confluence of gametes in the fertilized egg (zygote). The hen (the man, the tree) is largely irrelevant except, as Butler said, as a device for producing another egg.

The most widely held modern theory of evolution may be presented as a reconciliation between the naturalists' hen-evolution and the geneticists' egg-evolution. It reinstates behavior not merely as something to which evolution has happened but as something that is itself one of the essential determinants of evolution. Accepting the geneticists' knowledge of egg-processes, it shows that these are not autonomous but are strongly influenced by hen-processes. The means of that influence is, as Darwin thought, natural selection. In the course of this theoretical synthesis natural selection has turned out to be something broader than and in some respects different from Darwin's concept.[2]

Methods of Evolutionary Study

The topic assigned for this chapter requires some notice of methods before proceeding to summarize the present status of evolutionary theory. Methods are, indeed, so numerous and diverse that a catalogue of them would be redundant to those who are using them, confusing to those who are not, and of little interest or usefulness in either case. It will be best to avoid detail and to present only a few broad considerations as to aims, the ways of achieving them, and implications or criteria involved in those ways.

In the first place, most of the aims of evolutionary study involve either events or processes. The study of events is historical; it seeks to reconstruct the whole history of organisms on this planet. That (unattainable) goal is of course approached by accumulation of restricted studies of the histories of particular groups of organisms, of particular anatomical or physiological features, and the like. The procedure is by levels: comparative descriptive studies, then inferential placing of the units of description in phylogenetic sequences, and finally, generalizations as to the kinds of sequences that have most frequently occurred and the conditions that accompany and therefore may determine a particular kind of sequence.

The objective data for historical study, the things described at the first level of research, are characteristics of (1) organisms or parts thereof, (2) their activities, (3) the conditions surrounding and influencing them, and (4) the temporal sequence of the items observed.[3] It is especially pertinent to the subject of this book that all four kinds of data are only very exceptionally available in any one study. There are in this respect two quite different cases, each with its distinct methodological problems. A temporal sequence long enough to involve marked evolutionary change usually extends into geological time, and the organisms involved are, or include, fossils. Then the documents are directly historical in nature, but their data are primarily of classes (1), mainly morphological, and (4), sequen-

[2]In justice, however, it should be emphasized that practically nothing that Darwin wrote about natural selection is invalidated by the modern concept. Darwinian selection still stands, but its complexities and bearings are better understood and it becomes part of a more inclusive principle.

[3]The temporal order of a really long sequence is rarely directly observed but it is commonly on so factual a basis that it may be considered an objective datum.

tial. Observations of class (3), environmental, are limited and more often involve inferences than direct observation. Direct observations of class (2), including behavior, are almost entirely lacking.[4] Morphological evolution of, for instance, a bone in the lower jaw of a group of reptiles can sometimes be observed without the slightest ambiguity in a directly historical record. Behavioral evolution cannot be so observed. Inferences as to behavior can be based on the morphology of fossils and analogy with living animals. That can, for instance, usually be done for food habits and locomotion, but such possible inferences include little beyond what might be called elemental or first-order behavior. For example, practically all of the habitual or possible movements of a bird may be inferred from its fossilized skeleton, and those movements are the elements from which the bird's total behavior was necessarily compounded. But it would be impossible to infer just what series of movements occurred in courtship, an example of compound or second-order behavior. The evolution of first-order behavior is important and interesting, and we have some good examples documented by the fossil record, such as the evolution of locomotion in the horse family. Nevertheless, the evolution of second-order behavior is even more important and more interesting, and this is quite properly the principal preoccupation of the evolutionary psychologist. In that field the fossil record is of almost no direct (although it is of some indirect) help.

In the second main sort of historical study the documents are essentially contemporaneous. If the organisms under study are dead (fossils; the usual taxonomic collections of recent organisms; specimens for post-mortem dissection) the limitations are even greater than for fossil sequences, and data for the study of behavioral evolution are few, indeed. If, however, the subjects of study are living, data of classes (1), (2), and (3) are freely available. This is the source of practically all of our observational information on behavior. That is almost too obvious to require statement, but the point to be emphasized is that *such information is in itself completely nonhistorical;* it includes no data of class (4). Almost all students agree with that statement when it is made, but many of them do not really keep it in mind in their own work. In comparative anatomy some such sequence as dogfish-frog-cat-man is still fre-

---

[4]There are, to be sure, surprisingly numerous examples of what may be called "fossilized behavior": tracks, burrows, wounds and tooth marks, even animals fossilized in the act of parturition or copulation. Nevertheless I know of only one or two rather unimportant examples in which change, actual evolution, of behavior can be observed in such materials.

quently taught as "evolutionary," i.e. historical. In fact the anatomical differences among those organisms are in large part ecologically and behaviorally determined, are divergent and not sequential, and do not in any useful sense form a historical series. The same objection applies with perhaps even greater force to studies of behavior which state or assume an evolutionary (historical) sequence in, for instance, comparison of an insect[5] ("invertebrate level"), a rat[5] ("primitive mammalian level"), and a man.

The three main bases for inference from contemporaneous data to historical sequence are well known. (1) Related lineages often evolve more or less in parallel but some faster than others; at any one time, then, the contemporaneous representatives of the various lineages may form a series that approximates the historical sequence leading to the more advanced members of the group. (2) Certain historical trends (e.g. from smaller to larger size, from simpler to more complex behavior) are so frequent or logical that they may be assumed to have occurred in a given case. (3) Characteristics shared by contemporaneous organisms are likely to have been present in their common ancestry. There is no reason to doubt that methods based on these principles, long used in comparative anatomy, are equally pertinent for the historical study of behavior. There are, however, many pitfalls in these methods, and these are probably (at least in the present state of the subject) even more serious for behavioral studies than they have proved to be for morphological studies. Problems and precautions cannot be further discussed here than to indicate the general nature of a few of the more serious in each category. (1) Divergence is more common than parallelism, and a contemporaneous series may not at all resemble an ancestral sequence; different characteristics commonly evolve at different rates so that the animal most primitive in one respect may be most advanced in another; truly ancestral stages are liable to complete replacement and are frequently totally unrepresented at the present time. (2) No trends have been universal and comparatively few are established as usual; trends may go in either direction, or both ways from the middle, and data without an objective

[5] Apart from the point that there are hundreds of thousands of different kinds of insects, with almost incredibly diverse behavior patterns, and hundreds of kinds of rats, with much less but still important behavioral differences. In the conferences on which this symposium is based, the naturalists present repeatedly had occasion to call attention to the absurdity of speaking of "the insect," "the rat," or "the monkey" in studies of behavior, as if there were only one insect, rat, or monkey, or as if all insects, rats, or monkeys behaved alike.

time factor provide no directional signpost; any array of data can be arranged in a logical sequence, but if the data are contemporaneous the logical sequence may have no relationship to a true historical sequence. (3) Parallelism and convergence in evolution have been extremely common and they produce resemblances not present in a common ancestor; homoplasy is, therefore, widespread and is difficult to distinguish from homology, especially when, as in most studies of behavior, direct historical evidence is lacking.

The second main class of evolutionary studies involves processes rather than (historical) events. Study of a process necessarily includes study of the mechanism that performs it; joint study of genetic mechanisms and processes is an example more or less familiar to everyone with any interest in biology or evolution. The methods are for the most part experimental, and it is really not necessary to discuss them here: they are most familiar to the students least familiar with the matter of the present chapter, and they are richly exemplified in other chapters of this book. It is perhaps well just to point out that there is no natural, deep cleavage between the study of events and that of processes, or between the observational methods characteristic of the former and the experimental methods usual in the latter. Both sorts of methods are used to some extent in both fields, and the two can sometimes hardly be distinguished. Processes can to some extent be inferred from the historical record, and prior events lie implicitly behind existing processes. The importance and long-range effects of processes established by experimentation are best judged in the light of the historical record. Alternative possible interpretations of historical sequences must be judged by compatibility with known processes.

Elements of the Synthetic Theory of Evolution

Among students of evolution the world around there are still neo-Lamarckians, old-line Darwinians, vitalists, finalists, orthogeneticists, hologeneticists, mutationists, even spiritualists, not to mention theories so particular to certain individuals that they hardly fall into an -ism. All those now heterodox views are interesting, and many of them have points of emphasis, at least, that still should be kept in mind. Nevertheless, in a brief review of the present status of evolutionary theory it is now possible and proper to concentrate on a single school of theory. No one would maintain either that this theory is complete or that it is correct in all details. An overwhelming majority of students really familiar with the evidence do maintain that the theory has a sound basis and is proving most fertile in increasing understanding of the tremendously intricate course and process of evolution. This strong consensus, if not near unanimity, is a comparatively recent development. The name here preferred is the *synthetic theory*,[6] so-called because it is a new synthesis from all fields of biology and not the offspring exclusively of any one of the numerous preceding theories. Works cited at the end of this chapter consider various aspects of the synthetic theory in more detail, and several of them discuss and give references to various alternative theories not considered here.

GENETIC MECHANISMS. The medium of evolution, the thing in which the processes of evolution occur and hence the thing that is actually evolving, is a population. A population, in this sense, is a group of organisms, similar among themselves and dissimilar from other organisms with which they live, descended from a not remote common ancestry, living in the same general region and environment, and with a continuity of many generations through time. The inclusiveness of the term is vague and necessarily variable. At its least inclusive it is synonymous with the deme or local population of the biogeographers and systematists or (in a biparental population) the so-called Mendelian population of the geneticists. At its most inclusive it is practically synonymous with the species of most modern students. In the usual case of biparental organisms, the population is also characterized and unified by interbreeding among its actively sexual members. In the less common case of uniparental (asexual, apomictic, etc.) organisms, the unity of the population is still real but is looser and the evolutionary mechanisms are simpler but less flexible and potent.

The characteristics of any individual organism within a population are determined by interaction of its heredity with its environment, in the broadest sense, as the organism develops and, to less extent, thereafter as long as it lives. Heredity may be determined in part by the nature and organization of directly inherited cytoplasm (in metazoans mostly or entirely maternal, in the egg) and

[6]Numerous other tags have been applied, especially "neo-Darwinian," because of the large role assigned to natural selection in the theory. But "neo-Darwinian" in this application is misleading on two important counts. First, natural selection (itself no longer purely Darwinian) is here synthesized with equally important factors unknown to Darwin and even in strong contradiction with his views, especially on heredity. Second, the label "neo-Darwinian" historically belongs to a school that was literally neo-Darwinian, quite distinct from the present synthetic theory and only one of the several forerunners incorporated in the synthesis.

sometimes by extranuclear bodies (plastids in plants, etc.), but to far greater degree it is determined by the chromosomes in the nucleus. Chromosomes are differentiated longitudinally, and the irreducible (or at least experimentally unreduced) units of that differentiation are called genes. Different genes have different effects (necessarily, in practice, because the genes are distinguishable or recognizable in no other way), but the whole chromosomal complement acts and interacts, and it is that complement as a complex unit that is the main determinant of heredity. It may be considered as setting a reaction range, sometimes rigidly narrow and sometimes very broad, within which the characteristics of the developing organism must lie. The characteristics actually arising at one point or another of the reaction range, for instance the exact size of an organism when the range permits much variation in size, depend for the most part on environmental influences during development.

The population as a whole has characteristics likewise determined by the interaction of the genetic mechanism and of the environment. Its total genetic structure at any one time usually depends almost entirely on the kinds and combinations of chromosomes and genes present and their relative frequencies. Continuity of the population depends on the processes of reproduction in which sets of chromosomes are passed on from parent to offspring. In asexual reproduction the parental set (generally double) is simply passed on, usually unchanged. In sexual, biparental reproduction two homologous sets (each usually single) are received, one from each parent. Then there is reduction of a parental double set to a single set in the gamete, and this involves the mechanism of meiosis, with two concomitants of special importance for evolution: (1) the single chromosome set of the gamete is a random assortment from each of the two sets of the parent, and (2) occasional crossing over from one homologous parental chromosome to the other produces different combinations of genes in the chromosomes received by the offspring. Fusion of gametes into a zygote brings together sets of homologous chromosomes from different sources. That factor means that the combinations actually realized will be influenced by breeding structure and habits in the population. The extent to which breeding is random or promiscuous, monogamous, polygamous, etc., becomes important, and above all any influence which makes individuals with certain genetic characteristics more likely than others to have offspring. Also important is the likelihood of hybridization between different populations or, much less commonly, different species.

Changes in characteristics induced by changing environmental influences on identical genetic reaction ranges are not heritable. Such changes may affect evolution quite indirectly, but they cannot in themselves constitute secular evolutionary change. True evolutionary change involves changes in the genetics of the population, which are almost always changes in the relative frequencies of the various kinds of genes and of chromosomes and of their combinations. In sexual, biparental populations constant changes in individual combinations are guaranteed by the mechanisms already mentioned: random assortment of chromosomes and crossing over in meiosis, and biparental origin of chromosomes. These may but, as will be seen, usually do not in themselves bring about changes in relative frequencies in the population as a whole.

The mechanisms hitherto mentioned make for constant and radical individual rearrangements of genetic factors already present in any biparental population. The appearance of new factors in both biparental and uniparental populations is due to mutations which, broadly speaking, include changes in the numbers of chromosomes, in the internal structure of chromosomes (other than by simple crossing over), and in genes. It is the past occurrence of mutations that guarantees that homologous chromosomes rarely have exactly the same forms (alleles) of homologous genes and often are structurally different (have, for instance, the genes arranged in different sequence). Occurrence of new mutations, unless counteracted in various ways, further tends slowly but steadily to change the genetics of a population.

RANDOM PROCESSES AND EVOLUTION. It is an extraordinary fact that most of the processes inherent in the genetic mechanism of evolution occur at random. It must be understood that the word "random" in this connection (and, indeed, etymologically) does *not* mean that all of a number of possible outcomes are equally probable. It means that the results of the processes are not oriented toward some end external to the processes themselves. In evolution the relevant end is the adaptedness of the population as a whole, its capacity to continue through future generations within an available environment. The random genetic processes are those that are not inherently adaptive for the population. Assortment of chromosomes in meiosis does seem normally to be random not only in this sense but also in the fullest possible sense that all combinations are about equally probable. Crossing over, as it affects association of any two genes, has probabilities almost directly proportional to the distance (along the chromosome) between the genes, but still is random as regards adaptation. For reasons yet unknown, different genes mutate at quite different rates and mutations of a given gene to (or from) different alleles also have decidedly different rates, so that possible gene mutations—and the same is true also of chromosome mutations —have very diverse probabilities, but these processes are still random by the pertinent definition of that word. Mating or more broadly reproduction is usually not entirely random, a fact to be stressed in the next section, but it may be at least approximately so. Here randomness involves likelihood that parents of given genetic types occurring with given frequencies in the population tend to produce offspring in about the same frequencies, or, what comes to the same thing, that relatively higher production of offspring is not significantly correlated with genetic factors in the parents.[7]

If reproduction is random, in combination with the inherently random processes in meiosis, there is no statistical tendency for change in frequencies of genetic factors within a population; in other words there is no tendency for directional evolutionary change to occur. That is the so-called Hardy-Weinberg law, the mathematical expression and derivation of which are given in most textbooks of genetics. Even if mutation is taken into account, there is a point of equilibrium where a given mutation is balanced by back-mutation and random loss (see below), and there is no (or no further) tendency toward evolutionary change in the population. Thus the random genetic processes, all together, do *not* tend statistically to produce evolution. That statement applies equally to sexual populations with mutation, meiosis, and fertilization and to asexual populations with mutation and mitosis, only.

Although the random processes noted do not tend systematically to change the mean frequencies of genetic factors in a population, those frequencies through the generations do tend to fluctuate around the mean. Populations of organisms are of course always finite, and each generation is in effect a sample drawn from the long-range total population of all generations or from the purely theoretical infinite population of statistical estimation. The genetical constitution of each generation is thus subject to statistical sampling error, which is its departure from the mean of the long-range or infinite population. Such departures or statistical sampling

---

[7]Because of doubts or equivocation as to the precise meanings of "random" in application to these various processes, they are sometimes called "stochastic." Appropriate definition may, nevertheless, be as readily made for "random" as for "stochastic."

errors also occur, and may be quite radical, when a new area is populated by a few individuals spreading from a larger population elsewhere, or when for any reason a segment of a large population becomes reproductively isolated from the rest of that population. Sampling errors are larger the smaller the population. In very large populations they are so small as to be negligible, at least in comparison with effects of selection (below), but they are never reduced to zero in populations of finite size.

Under the influence of random sampling error, commonly called "genetic drift" in this connection, the frequency of a given chromosome number or arrangement or of a given gene allele may increase, even to 100 per cent, or decrease, even to zero. Evolution has then obviously occurred, and as far as now known this is the *only* process by which random (unoriented with respect to adaptation) evolution can occur. That it does occur, for instance in the colonization of an oceanic island from a mainland, is beyond any question. How commonly it occurs and how important it is in the overall picture of evolution are still strongly disputed questions. The present consensus seems to be that it is rather common but that its importance in long evolutionary sequences or radical evolutionary transformations is largely, or almost completely, overshadowed by the nonrandom effects of selection. One special case of completely demonstrated reality has evidently played an important role in the diversification of plants, at least, on lower taxonomic levels. Polyploid mutants or hybrids, with increased (usually doubled) numbers of chromosomes, may be unable to breed back with a parental stock. If they do survive and increase to become populations, they are thus genetically distinct samples isolated forthwith from their ancestral populations.[8]

ORIENTED PROCESSES AND ADAPTATION. Thus the usual random processes of the genetic mechanism tend to produce either no evolutionary changes at all or changes that are sampling errors and that are nonadaptive or, so to speak, only accidentally adaptive. Yet it is perfectly clear that evolution does occur and that it is, to say the least, often adaptive and not entirely random. It was often urged against Darwin and, with more basis, against De Vries and other early geneticists who assigned too exclusive a role to mutation that evolution cannot have occurred "by accident." The fairly obvious

[8]It is not usual to consider the origin of a polyploid species as an example of sampling error, but it does seem logically to fall into that category as an example of random evolutionary change.

answer, which was in fact already emphasized and soundly established by Darwin, is that the adaptive orientation of evolution must involve the one genetic process that is not necessarily or, as a matter of conclusive observation, usually random: reproduction. If reproduction is differential, if there is a correlation between distinctive genetic factors in the parents and their relatively greater success in reproduction, then there will be an increase in the frequencies of those genetic factors (and combinations of them) within the population from one generation to another. Evolution will occur, and it will be oriented, not random. That, in brief and shorn of numerous complications, is the modern concept of natural selection. Natural selection, as defined, is known really to exist and to be effective, both by observation in nature and by experimentation. No other nonrandom genetic factor has been objectively demonstrated, even though several have been postulated (e.g. Lamarckian influence of use or disuse, nonrandom mutation, inherent tendency—whatever that may mean—to progress toward a goal). Most students now believe that this only demonstrably real nonrandom process is also sufficient to account for all the observed nonrandom events in the course of evolution. *Proving* sufficiency amounts to proving a negative, which is generally deemed impossible; but sufficiency is the stand of the synthetic theory, and the burden of proof would seem to lie with its (now few) opponents.

Reproductive success may be comparatively simple in asexual organisms. It often amounts only to this: a genetic difference arises by mutation, there is direct competition between mutant and nonmutant forms, members of one group or the other survive more often to reproduce, and the less successful group eventually disappears. Even there complications are ignored, and in biparental populations the matter becomes highly intricate. (1) Male and female must occur in proximity or must find each other. (2) In many, especially the more complex, animals they must be sexually acceptable to each other and must mate. (3) Fertilization must occur. (4) The gametes must be genetically compatible. (5) Normal embryological development must occur. (6) Offspring must survive to breeding age and become successful reproducers in their turn. Relatively greater or less success may occur at any one of these stages, and at substages within them, and selection depends on the total outcome.

Darwin was aware of the selective possibilities of all the listed stages, but he stressed (6) above all others, and some of his followers did so almost to the exclusion of any others. Thus Darwinian natural selection was based mainly on differential mortality, and the Darwinians and neo-Darwinians hardly grasped the whole process as one of differential reproduction. Darwin also devoted much attention to stage (2) as involving sexual selection, which he distinguished from natural selection.

Until quite recently it was generally implied or assumed that selection always favors individual survival or, more in the spirit of the modern theory, individual success in reproduction. Now it is evident that selection favors successful reproduction of the population and not necessarily of any or of all particular individuals within it. A striking, although rather exceptional, example of that fact is provided by the social insects, among which only a very small fraction actually reproduce although their success in reproduction is completely dependent on the nonreproducing individuals. Of more general import is the recently accumulating evidence that the most successful populations usually have considerable genetic heterogeneity and much heterozygosity in individuals. But that favored characteristic of a population can be maintained only at the expense of constantly producing a certain proportion of definitely inferior, less heterozygous individuals.

A central problem of evolutionary theory has always been the explanation of adaptation, and the synthetic theory maintains (as did Darwin, but with a different understanding of the mechanism) that adaptation is a result of natural selection. But it also demonstrates that natural selection always favors reproductive success of a population, and nothing else. It might be suitable to redefine adaptation as such reproductive success, but some confusion might arise from the fact that most of the characteristics generally considered adaptive seem to be so in the old Darwinian sense of promoting survival of the individual and seem to have little or nothing to do with population reproduction *per se*. The anomaly is only apparent, however, for clearly reproductive success of the population involves all phases of individual life cycles and will incomparably more often than not be favored by individual adaptation to the environment. Such adaptation will therefore almost always be favored by natural selection. Nevertheless the possibility remains that selection, as here defined, could favor population reproduction at the expense of individual adaptation. We have already noted that it does so, indeed, in the cases of homozygous individuals in heterotic populations. It has also been variously claimed that a species may become so specialized for reproductive ends, for example in development of sexual weapons and competition, as to put the whole population at a disadvantage in competition with other species. The reality or importance of such possible phenomena are not, however, clearly established.

An aspect of the synthetic theory especially pertinent here is that it again brings in behavior as a central element. It not only points the way to evolutionary, historical explanations of existing behavior patterns but also involves behavior as one of the factors that produce or guide evolution. Some phases of selection, as in zygote and embryo, are not directly behavioral, but aspects of breeding, care of young, and subsequent survival are pre-eminently so and are obviously crucial elements in selection.

Some Historical Generalizations and Principles

Those, in brief, are the most essential features of the mechanisms and processes now believed to underlie the phenomena of evolution. An understanding of comparative behavior, or other biological aspects of our contemporary world, further involves consideration of what those phenomena have, in fact, been, of how the processes have worked out in the prodigious history of life. A review of the vast body of information and theory on this subject is of course beyond the present scope. There are, however, certain generalizations and principles that stand out from that record and that can be particularly useful in any reconstruction of behavioral (or other) evolution. Just a few of the most important of these will be mentioned.

IRREVOCABILITY, OPPORTUNISM, AND TRANSFORMATION. From a certain point of view all study and knowledge of nature can be divided into processes, immanent and changeless characteristics of the universe, and configurations that result from those processes, transient and historically cumulative states of the universe. The difference is that between gravity, a timeless structural feature of our world, and a falling stone, acted on by gravity but determined as to time, place, and condition by the whole previous history of the matter in the stone. The configuration of the living, as of any other, world depends from instant to instant on its last previous configuration and on how the immanent processes, the "laws" of nature, tend to act on any given configuration. Involved is historical causation, which includes everything that has ever happened and which is thus an inherently nonrepeatable accumulation.

In application to evolution, those rather abstract considerations mean that the actual course of evolution is determined not only by its processes but also by the cumulative total of *all* previous events. It follows that evolution is irrevocable. That law (it seems to be about as near to a true law as anything in the realm of biology) has two major corollaries. One is the famous doctrine of the irreversibility of evolution. No organism, no population, no community returns precisely to any antecedent structure or state. A gross but impressive example: whales are descended from fishes; they have returned to the water and resumed the ecological status of fishes; but they have not again become fishes, and every system, organ, tissue, or cell of a whale is radically distinct from that of any fish that is or ever was. The other corollary of irrevocability is that the effects of previous conditions are never wholly lost. A whale, again, carries not only in general but also in detail down to the last cell unmistakable effects of its ancestors' sojourn on the land.[9]

As each configuration is derived from the last, and from all previous ones, each can only be a modification of or an addition to what was already there. This gives evolution an opportunistic aspect. Changes take place on the basis of the previous condition and not as a wholly new construction most efficiently adapted to new conditions. Early fishes had lungs. In many later fishes the pre-existing lungs evolved into hydrostatic organs, which, in spite of their radically different function, did not arise *de novo*. In land animals the lungs retained and considerably perfected their respiratory structure and function. Land snails, requiring an organ for the same function, had no lungs in their ancestry and did not evolve lungs, but a structure that was pre-existent, the mantle cavity, could and did evolve to serve that function.

When a way of life is changing in the course of evolution it is evidently simpler, that is, it is genetically more likely, to remodel the existing than to introduce something completely new. That is the principle of transformation. The evolution of lung to swim bladder, already mentioned, is an example. Another striking and widely familiar example is the incorporation of the bones hinging

---

[9]Exceptions to both aspects of irrevocability are conceivable, but none are known or likely. The genetic processes of evolution are all reversible, but that all should reverse to just the same extent in conjunction and within an intricate and changing environmental framework is so improbable that it is not likely to have happened in only a few billion years. An event such as a mutation may seem to be quite canceled out if the mutant allele is subsequently eliminated from the population, but again the probability that even the transient presence of the allele left no effects at all is infinitesimal.

skull and jaw in early reptiles (quadrate and articular) into the middle ear of mammals (where they are renamed incus and malleus).

The principles of irrevocability, opportunism, and transformation are based mainly on anatomical and physiological data, but in the nature of things they must also apply, *mutatis mutandis*, to the evolution of behavior.

TRENDS AND ORTHOGENESIS. It is a common observation, backed by hundreds of concrete examples in the fossil record, that evolutionary change in a given direction once started may tend to continue for a long time. In terms of years, as nearly as highly inaccurate approximations permit conclusion, it is the rule for trending changes to continue for more than 10^6 years and common for them to last on the order of 10^7 years. Much longer trends, however, as of the order of 10^8 years without stop or pronounced change of direction, have apparently not been substantiated. For instance the recorded history of the horse family shows several well-marked trends, as has become common knowledge, but it is less widely known by nonspecialists that no single recognized trend in that family was continuous throughout the 6×10^7 years of its known history. The longest of the known trends did not continue with even approximate constancy for more than about 2×10^7 years. Some trends reached an inherent limit, for instance the premolars (all but the first) once fully molarized could not become more so. Other trends stopped without having reached such an apparent limit; for instance increase in size stopped far short of any mechanical limit.

Similar trends often appear simultaneously or successively in multiple related lines, such as a tendency for the shells to become coiled in relatives of the oyster. Others may appear over and over again in widely diverse groups, for example increase in individual size. Yet there has been no universal trend, no trend that did not stop or change before about 10^8 years and usually much less, and even no trend that was not on occasion reversed.[10] The trend toward larger size noted above for some of the horses and here in a more general sense is probably the most widespread to be detected among

[10]There has been some confusion on the subject of trends and the irreversibility of evolution, with the argument that either trends do not become reversed or else evolution is reversible. The difficulty is semantic, only. A lineage that becomes smaller and to that degree more like an ancestral stage has not except in this one artificially segregated characteristic returned to the ancestral condition.

animals. It has occurred repeatedly in groups as diverse as protozoans and primates. Yet it has obviously been neither universal nor, in any one group, constant. If it had been, all animals would by now be elephantine or cetacean in bulk. The opposite trend, toward smaller size, has evidently been less frequent but has certainly occurred many times, and absence of trend, maintenance of about the same size, has probably been the rule.

The foregoing and many other facts about trends lead to the essential conclusion that there is no mysterious, inherent tendency for evolution to proceed indefinitely in straight lines. It accords with everything really known about trends, to the limited extent that they do characterize evolution, to conclude that they occur only when and only as long as they are adaptive. This pre-eminently oriented feature of evolutionary history is adequately explained by the known orienting (nonrandom or antichance) process of evolution: natural selection. The opposite view, that trends may or do occur without relationship to natural selection generally is labeled as "orthogenesis," and there has been widespread belief that the fossil record supports or even proves the postulate of orthogenesis. That idea has always been most widespread among those least familiar with the fossil record. Most paleontologists have long since rejected it.

The facts that trends are adaptive, begin and end at fairly definite times, and rarely persist long, geologically speaking, have another bearing, harking back to methods of inference mentioned early in this chapter. In the absence of really historical documents, it is generally impossible to extrapolate far and accurately from brief sequences or by postulating a previous trend on the basis of comparative data on living animals. It is, for instance, unjustified to conclude that a behavioral sequence from simple to complex among recent primates can be correctly superimposed as a continuing historical trend from Paleocene prosimian to Recent man.

PATTERNS OF EVOLUTION. The fabric of evolution is phylogeny, and above the level of interbreeding and hybridization it has only two elements: splitting and succession. The basic process of evolutionary splitting is speciation, the rise of two or more species from a single species. Isolation of a segment of the population is accompanied or followed by genetic divergence, with more or less divergence also in morphology, physiology, and behavior. In uniparental populations no genetic nexus unites the individuals and speciation is a comparatively simple result of mutation and selection. In biparental populations the crucial feature is the breaking of the nexus of inter-breeding. Usually (some would say "always") an initial requirement is some degree of geographic separation. Isolating mechanisms that then reduce and finally stop interbreeding, even if the incipient species do come into contact, are almost innumerable. Many of them are behavioral, for instance in decreasing willingness to mate or success in mating. The eventual and complete barrier, which always does arise finally if the now separate species survive but which may be long delayed, is genetic divergence that makes the gametes so incompatible that hybrid zygotes cannot develop.

The significance of phylogenetic splitting in over-all evolutionary history is increase in diversity, with the occupation of new regions and environments and, within each area of occupation, a parceling out into increasingly numerous and narrow ecological niches, each occupied by a distinctive species. If we had no fossil record, it would be irresistible to visualize a single, broadly adapted, primordial marine species the descendants of which expanded to occupy all the waters and lands and specialized for close fit in each available niche. Expansion and diversification complete, evolution would end. Expansion and diversification are, of course, the main motifs in the rich fabric of life's history, but the whole pattern is astonishingly more complex. Most species, even though already well fitted into a niche or adaptive zone, continue to change. The overwhelming majority finally become extinct without issue and are replaced by other, perhaps quite different organisms.

A few organisms have reached a sort of evolutionary stasis, adequate adaptation to a sufficiently constant environment, and have continued without marked change thereafter to become "living fossils": the horseshoe crab, the opossum, and others. Most environments change enough so that the organisms in them must do so too. The mere fact that some one species in a community changes, for any reason, means that the environment of all the others is different to some degree. The environmental change requiring adaptive adjustment for a species may even reside within the species itself—that is probably true of many of the trends toward larger size, the smaller animals of a population always being at a slight competitive disadvantage compared with the larger. Such usually slow shifts of environment and adaptation are nearly, but not quite, universal and they account for the commonest trends in evolution.

Rarer but more striking events result from not merely maintaining adaptation in a changing world but also changing or improving the quality of adaptation. Then there is likely to occur on a smaller or larger scale what has been aptly called a breakthrough. Increased competitive efficiency may permit expansion into already occupied adaptive zones, with extinction for their former occupants, as among the fishes the teleosts have ousted all but a tithe of their ancient competitors. Or new ways of life may be achieved, as the reptiles spread over the lands then effectively empty of competitors. In such episodes more or less radical changes in structure, physiology, and behavior are involved. Selection is then particularly intense, and change is correspondingly rapid. The changes do usually take an appreciable time, apparently as a rule on the order of 10^6 years and upward, but the effect in the over-all picture is steplike, not a trend but a steep transition from one level to another. The behavioral change when man became adept with tools—supposing, as one must, that this was accompanied by a biological and not entirely a cultural evolutionary advance—was such an event, probably one of exceptional rapidity and certainly one of exceptional portent.

References

CARTER, G. S. 1951. Animal evolution. London, Sidgwick and Jackson.

DOBZHANSKY, TH. 1951. Genetics and the origin of species. 3d ed. New York, Columbia Univ. Press.

DOBZHANSKY, TH. 1955. Evolution, genetics, and man. New York, Wiley.

HUXLEY, J. S. 1943. Evolution: the modern synthesis. New York, Harper.

LERNER, I. M. 1954. Genetic homeostasis. New York, Wiley.

MAYR, E. 1942. Systematics and the origin of species. New York, Columbia Univ. Press.

MOODY, P. A. 1953. Introduction to evolution. New York, Harper.

SIMPSON, G. G. 1953. The major features of evolution. New York, Columbia Univ. Press.

SIMPSON, G. G., PITTENDRIGH, C. S., and TIFFANY, L. H. 1957. Life: an introduction to biology. New York, Harcourt, Brace.

STEBBINS, G. L., JR. 1949. Variation and evolution in plants. New York, Columbia Univ. Press.

The Evolution of Living Systems*

ERNST MAYR

(*Editor's Note*) For a sexually reproducing animal to adapt, it needs (1) a ready surplus of genetic variability and (2) a "gene-proof" maximal population in which to reproduce. The species is such a unit, for it has boundaries that do not permit gene flow to any adjacent species. Without such boundaries no adaptation could occur; more specifically, no evolution could occur since it would be impossible to concentrate the adapted genotypes in any one group of animals. Even before Darwin the species was recognized as an actually existing natural unit unlike genera and other higher classificatory units which are arbitrary. But this approach implied to the early naturalists that the species was immutable. Darwin showed that a species could change over time. He proposed anagenic or sequential change, but it has been only recently that the mechanisms required for the origin of new species by divergence or cladogenesis have been understood. For that to happen some member population of the maximum population (the species) must "bud off" and become isolated genetically long enough to eventually become reproductively incompatible. The new species gradually responds to a new environment and eventually, due to adaptation and to chance factors, develops a distinct genetic system. Such divergent speciation is very common in nature, yet there are some factors that militate against it. Naturally, the population in possession of genes capable of adjusting the constituent individuals to a wide range of environmental differences will not have to resort to specialization via the elimination of unfavorable genes. Mayr points out that the genes responsible for the learning capacity in the human

*From *Proceedings of the National Academy of Sciences*, vol. 51, May 1964, pages 934–941. By permission of the author and the publisher.

24

provide such flexibility and mitigate against specialization and speciation. While man is certainly still evolving and still under selective pressure, it is also true that culture does do a great deal of the "adapting" for us and thus may permit the retention of a great amount of variation in the species.

THE number, kind, and diversity of living systems is overwhelmingly great, and each system, in its particular way, is unique. In the short time available to me, it would be quite futile to try to describe the evolution of viruses and fungi, whales and sequoias, or elephants and hummingbirds. Perhaps we can arrive at valid generalizations by approaching the process in a rather unorthodox way. Living systems evolve in order to meet the challenge of the environment. We can ask, therefore, what *are* the particular demands that organisms have to meet? The speakers preceding me have already focused attention on some of these demands.

The first challenge is to cope with a continuously changing and immensely diversified environment, the resources of which, however, are not inexhaustible. Mutation, the production of genetic variation, is the recognized means of coping with the diversity of the environment in space and time. Let us go back to the beginning of life. A primeval organism in need of a particular complex molecule in the primordial "soup" in which he lived, gained a special advantage by mutating in such a way that, after having exhausted this resource in his environment, he was able to synthesize the needed molecule from simpler molecules that were abundantly available. Simple organisms such as bacteria or viruses, with a new generation every 10 or 20 minutes and with enormous populations consisting of millions and billions of individuals, may well be able to adjust to the diversity and to the changes of the environment by mutation alone. In addition, they have numerous mechanisms of phenotypic adaptation. A capacity for mutation is perhaps the most important evolutionary characteristic of the simplest organisms.

More complex organisms, those with much longer generation times, much smaller population size, and particularly with a delicately balanced coadapted genotype, would find it hazardous to rely on mutation to cope with changes in the environment. The chances that the appropriate mutation would occur at the right time so that mutation alone could simply appropriate genetic variability for sudden changes in the environment of such organisms are virtually nil.

What, then, is the prerequisite for the development of more complex living systems? It is the ability of different organisms to exchange "genetic information" with each other, the process the geneticist calls recombination, more popularly known as *sex*. The selective advantage of sex is so direct and so great that we can assume it arose at a very early stage in the history of life. Let us illustrate this advantage by a single example. A primitive organism able to synthesize amino acid *A*, but dependent on the primordial soup for amino acid *B*, and another organism able to synthesize amino acid *B*, but dependent on the primordial soup for amino acid *A*, by genetic recombination would be able to produce offspring with the ability to synthesize both amino acids and thus able to live in an environment deficient in both of them. Genetic recombination can speed up evolutionary change enormously and assist in emancipation from the environment.

Numerous mechanisms evolved in due time to make recombination increasingly precise in every respect. The result was the evolution of elaborately constructed chromosomes; of diploidy through two homologous chromosome sets, one derived from the father, the other from the mother; of an elaborate process of meiosis during which homologous chromosomes exchange pieces so that the chromosomes of father and mother are transmitted to the grandchildren not intact, but as newly reconstituted chromosomes with a novel assortment of genes. These mechanisms regulate genetic recombination among individuals, by far the major source of genotypic variability in higher organisms.

The amount of genetic diversity within a single interbreeding population is regulated by a balance of mechanisms that favor inbreeding and such that favor outbreeding. The extremes, in this respect, are much greater among plants and lower animals than among higher animals. Extreme inbreeding (self-fertilization) and extreme outbreeding (regular hybridization with other species) are rare in higher animals. Outbreeders and inbreeders are drastically different living systems in which numerous adaptations are correlated in a harmonious manner.

The result of sexuality is that ever-new combinations of genes can be tested by the environment in every generation. The enormous power of the process of genetic recombination by sexual reproduction becomes evident if we remember that in sexually reproducing species no two individuals are genetically identical. We must admit, sex is wonderful!

However, even sex has its drawbacks. To make this clear, let me set up for you the model of a universe consisting entirely of genetically different individuals that are *not* organized into species. Any individual may engage in genetic recombination with any other individual in this model. New gene complexes will be built up occasionally, as a result of chance, that have unique adaptive advantages. Yet, because in this particular evolutionary system there is no guarantee that such an exceptional individual will engage in genetic recombination *only* with individuals having a similarly adaptive genotype, it is inevitable that this exceptionally favorable genotype will eventually be destroyed by recombination during reproduction.

How can such a calamity be avoided? There are two possible means, and nature has adopted both. One method is to abandon sexual reproduction. Indeed we find all through the animal kingdom, and even more often among plants, a tendency to give up sexuality temporarily or permanently in order to give a successful genotype the opportunity to replicate itself unchanged, generation after generation, taking advantage of its unique superiority. The history of the organic world makes it clear, however, that such an evolutionary opportunist reaches the end of his rope sooner or later. Any sudden change of the environment will convert his genetic advantage into a handicap and, not having the ability to generate new genetic variability through recombination, he will inevitably become extinct.

The other solution is the "invention," if I may be pardoned for using this anthropomorphic term, of the biological species. The species is a protective system guaranteeing that only such individuals interbreed and exchange genes as have largely the same genotypes. In this system there is no danger that breakdown of genotypes will result from genetic recombination, because all the genes present in the gene pool of a species have been previously tested, through many generations, for their ability to recombine harmoniously. This does not preclude considerable variability within a species. Indeed, all our studies make us realize increasingly how vast is the genetic variability within even comparatively uniform species. Nevertheless, the basic developmental and homeostatic systems are the same, in principle, in all members of a species.

By simply explaining the biological meaning of species, I have deliberately avoided the tedious question of how to define a species. Let me add that the species can fulfill its function of protecting well-integrated, harmonious genotypes only by having some mechanisms (called "isolating mechanisms") by which interbreeding with individuals of other species is prevented.

In our design of a perfect living system, we have now arrived at a system that can cope with the diversity of its environment and that has the means to protect its coadapted, harmonious genotype. As described, this well-balanced system seems so conservative as to offer no opportunity for the origin of additional new systems. This conclusion, if true, would bring us into a real conflict with the evolutionary history of the world. The paleontologists tell us that the number of species has increased steadily during geological time and that the multiplication of species, in order to compensate for the extinction of species, must occur at a prodigious rate. If the species is as well-balanced, well-protected, and as delicate as we have described it, how can one species be divided into two? This serious problem stumped Darwin completely, and evolutionists have argued about it for more than one hundred years.

Eventually it was shown that there are two possible solutions, or perhaps I should say two normally occurring solutions. The first mode occurs very frequently in plants, but is rare in the animal kingdom. It consists in the doubling of the chromosome set so that the new individual is no longer a diploid with two sets of homologous chromosomes, but, let us say, a tetraploid with four sets of chromosomes, or if the process continues, a higher polyploid with an even higher chromosome number. The production of a polyploid constitutes instantaneous speciation; it produces in a single step an incompatibility between the parental and the daughter species.

The other mode of speciation is simplicity itself. Up to now, we have spoken of the species as something rigid, uniform, and monolithic. Actually, natural species, particularly those that are widespread, consist like the human species of numerous local populations and races, all of them differing more or less from each other in their genetic composition. Some of these populations, particularly those at the periphery of the species range, are completely isolated from each other and from the main body of the species. Let us assume that one of these populations is prevented for a long time from exchanging genes with the rest of the species, because the isolating barrier—be it a mountain range, a desert, or a waterway—is impassable. Through the normal processes of mutation, recombination, and selection, the gene pool of the isolated population becomes more and more different from that of the rest of the species, finally reaching a level of distinctness that normally characterizes a different species. This process, called "geographic speciation," is by far the most widespread mode of speciation in the animal kingdom and quite likely the major pathway of speciation also in plants.

Before such an incipient species qualifies as a genuine new species, it must have acquired two properties during its genetic rebuilding.

First, it must have acquired isolating mechanisms that prevent it from interbreeding with the parental species when the two again come into contact. Secondly, it must also have changed sufficiently in its demands on the environment, in its niche utilization (as the ecologist would say), so that it can live side by side with mother and sister species without succumbing to competition.

KINDS OF LIVING SYSTEMS. In our discussion of the evolution of living systems, I have concentrated, up to now, on major unit processes or phenomena, such as the role of mutation, of genetic recombination and sex, of the biological species, and of the process of speciation. These processes give us the mechanisms that make diversification of the living world possible, but they do not explain why there should be such an enormous variety of life on earth. There are surely more than three million species of animals and plants living on this earth, perhaps more than five million. What principle permits the coexistence of such a wealth of different kinds? This question troubled Darwin, and he found an answer for it that has stood the test of time. Two species, in order to coexist, must differ in their utilization of the resources of the environment in a way that reduces competition. During speciation there is a strong selective premium on becoming different from pre-existing species by trying out new ecological niches. This experimentation in new adaptations and new specializations is the principal evolutionary significance of the process of speciation. Once in a long while one of these new species finds the door to a whole new adaptive kingdom. Such a species, for instance, was the original ancestor of the most successful of all groups of organisms, the insects, now counting more than a million species. The birds, the bony fishes, the flowering plants, and all other kinds of animals and plants, all originated ultimately from a single ancestral species. Once a species discovers an empty adaptive zone, it can speciate and radiate until this zone is filled by its descendants.

To avoid competition, organisms can diverge in numerous ways. Dr. Hutchinson has already mentioned size. Not only has there been a trend toward large size in evolution, but also other species and genera, often in the same lines, have evolved toward decreased size. Small size is by no means always a primitive trait.

Specialization for a very narrow niche is perhaps the most common evolutionary trend. This is the characteristic approach of the parasites. Literally thousands of parasites are restricted to a single host, indeed restricted to a small part of the body of the host. There are, for instance, three species of mites that live on different parts of the honey bee. Such extreme specialization is rare if not absent in the higher plants, but is characteristic for insects and explains their prodigious rate of speciation. The deep sea, lightless caves, and the interstices between sand grains along the seashore are habitats leading to specialization.

The counterpart of the specialist is the generalist. Individuals of such species have a broad tolerance to all sorts of variations of climate, habitat, and food. It seems difficult to become a successful generalist, but the very few species that can be thus classified are widespread and abundant. Man is the generalist par excellence with his ability to live in all latitudes and altitudes, in deserts and in forest, and to subsist on the pure meat diet of the Eskimos or on an almost pure vegetable diet. There are indications that generalists have unusually diversified gene pools and, as a result, produce rather high numbers of inferior genotypes by genetic recombination. Widespread and successful species of Drosophila seem to have more lethals than rare or restricted species. It is not certain that this observation can be applied to man, but this much is certain, that populations of man display much genetic variation. In man we do not have the sharply contrasting types ("morphs") that occur in many polymorphic populations of animals and plants. Instead we find rather complete intergradation of mental, artistic, manual, and physical capacities (and their absence). Yet, whether continuous or discontinuous, genetic variation has long been recognized as a useful device by which a species can broaden its tolerance and enlarge its niche. That the same is true for man is frequently forgotten. Our educators, for instance, have tended far too long to ignore man's genetic diversity and have tried to force identical educational schedules on highly diverse talents. Only within recent years have we begun to realize that equal opportunity calls for differences in education. Genetically different individuals do not have equal opportunities unless the environment is diversified.

Every increase in the diversity of the environment during the history of the world has resulted in a veritable burst of speciation. This is particularly easily demonstrated for changes in the biotic environment. The rise of the vertebrates was followed by a spectacular development of trematodes, cestodes, and other vertebrate parasites. The insects, whose history goes back to the Paleozoic nearly 400 million years ago, did not really become a great success until the flowering plants (angiosperms) evolved some 150 million years ago. These plants provided such an abundance of new adaptive zones and niches that the insects entered a truly explosive stage in their evolution. By now three quarters of the known species of animals are insects, and their total number (including undiscovered species) is estimated to be as high as two or three million.

PARENTAL CARE. Let me discuss just one additional aspect of the diversity of living systems, care of the offspring. At one extreme we have the oysters that do nothing whatsoever for their offspring. They cast literally millions of eggs and male gametes into the sea, providing the opportunity for the eggs to be fertilized. Some of the fertilized eggs will settle in a favorable place and produce new oysters. The statistical probability that this will happen is small, owing to the adversity of the environment, and although a single full-grown oyster may produce more than 100 million eggs per breeding season, it will have on the average only one descendant. That numerous species of marine organisms practice this type of reproduction, many of them enormously abundant and many of them with an evolutionary history going back several hundred million years, indicates that this shotgun method of thrusting offspring into the world is surprisingly successful.

How different is reproduction in species with parental care! This always requires a drastic reduction in the number of offspring, and it usually means greatly enlarged yolk-rich eggs, it means the development of brood pouches, nests, or even internal placentae, and it often means the formation of a pair-bond to secure the participation of the male in the raising of the young. The ultimate development along this line of specialization is unquestionably man, with his enormous prolongation of childhood.

Behavioral characteristics are an important component of parental care, and our treatment of the evolution of living systems would be incomplete if we were to omit reference to behavior and to the central nervous system. The germ plasm of a fertilized egg contains in its DNA a coded genetic program that guides the development of the young organism and its reactions to the environment. However, there are drastic differences among species concerning the precision of the inherited information and the extent to which the individual can benefit from experience. The young in some species appear to be born with a genetic program containing an almost complete set of ready-made, predictable responses to the stimuli of the environment. We say of such an organism that his behavior is unlearned, innate, instinctive, that his behavior program is closed. The other extreme is provided by organisms that have a great capacity to benefit from experience, to learn how to react to the environment, to continue adding "information" to their behavior program, which consequently is an open program.

Let us look a little more closely at open and closed programs and their evolutionary potential. We are all familiar with the famous story of imprinting explored by Konrad Lorenz. Young geese or ducklings just hatched from the egg will adopt as parent any moving object (but preferably one making appropriate noises). If hatched in an incubator, they will follow their human caretaker and not only consider him their parent but consider themselves as belonging to the human species. For instance, upon reaching sexual maturity they may tend to display to and court a human individual rather than another goose. The reason for this seemingly absurd behavior is that the hatching gosling does not have an inborn knowledge of the Gestalt of its parent; all it has is readiness to fill in this Gestalt into its program. Its genetically coded program is open; it provides for a readiness to adopt as parent the first moving object seen after hatching. In nature, of course, this is invariably the parent.

Let us contrast this open program with the completely closed one of another bird, the parasitic cowbird. The mother cowbird, like the European cuckoo, lays her eggs in the nests of various kinds of songbirds such as yellow warblers, vireos, or song sparrows, then to abandon them completely. The young cowbird is raised by its foster parents, and yet, as soon as he is fledged, he seeks other young cowbirds and gathers into large flocks with them. For the rest of his life, he associates with members of his own species. The Gestalt of his own species is firmly imbedded in the genetic program with which the cowbird is endowed from the very beginning. It is—at least in respect to species recognition—a completely closed program. In other respects, much of the behavioral program of the cowbird is open, that is, ready to incorporate experiences by learning. Indeed, there is probably no species of animals, not even among the protozoans, that does not, at least to some extent, derive benefit from learning processes. On the whole, and certainly among the higher vertebrates, there has been a tendency to replace rigidly closed programs by open ones or, as the student of animal behavior would say, to replace rigidly instinctive behavior by learned behavior. This change is not a change in an isolated character. It is part of a whole chain reaction of biological changes. Since man is the culmination of this particular evolutionary trend, we naturally have a special interest in this trend. Capacity for learning can best be utilized if the young is associated with someone from whom to learn, most conveniently his parents. Consequently there is strong selection pressure in favor of extending the period of childhood. And since parents can take care of only a limited number of young, there is selection in favor of reducing the number of offspring. We have here the paradoxical situation that parents with a smaller number of young may nevertheless have a greater number of grandchildren, because mortality among well cared for and well-prepared young may be reduced even more drastically than the birth rate.

The sequence of events I have just outlined describes one of the dominating evolutionary trends in the primates, a trend that reaches its extreme in man. A broad capacity for learning is an indispensable prerequisite for the development of culture, of ethics, of religion. But the oyster proves that there are avenues to biological success other than parental care and the ability to learn.

One final point: how can we explain the harmony of living systems? Attributes of an organism are not independent variables but interdependent components of a single system. Large brain size, the ability to learn, long childhood, and many other attributes of man, all belong together; they are parts of a single harmoniously functioning system. And so it is with all animals and plants. The modern population geneticist stresses the same point. The genes of a gene pool have been brought together for harmonious cooperation, they are coadapted. This harmony and perfection of nature (to which the Greeks referred in the word *Cosmos*) has impressed philosophers from the very beginning. Yet there seems to be an unresolved conflict between this harmony of nature and the apparent randomness of evolutionary processes, beginning with mutation and comprising also much of reproduction and mortality. Opponents of the Darwinian theory of evolution have claimed that the conflict between the harmony of nature and the apparent haphazardness of evolutionary processes could *not* be resolved.

The evolutionist, however, points out that this objection is valid only if evolution is a one-step process. In reality, every evolutionary change involves two steps. The first is the production of new genetic diversity through mutation, recombination, and related processes. On this level randomness is indeed predominant. The second step, however—selection of those individuals that are to make up the breeding population of the next generation—is largely determined by genetically controlled adaptive properties. This is what natural selection means; only that which maintains or increases the harmony of the system will be selected for.

The concept of natural selection, the heart of the evolutionary theory, is still widely misunderstood. Natural selection says no more and no less than that certain genotypes have a greater than average statistical chance to survive and reproduce under given conditions. Two aspects of this concept need emphasis. The first is that selection is not a theory but a straightforward fact. Thousands of experiments have proved that the probability that an individual will survive and reproduce is not a matter of accident, but a consequence of its genetic endowment. The second point is that selective superiority gives only a statistical advantage. It increases the probability of survival and reproduction, other things being equal.

Natural selection is measured in terms of the contribution a genotype makes to the genetic composition of the next generation. Reproductive success of a wild organism is controlled by the sum of the adaptive properties possessed by the individual, including his resistance to weather, his ability to escape enemies, and to find food. General superiority in these and other properties permits an individual to reach the age of reproduction.

In civilized man these two components of selective value, adaptive superiority and reproductive success, no longer coincide. The individuals with above average genetic endowment do not necessarily make an above average contribution to the gene pool of the next generation. Indeed the shiftless, improvident individual who has a child every year is sure to add more genes to the gene pool of the next generation than those who carefully plan the size of their families. Natural selection has no answer to this predicament. The separation in the modern human society of mere reproductive success from genuine adaptedness poses an extremely serious problem for man's future.

In this brief discussion of the evolution of living systems, I have been unable to do more than outline basic problems. We are beginning to understand the role of mutation, of genetic recombination, and of natural selection. The comparative study of the overwhelming multitude of diverse living systems has only begun. Because much of our environment consists of living systems, their study is of great importance. Indeed it is a prerequisite for understanding ourselves, since man also is a living thing.

Mendelism, Darwinism, and Evolutionism*

THEODOSIUS DOBZHANSKY

(*Editor's Note*) One way of attaining a thorough understanding of the theory of evolution is by retracing the historical steps in its synthesis. This is far more than an academic exercise, particularly for the beginning student who tends to approach the study of evolution with a number of nineteenth-century ideas. Dobzhansky's article describes what was perhaps the major step toward the modern theory, the gradual recognition of the relevance of Mendelism to Darwinism. But between the mechanism of heredity and the phenomenon of natural selection lies a process which causes organisms to change over generational time. While it is now clear how nonblending inheritance provides the variation upon which natural selection feeds, exactly how this process operates to bring about adaptation is still incompletely understood. In other words, there remains a lot of unknown ground between a knowledge of the biology and chemistry of the hereditary mechanisms and the evolution of adapted populations of organisms. This article discusses some of the problems involved here and some of the solutions that have been proposed. Dobzhansky emphasizes that to understand evolution the scientist must maintain a balance between reductionism and compositionism. This is particularly true for the student of human evolution who must deal with a host of socio-cultural factors not generally considered by the natural scientist. There is a tendency, and Dobzhansky discusses it, for the various specialists to go off into their own corners with the micro-biologists investigating "molecular evolution"; zoologists, "organismal evolution"; anthropologists, "cultural evolution", etc. When such divisions

*From *Proceedings of the American Philosophical Society*, vol. 109, August 1965, pages 205–215. By permission of the author and the publisher.

of labor occur, any opportunity to consider interaction between variables artificially classified as different ceases, and attempted syntheses turn out to be based on analogies. Specialization is not a substitute for broad theoretical comprehension nor does it release one from the responsibility of being aware of the tremendous problem that faces the student of human evolution. Dobzhansky, with a lifetime of contributions to basic research in genetics, is also a masterful "compositionist" as evidenced in this article.

MENDEL is one of the tragic figures in the history of science. During the autumn of his life he must have felt that his work as a scientist was a dismal failure. It was overlooked and ignored. He could hardly have foreseen that it would be rediscovered and appreciated in 1900, i.e., sixteen years after his death. It was published in an obscure provincial journal, but this was only a partial explanation of its having been disregarded. The scientific literature was then not yet the flood that it has become now. Biologists of 1865 were evidently less well prepared to understand Mendel's insights than were biologists of 1900. There was, however, a biologist living in 1865 to whom the above statement did not apply. This biologist was Darwin. Unluckily for both parties, Darwin did not know about Mendel's discovery. The library of Mendel's Brünn monastery had copies of some books by Darwin with marginal notations in Mendel's handwriting. Mendel failed to send a copy of his publication to Darwin; perhaps by the time he became familiar with Darwin's books he had given up hope of having his contribution understood by anybody.

Mendel was not a great generalizer of masses of heterogeneous data, as Darwin so pre-eminently was. Mendel's genius was in depth rather than in breadth. His place among the greatest of scientists is due to a single published work of modest size. In this work he was able, however, to analyze fully his experimental results, and to apprehend with perfect clarity the causal nexus which these results revealed. A really new discovery in depth is apt to be less easily understood than a discovery in breadth. Darwin, not knowing of Mendel's work, was making some experiments of his own, which led him within an ace of obtaining results paralleling Mendel's. Whether or not he would have analyzed the results as masterfully as Mendel did is a moot point. The late J. B. S. Haldane thought that

Mendel's analysis was somehow facilitated by his familiarity with Thomist philosophy. This is an extraordinary compliment for Thomistic philosophy, but I am not convinced that it is warranted.

II

Darwin was certainly aware of the importance of understanding heredity for understanding evolution. In his books, especially in that dealing with domesticated animals and plants, he painstakingly collated every bit of information about heredity that he found in the literature. Evolution is a complement of heredity, or rather a negation of heredity. Heredity tends to make the progeny resemble the parents and other ancestors. Evolution makes the descendants unlike the ancestors. If heredity were always exact, evolution could not happen. An offspring of a pair of parents consists, however, of individuals which differ to some extent from the parents and from each other. This is variation.

Variation is the fountainhead of evolution. Taking variation for granted, Darwin proceeded to describe how natural selection molds it into shapes which make living beings adapted to their environments. He was satisfied that the variation was universal, observable in all organisms. He acknowledged, however, that the origin of variation was unknown. So long as this ignorance was unbroken the theory of evolution was incomplete. One could even say that this theory was a colossus with feet of clay. This was pointed out in 1867 by Fleming Jenkin, an engineer rather than a biologist. Suppose that a light-skinned individual appears in a dark-skinned population. Could the light-skinned variant eventually replace the original form? It seemed that it could not. The new variant, a mutant as we would call it now, is unlikely to arise in many individuals in any one place and at any one time. The mutant will have to mate with an individual of ordinary color. Their children will presumably be intermediate between the parents, and they too will have to marry partners of the usual color. After a few generations of intermarriage, the mutant will disappear like a drop of a soluble dye in a sea. It will be dissolved in the prevailing norm.

Jenkin's argument tacitly assumes that the heredity of a child is a blend of the parental heredities, and that the components of the blend never regain their purity. This is the vernacular notion, sometimes dignified by the name of "blood theory of heredity," which Darwin and Jenkin, and everybody else in their day, assumed to be correct. Everybody, that is, except Mendel, who showed it to be erroneous. Mendel's paper was, however, reposing on some library shelf which Darwin did not reach. Darwin doubtless felt that the blood theory contained some hidden fallacy, which he was, however, unable to pinpoint. Heslop-Harrison (1958) even argued that Darwin did not really accept the blood theory as valid, because he knew that some hybrids do not show blending but show instead what we at present call Mendelian segregation, i.e., reappearance of individuals resembling the parents of the cross. Darwin did know this, from the literature and from his own experiments. He also knew, however, that in many, in fact in most hybrids, segregation is not easily perceptible. This is called at present polygenic inheritance; it is basically Mendelian but technically difficult to analyze. Darwin's judicious objectivity made in this case a disservice. He drifted towards Lamarckian notions, which happened to be incorrect.

The rediscovery in 1900 of Mendel's forgotten work should have at once laid the ghost of the blood theory of heredity. It was not quite that simple. The early stages of the development of genetics are analyzed for you by Drs. Dunn and Sturtevant. I had the opportunity to discuss the genetics of the origin of variations before the American Philosophical Society six years ago, when we commemorated the Darwin Centennial (Dobzhansky, 1959). I can limit myself here to only a few remarks concerning these matters.

Some log jams had to be cleared before Darwinism and Mendelism could join forces. For a time, it did not seem unreasonable to entertain a kind of dualistic theory of heredity, assuming that some of the inheritance is transmitted from parents to offspring by miscible "bloods," and other inheritance by immiscible genes. For example, the variation of the eye color in man is nearly (though not quite) discontinuous. Segregation of brown-eyed and blue-eyed types of progeny is observable in many families. On the other hand, the variation of human stature seems to be continuous and the inheritance blending. It took close to thirty years to have almost everybody convinced that continuous variability is fundamentally Mendelian.

Mutation is the source of the hereditary variation which Darwin was looking for. How tantalizingly close he was to its discovery is evident from his following statement:

All the characters . . . which are transmitted in a perfect state to some of the offspring and not to others, such as distinct colors, nakedness of skin, smoothness of leaves, absence of horns or tail, additional toes, pelorism, dwarfed structure, etc., have all been known to appear suddenly in individual animals and plants. From this fact, and from the several slight, aggregated differences which distinguish domestic races and species from each other, not being liable to this peculiar form of transmission, we may conclude that it is in some way connected with the sudden appearance of the characters in question.

And yet, de Vries, the pioneer student of mutation, contrasted the mutational variability with the ubiquitous continuous hereditary variation, which Darwin believed to represent the raw materials with which natural selection operates.

De Vries dealt with mutations so sharply distinct from the parental form that he believed them to be new biological species. Mutationism was construed not as an integral part of, but as an alternative to Darwinism and Mendelism. The work of T. H. Morgan and his school at last resolved the puzzle. Mutations come, so to speak, in all sizes, from so drastic ones that the mutants are inviable, to so slight ones that a very keen eye or a statistical refinement is needed to detect them at all. No matter how drastic a mutation may be, it does not create a new species (except for the special case of doubling the chromosome complement in some otherwise sterile hybrids between distinct species). All the numerous mutants observed in *Drosophila* flies still belong to the same species in which they have arisen. Mutants do, however, possess all the characteristics which seem requisite in the materials from which natural selection could compound species differences. They are hereditary variants that cannot be swamped by blending with the ancestral form, but they can become more and more frequent if they are favored by natural selection and can eventually replace the ancestral form. Hardy and Weinberg showed independently, both in 1908, that the Mendelian mechanism tends to preserve the variant genes in the population, from one generation to the next, with constant frequencies, unless they are either eliminated or multiplied by natural selection.

The stage was now set for further advances. Chetverikov in 1926 had sketched the outlines of what has more recently come to be called the biological, or synthetic, theory of evolution (an English translation of Chetverikov's classic was published in the *Proceedings* of the American Philosophical Society in 1961). Fisher (1930), Wright (1931), and Haldane (1932), largely independently of each other and unacquainted with Chetverikov's contribution, gave more rigorous mathematical formulations of the basic tenets of the theory. This was unprecedented in biology—a theory was deduced mathematically from a single fundamental premise—Mendel's law of segregation. Some additions and elaborations, but no basic changes were made in this deductive theory for about thirty years. The mathematical theory has, however, far outstripped its biological foundation —again for the first time in the history of biology. Significant developments since Haldane-Wright-Fisher halcyon days were generalizing works which examined the factual data accumulated in several biological disciplines, and found that those data make sense in the light of the deductive theory. Mayr, Simpson, Rensch, Schmalhausen, Stebbins, Darlington, White, Ford, and Grant are the outstanding names among the founders of the modern biological theory of evolution. This theory has also been named "synthetic." It is synthetic, in the sense that it embodies a synthesis of data from biology as a whole. The word "synthetic" may, however, also mean artificial or factitious, as contrasted with genuine, and this makes the designation "biological" preferable in my opinion.

III

In Mendelian terms, the process of organic evolution can be described as a sequence of substitutions in consecutive generations of some genes for others. Genes, let it be noted, are carried mostly, though not exclusively, in the chromosomes, and a definition of evolution must accordingly be framed to include the chromosomal and the cytoplasmic heredity. This definition is satisfactory as far as it goes, but it does not go far enough. It describes adequately only the elementary components, and not the way the components compose the evolution. The definition is reductionist, and it needs a compositionist counterpart, to use the expression suggested by Simpson (1964a). For evolution is not only substitution of independent components; it is also integration of the components to form adaptively coherent systems. My favorite analogy is that genes act not like solo players but more like members of a symphony orchestra.

The origin of strains of bacteria resistant to antibiotics can serve as a paradigm of elementary evolutionary events which are experimentally reproducible. The origin of insect populations resistant to pesticides is less easily reproducible but equally clear. What is involved is adaptation of organisms to man-made environmental factors. Antibiotic-resistant bacteria and insecticide-resistant insects can live in environments in which bacteria and insects ordinarily do not live. The adaptation occurs through a mutation-selection mechanism. Mutation is a change in a gene, or in a chromosome which carries the genes. It is adaptively ambiguous; i.e., mutations arise regardless of whether they will be useful or harmful to their carriers, and a great majority of mutations are in fact harmful. Mutation is not evolution, but, as pointed out above, it supplies the raw materials from which evolution can be built in response to challenges of the environment. The builder is natural selection.

Mutant bacteria resistant to antibiotics, and insects resistant to insecticides, arise in the species whose genes are capable of producing these mutants, irrespective of whether antibiotics or insecticides are present or absent in the environment. A bacterial culture containing many millions or billions of cells, or an insect population of many millions of individuals, would usually include a few resistant variants. Resistant variants have no advantage, and they are likely to be at a disadvantage in survival and reproduction, in environments free of antibiotics or insecticides. Natural selection not only does not increase their frequencies in the bacterial cultures or the insect populations, but keeps the frequencies down. The situation changes when the antibiotics or insecticides arrive on the scene. What was disadvantageous becomes advantageous, and it may be the only form able to survive. The nonresistant forms fail to be perpetuated, and the resistant ones take their place. The speed of the replacement depends, of course, on how great the respective advantages and disadvantages are. It may be that, at high concentrations of an antibiotic or an insecticide, only the resistants survive and all the sensitives are killed. The change is accomplished in one generation. On the other hand, one form may produce 100 offspring in an environment in which the other produces only 99. The replacement by natural selection will then take many generations. It is nevertheless important to know that, given enough time, natural selection will be effective even when operating with small fitness differences.

Another kind of experimentally reproducible genetic changes should be mentioned. A form of natural selection, called balancing selection is particularly important in higher organisms. It leads not to replacement of one gene by another but rather to maintenance of both. Contrary to what some geneticists liked to think, natural selection does not usually establish some kind of an optimum genetic endowment shared by all members of a species, but rather sustains a genetic diversity. The population becomes polymorphic, consisting of two or more genetically distinct kinds of individuals. Human populations, like those of most sexually reproducing organisms, are highly polymorphic; so much so, that no two individuals, identical twins excepted, are at all likely to have the same genotypes, complements of genes.

The two most interesting kinds of balancing selection are the heterotic and the diversifying. Heterotic selection occurs when the heterozygote, the genotype having two variants of the same gene or gene complex, enjoys hybrid vigor, heterosis, compared to the homozygotes, carrying the same gene in double dose. Diversifying selection depends on the complexity of the environment. Suppose, for example, that there are two kinds of food available, and two genotypes, one of which thrives better on one and the other on the other food. In human societies there may be different occupations or professions which are most congenial to, or which can be performed most successfully by, carriers of different genotypes. Natural selection will, then, tend to make each kind of genotype reach a frequency in the population conforming to the prevalence of the respective foods or opportunities.

In many species of *Drosophila* flies, the populations in their natural habitats are polymorphic for the structure of their chromosomes. Some individuals have chromosomes differing from others by inversions of blocks of genes. The chromosomal variants interbreed freely. The chromosomal polymorphism is maintained by heterotic balancing selection. The highest fitness is found in flies which have the two chromosomes of a pair different in structure (heterozygotes), while flies with pairs of similar chromosomes (homozygotes) are inferior in fitness. The exciting thing is that the selection pressures acting on these naturally occurring variants are so great that the natural selection can be reproduced and measured in the laboratory. We can make experimental populations, maintained in special cages made of wood or of plastic, and observe the chromosomal variants change in frequencies from generation to generation, until they reach stable equilibria. The selection is not only strong, but exquisitely responsive to environmental changes. Two chromosomes found in the populations of *Drosophila pseudoobscura* in the western United States give a heterozygote which has a fitness more than twice that of one of the homozygotes, in the experimental populations kept at 25°C and fed on a certain food. Lowering the temperature by only 9 degrees, to 16°, makes these heterozygotes and homozygotes identical in fitness, within the limits of precision of the experimental technique. Altering the food on which the populations are kept also produces considerable changes in fitness relationships.

IV

Natural selection is often compared, especially in popular writings, to a sieve. It retains the useful genetic variants, and lets the harmful ones become lost. So crude a mechanical analogy is of limited usefulness. It does fit the simplest situations, like the selection of antibiotic-resistant and insecticide-resistant strains, or the elimination of hereditary diseases and malformations which many mutations produce. These elementary processes are repeatable, predictable, and reversible, at least in principle. Provided that mutations resistant to streptomycin are produced in a species of bacteria, exposing to streptomycin a number of bacterial cells large enough to contain at least one mutant makes it very probable that a streptomycin-resistant strain will be obtained. Conversely, placing a streptomycin-resistant strain on a nutrient medium without streptomycin encourages the selection of mutants reverting to the original form.

The sieve analogy is less appropriate to describe balancing natural selection. Here the "sieve" would have to be so contrived that it will retain genetic variants when they are rare and remove them when they become frequent. Adaptation to heterogeneous environments is most readily achieved by genetic diversity. Genetic diversity, polymorphism, raises a new problem, to which the sieve analogy is irrelevant. This is mutual adjustment, coadaptation, of constituents of a genetic system. Let me reiterate that the analogy most appropriate to describe the gene action in ontogeny, the development of an individual, is a symphony orchestra. The ontogeny, from fertilization to birth, adulthood, and death, is not a sequence of independent gene effects following each other, but a marvelously well-integrated system of feedbacks. To be adapted to an external environment, the components of a genotype must be internally coadapted, i.e., must fit harmoniously together. A gene, A, may interact favorably with B but not with C; natural selection will favor A if it arises in a genotype containing B, and will discriminate against A if it arises with C.

This has important consequences. Evolutionary changes depend on the changes that preceded them, and condition the changes that follow them. The role of the environment in evolution is now seen in a new light. In the origin of antibiotic-resistant strains the environment is the determining factor. In the presence of an antibiotic, the bacteria must either become resistant or be destroyed. Even here, it appears that the organism has a certain amount of "freedom"— there are several genes, any one of which may mutate to produce a resistance. With genetically more complex changes, the environment can only be described as presenting challenges, to which the organism may respond by any one of the many possible adaptive reconstructions. Which response will actually be given depends on the genetic materials which will happen to be available when and where the challenge is to be met.

Another consequence is the so-called "law" of irreversibility of evolution. As pointed out above, the elementary evolutionary events, sometimes called microevolutionary, such as the mutation-selection episodes yielding the antibiotic-resistant bacterial strains, are reversible. Not so with macroevolutionary processes. The changes which led to the origin of mankind from its pre-human ancestors are irreversible. The reason is that the series of consecutive changes which took place in, presumably, thousands of genes are infinitely unlikely to be retraced in the same sequence in which they occurred before. By the same token, they are unlikely to be re-enacted. Microevolution is repeatable; macroevolution is unrepeatable. In recent years this matter has been debated in connection with the speculations concerning the likelihood of existence elsewhere in the universe of living beings, including humanoids resembling those on earth. Dobzhansky (1960) and Simpson (1964a) have discussed the problem in more detail. Very briefly, even assuming that some sort of life arose in many places in the cosmos, it seems highly improbable that it would evolve into anything resembling the creatures met with on earth. Those who hold the contrary opinion, usually argue that the adaptive features of the living beings fit remarkably the demands of the environment. This is true, but beside the point. The problem of becoming adapted to a given environment can be "solved" in evolution usually in many different ways. It cannot be lightly assumed that whenever a "solution" is possible it will in fact be achieved. Microevolution is deterministic, macroevolution is creative. The results of a creative process are uncertain—it may succeed or fail.

Experimental evidence bearing on macroevolution must, of necessity, be indirect. We cannot re-enact the evolution of the horses during the Tertiary, or the emergence of the land-dwelling from the water-dwelling vertebrate animals. At best, experiments can be made on complex kinds of microevolutionary changes, for which I have suggested the designation "mesoevolution" (Dobzhansky, 1954). Two examples of such experiments can be briefly reviewed here. In both of them the chromosomal variants of *Dropsophila pseudoobscura* are utilized as materials. As mentioned above, these variants are maintained in natural populations of this fly by the heterotic balancing selection. Now, the cultures in which the flies are kept in laboratories have environments obviously not identical with the natural ones. The laboratory flies are maintained either in culture bottles, or in the population cages mentioned above. Natural selection taking place in these highly artificial, or if you wish unnatural, conditions makes the flies progressively more fit to live in the respective laboratory environments, the culture bottles or the population cages.

Suppose, then, that one has strains of two chromosomal variants, *A* and *B*, which have lived for a series of generations in culture bottles, and other strains which lived in population cages. Strickberger (1963) made two kinds of experimental population cages; in the first kind, the *A* parents were from bottles and *B* from cages, and in the second *A* from cages and *B* from bottles. The equilibrium frequencies which the chromosomes *A* and *B* attained in the experimental populations were different; *A* chromosomes were less frequent, and *B* more frequent, in the first than in the second kind of population. The difference persisted generation after generation. The chromosomes had their histories, as it were, inscribed in their genes.

The evolutionary histories of natural populations which live in territories with different climatic and other conditions are also "inscribed" in their genes, in the sense that such populations become different races, each adapted to its environment. The chromosomal types, which we have denoted above as *A* and *B*, often occur in the populations of different territories. Experimental laboratory populations containing *A* and *B* may be arranged in two ways. In experimental populations of geographically uniform origin the chromosomes *A* and *B* are descended from wild ancestors collected in the same locality; in populations of geographically mixed origins the chromosomes *A* come from one locality and *B* from another. Dobzhansky and Pavlovsky (1953) and Dobzhansky and Spassky (1962) found an interesting difference between the behavior of the populations of uniform and of mixed origins. The results obtained in populations of geographically uniform origin are repeatable and predictable; if one arranges several replicate populations with flies from the same cultures, and keeps them in the same controlled environment, all the populations reach, within the limits of experimental errors, the same equilibrium frequencies of the chromosomal forms. Scientists take it almost for granted that well-executed experiments should be repeatable; if a repetition fails to yield the same result as obtained formerly, one looks for undetected flaws in the experimental procedure. And yet, replicate experimental populations of geographically mixed origins often reach quite diverse equilibrium frequencies of the chromosomal forms.

This, at first sight, complex and confusing situation has a simple explanation. Assume that two geographic areas are inhabited by populations differing in *n* genes. Mendelian segregation and recombination in the progenies of hybrids between such populations may produce as many as 3^n different genotypes. If n is in tens, not to speak of hundreds, the numbers of potentially possible genotypes become vastly greater than the numbers of individuals in any experimental or natural populations. In other words, many potentially possible genotypes will not in fact be formed. Consider now the situation presented by several replicate experimental populations. The genotypes which will arise will usually not be the same in any two populations. How will natural selection act in these circumstances? It will encourage the propagation of whatever favorable genotypes will happen to be present in any given population. Replicate populations give therefore dissimilar and diverging results. We observe, in miniature, what we called above the creativity of the evolutionary process. The "problem" of becoming adapted to a given environment may be solved in a variety of ways.

V

According to Wald (1963), "living organisms are the greatly magnified expressions of the molecules that compose them." This trenchant aphorism is, of course, a restatement of the organism-the-machine theory of Descartes. But as Wald himself said on another occasion (Wald, 1958),

> Confronting any phenomenon in living organisms, the biologist has always to ask three kinds of questions, each independent of the others: the question of mechanism (how does it work?), the question of adaptation (what does it do for the organism?), the twin questions of embryogeny and evolution (how did it come about?).

The first kind of questions call for Cartesian, reductionist; the other kinds for Darwinian, compositionist, answers (Dobzhansky, 1964; Simpson, 1964b). Organisms do not arise by accidental conflux of molecules. The creatures that are alive today are the products of unbroken sequences of patternings of molecular components; these sequences extend back to the origin of life, two or more billion years ago. Every generation involves formation and dissolution of a pattern, but the consecutive patterns are not independent. They are products of accumulation and storage of genetic information. Natural selection is a cybernetic process which transfers the information concerning the state of the environment to the genotype.

Already Darwin grappled with the difficulty that the formation in evolution of complex organs, such as the vertebrate eye, seems an improbable event. A few years ago, one of the outstanding living mathematicians sent me a long and closely argued private letter, in which he urged that a combination of many gene mutations adding up to such an organ is so absurdly improbable that we have to suppose that organic evolution is guided by a deity. I cannot gainsay his mathematics, but biological mathematics is at best only as valid as the biological assumptions on which it rests. The assumption implied in his argument was that, in order that an organ be formed, numerous mutants must arise and all come together in one place at the same time. This is, indeed, too far-fetched to credit. But it is the assumption that is at fault. Natural selection was working in a long succession of generations; it was not aiming to build the organ or the body which we now observe in a state of relative perfection; it was acting to modify the structures and the functions of a succession of ancestral organs and bodies in accord with the challenges coming from the ancestral environments.

The argument is out of focus also in another way. It tries to envisage the evolutionary development, the phylogeny, as though it were an individual development, an ontogeny. An individual begins as a single cell, a fertilized ovum, and proceeds to develop through a complex series of maneuvers. Body structures and functions that are formed fit together as if planned by some foresight for the purpose of making a body which can live in a certain environment. Ontogeny seems to be attracted by its end rather than impelled by its beginning. This is an astounding thing for a pile of molecules to do, and Sinnott (1950–1957) sees himself forced to assume that the development is governed by a psyche, a new name for the old vital force. This misrepresents both the ontogeny and the phylogeny.

Individual development is understandable only as part of the phylogenetic development of the species, not the other way around. The ontogeny follows a certain course, because it is a part of a cyclic (more precisely, a spiral) sequence of the developments of the ancestors. Organs in a developing individual are formed for future uses, because in evolution they were formed for contemporaneous utility. The development of an individual may be said to end in death; a better way of understanding it is to say that it continues in the progeny. It is a part of the process of the storage of genetic information which continues through time. Ontogeny may be likened to building an automobile or some other complex machine on an assembly line. The automobile is not being used while on the assembly line, it is being prepared for future uses. Phylogeny is more like the gradual derivation of the present automobile models from the primitive ones, and eventually from coaches, chariots, and push-carts. Natural selection performs the role of the engineer—it devises both the ways to improve the models and the techniques of manufacturing them.

VI

In discovering the genes, Mendel has, without knowing this, furnished the keystone of the arch which Darwin was building. With "blood" heredity, biological evolution would, at best, be exceedingly slow and inefficient; with gene heredity, evolutionary mechanisms are comprehensible. In turn, the theory of biological evolution is the keystone of the evolutionary world view. However, it is useful to be reminded that the cosmic and the cultural evolution theories were arrived at before the biological one. The nebular hypothesis of Kant (1755), Herschel (1791) and Laplace (1796) antedates the biological theory of Lamarck (1809), and the uniformitarian geology of Hutton (1795) and Lyell (1830) comes before *The Origin of Species* of Darwin (1859). The rise of the evolutionary view of man is less easy to date. Condorcet's (1793) inspired vision of the ten periods of historical development of mankind was clearly evolutionistic. Herder's *Ideas of the Philosophy of the History of Humanity* (1784) leads the way to the evolutionary speculations of Fichte (1806) and to Hegel's *Philosophy of History* (1837).

Evolutionist world views consider the inorganic, the organic or biological, and the human or cultural evolutions as integral parts of a universal evolutionary development. On the other hand, some people have objected that biological evolution is an extension of the inorganic, and human evolution an extension of the biological, only in a chronological sense. Is it legitimate to use the word "evolution" for such disparate processes? I believe that it is legitimate, and yet the objection contains a kernel of truth and deserves consideration. The elementary components of the biological evolution are mutations, changes in the hereditary materials. Mutation presupposes heredity, and heredity is self-reproduction, or self-copying, of certain molecular patterns, which exist only in living systems, and which are, in fact, the chief characteristics of life. These carriers of genetic information are the nucleic acids and, secondarily, proteins. Furthermore, the process of mutation supplies only the genetic raw materials, from which evolutionary developments may or may not be constructed by natural selection, Mendelian recombination, and other processes.

Natural selection is predicated on mutation and self-reproduction, and hence on life. To apply the term "mutation" on the human level to novel ideas and inventions, is to use a vivid but rather misleading analogy. The same must be said concerning "natural selection" of physico-chemical processes in the inorganic nature, which supposedly led to the origin of life on earth. To have natural selection, life must already be present, because natural selection is differential reproduction, and reproduction is a basic characteristic of life. Culture is learned behavior which is shared by members of a human group. In nonhuman animals only barest traces of such behavior can be found. Culture is not inherited biologically through some special genes; it is learned, i.e., acquired, by every individual in every generation. Acquired biological traits are not inherited; all the so-called cultural inheritance is, on the contrary, acquired.

Inorganic, organic, and human evolutions occur in different dimensions, or on different levels, of the evolutionary development of the universe. The changes in the organic evolution are more rapid than in the inorganic. Nevertheless, the inorganic evolution did not come to a halt with the appearance of life; organic evolution is superimposed on the inorganic. Biological evolution of mankind is slower than the cultural evolution; nevertheless, biological changes did not cease when culture emerged; cultural evolution is superimposed on the biological and the inorganic. The evolutionary changes in the different dimensions are connected by feedback relationships.

The attainment of a new level or dimension is, however, a critical event in the evolutionary history. I propose to call it evolutionary transcendence. The word "transcendence" is obviously not used here in the sense of philosophical transcendentalism. I am using it in the same sense as Hallowell (1960): "The psychological basis of culture lies not only in a capacity for highly complex forms of learning but in a capacity for transcending what is learned, a potentiality for innovation, creativity, reorganization and change." Erich Fromm (1959) wrote that man "is driven by the urge to transcend the role of the creature," and that "he transcends the separateness of his individual existence by becoming part of somebody or something bigger than himself."

Dubos (1962) said that "what is still so completely mysterious as to acquire for many human beings a mystical quality, is that life should have emerged from matter, and that mankind should have ever started on the road which so clearly is taking it farther and farther away from its brutish origin." This is just as mysterious, but I hope no more so, as is the ability of life to continue amidst hostile environments. Cosmic evolution went beyond the range of inorganic processes when it produced life. The origin of man was a transcendence of biological evolution, because it opened up a new range of potentialities, of processes and events, which occur exclusively in man or under the influence of man. These fateful transcendences are not, however, beyond hope of understanding. They may be envisaged as extreme cases of evolutionary innovation, lesser examples of which are also known. A quantitative difference may, to be sure, be large enough to appear as a qualitative one. The origin of terrestrial vertebrates from fishlike ancestors opened up a new realm of adaptive radiations in the terrestrial environments, which was closed to water-dwelling creatures. The result was what Simpson (1953) has called "quantum evolution," an abrupt change in the ways of life as well as in the body structures. Domestication of fire and the invention of agriculture were among the momentous happenings which opened new paths for human evolution. In a still more limited compass, the highest fulfillment of an individual human life is self-transcendence.

Rough stone tools have been found in association with australopithecine remains both in east-central and in South Africa. *Homo erectus* in China is the oldest known user of fire. The Neanderthalians were burying their dead. These are evidences of humanization. Some animals, birds, and even insects are known occasionally to use objects as tools, but intentional manufacture of a tool is a sign of a psychic organization known to exist in man alone. All animals die, but man alone knows that he will die; a burial is a sign of a death awareness, and probably of the existence of ultimate concern. The ancestors of man began to transcend their animality perhaps as early as 1,700,000 years ago. The process is under way in ourselves. Nobody has characterized this process more clearly than Bidney (1953):

Man is a self-reflecting animal in that he alone has the ability to objectify himself, to stand apart from himself, as it were, and to consider the kind of being he is and what it is that he wants to do and to become. Other animals may be conscious of their affects and the objects perceived; man alone is capable of reflection, of self-consciousness, of thinking of himself as an object.

And according to Hallowell (1959):

The great novelty, then, in the behavioral evolution of the primates, was not simply the development of a cultural mode of adaptation as such. It was, rather, the psychological restructuralization that not only made this new mode of existence possible but provided the psychological basis for cultural re-adaptation and change.

To an orthodox reductionist, the concept of evolution transcendence may sound faintly vitalistic. A similar view has, however, been arrived at by the simon-pure dialectical materialists in Russia. Despite his Marxist jargon, Present (1964) states it fairly clearly as follows:

> Wherever it arose, the human society must have come from the zoological world, and it was work, the process of production, that made man human. However, what has removed people from the animal way of life and gave a specificity to their (new) life, became the essence and the basis of the history that ensued. . . . Likewise, in the realm of living nature, what removed the novel form of material motion from its nonliving prehistory, necessarily became its essence, its fundamental basis.

Reductionism is not wrong, but it tells only a part of the story. Where man is concerned, it is only a small part. Reductionism must go hand in hand with compositionism, Cartesian with Darwinian inquiry and discovery.

VII

Mendel, a peasant's son, found an opportunity for his intellectual pursuits only behind a monastery's walls; Darwin, a wealthy English country squire, made the study room in his house his laboratory. Neither of them was a professional scientist, and unknown to each other (Mendel read some of Darwin's books probably after his own biological work was finished), they collaborated to lay the foundations for an evolutionary world view. The universe, life, a man, are evolving products of evolutionary developments.

It is often alleged that Darwin's evolution theory has rendered complete man's alienation from the world which he inhabits. Copernicus and Galileo showed that man is not the center of the world, and that the earth is but a speck of dust in the cosmic spaces. Before Darwin, man was believed to be only slightly "lower than the angels," Darwin showed that he is only slightly higher than brute animals. And animals are, to consistently reductionist biologists, automata only slightly more complicated than watches, and perhaps less complicated than some electronic computers. All this misses the main point. Evolution means that, whether one considers the present state of the world and of man satisfactory or otherwise, it is not necessarily fixed and unchangeable forever. It is at least thinkable that man may recast the whole situation in a direction which he believes to be good, even though a long time and much effort may be needed to accomplish the reform. Evolutionist world views range from deeply pessimistic to brightly optimistic ones.

To Sir Julian Huxley, H. J. Muller, Sir Charles Galton Darwin, and others, mankind is headed for biological twilight, unless something is very quickly done to rescue it. And what will a world without man be worth? The development of culture and civilization has brought about an unpremeditated reversal of the trend of the biological evolution from beneficial to nefarious. Mankind evolved as it did because natural selection fostered improvements of the genetic basis for intelligence, group solidarity, cooperation, and, so it is believed, for human ethical values. Civilization has tended increasingly to frustrate and pervert the action of natural selection. Many kinds of hereditary infirmities and weaknesses are cured or relieved by ministrations of the medical arts; the carriers of genetic defects are helped to survive and to reproduce, thus increasing the incidence of the same defects in future generations. Living in dense populations, particularly in crowded cities, may have also more subtle but sinister effects. When nuclear families and even individuals must be sufficient unto themselves, instead of mutual help being enjoined on all by custom, natural selection which in the past favored altruism may now favor selfishness.

The way out is an eugenic selection of desirable types. One must begin, with all deliberate haste, to collect and preserve in deep-frozen condition the semen of eugenically approved donors, particularly of great and illustrious men. This will be utilized for artificial insemination of numerous women. Eventually techniques should be developed to obtain and preserve also the egg cells of superior women. Even more ambitious methods may be possible in the future. Sir Charles Galton Darwin thinks, however, that the willingness of people to regulate their procreative activities taking in consideration the common good is itself a genetic trait. If so, those who fail to heed such considerations will outbreed those who do, and their uncoöperativeness will grow more and more frequent in future generations. A human flood, rising higher and higher, will overwhelm a multitudinous but degenerate mankind. The "next million years" will see the eclipse of the human species.

The evolutionary world view of Teilhard de Chardin is in a

different key.[1] Its consideration must, unfortunately, begin with a refutation of the author's statement in the first paragraph of the Preface to his most widely read book (1959: p. 29): "If this book is to be properly understood, it must be read not as a work on metaphysics, still less as a sort of theological essay, but purely and simply as a scientific treatise." Read as a scientific treatise, it is equivocal, as has been pointed out by scientific reviewers, sometimes in needlessly scathing ways. Teilhard was a Christian mystic, who happened to be also a scientist, a metaphysician, and a poet. This can be seen in his other books (e.g., Teilhard de Chardin, 1960, 1964), which expound the same evolutionary world view as *The Phenomenon of Man*, without claiming to be purely and simply scientific treatises. However, it is sheer misunderstanding to see in Teilhard's writings attempts to derive his religious beliefs from, or to prove them by, his science. What he is trying to do is rather to include his science in his total world view, which is basically a religious one. Such an attempt is of interest to scientists. We have heard a great deal in recent years about the divorce of the two, or several, "cultures," about science being a "glorious entertainment," etc. Teilhard attempts to effect a reunion.

Teilhard's basic insight is that the cosmic, biological, and human evolutions are not only components but are developmental stages of a single process of universal evolution. This single process has a discernible direction. It has advanced from matter, to life, to thought. Teilhard's extrapolation anticipates further advances, to the coming "mega-synthesis" and to the "Omega point." A difficulty arises because of his unfortunate use of the word "orthogenesis" to describe the directionality of the organic evolution. The directionality is indisputable. We do not know what the primordial life was like, but it must assuredly have been represented by some very simple forms. More complex organisms developed later. Land plants appeared in the Silurian period, land animals in the Devonian, first mammals in late Triassic and early Jurassic, first primates in Paleocene, hominids in late Pliocene or early Pleistocene. However, orthogenesis was not simply a word describing the fact of directionality, but a now almost defunct hypothesis pretending to explain the

---

[1]In the Introduction to the English translation of Teilhard's *The Phenomenon of Man* (1959), Sir Julian Huxley claims that Teilhard's ideas are mostly similar to those published earlier by himself. This is true only in so far as both authors are, of course, evolutionists. Beyond this, their ways of thinking are almost at polar opposites.

causation of this directionality. It postulated that evolutionary changes are the unfolding or manifestation of preexisting rudiments. Evolutionary changes are predetermined, in the same way that ontogenetic changes, from embryo to adult to death, are predetermined. The comparison between ontogeny and phylogeny is, to believers in orthogenesis, more than a simple analogy. It is envisaged as a causal similarity.

This is inconsistent with Teilhard's basic view that the organic as well as human evolution proceeds by "groping" (*tâtonnement*). Groping is "pervading everything so as to try everything, and trying everything so as to find everything." Ontogeny and orthogenesis do not try anything, because they move in a straight line toward a predetermined end result. The "grouping" leads to a succession of "layers" (*nappes*), of progressively more complex levels of organization of matter, of life, and of thought. This is neither orthogenesis nor vitalism. Mendelian recombination of genes is the way, on the biological level, of "pervading everything so as to try everything," i.e., to try out as many genotypes as can be formed. Teilhard did not know that the numbers of potentially possible genotypes are far greater than the numbers of individuals in which they can be realized and exposed to natural selection. "Trying everything so as to find everything" is a splendid metaphorical description of the operation of natural selection.

Teilhard was sceptical concerning the competence of natural selection to arrive at evolutionary "inventions." This seemed to him relying too much on "chance." He did not realize that natural selection is not building perfect organisms out of piles of unrelated genes; selection acts on a succession of parental and descendant generations modifying the organisms to fit their environments. Any orthogenetic theory of evolution postulates preformation; all that happens was bound to happen; man and animal and tree were equally present in the primordial life, and it just took time to have them gradually emerge from their hidden to their manifest state. This is completely contrary to Teilhard's basic philosophy of universal evolution being a creative process, not just an unveiling of what was there all the time in a concealed state. Creation implies the risk of miscreation, and Teilhard envisaged the possibility of the evolution being a failure: "There is a danger that the elements of the world might refuse to serve the world—because they think; or more precisely that the world should refuse itself when perceiving itself through reflection." Having been a paleontologist, Teilhard was familiar with the phenomenon of extinction of phyletic lines. Believers in orthogenesis assume that the cause of extinction is a "senescence" of the phyletic line, predetermined by the organization of the latter in much the same way as the senescence and death of an individual organism. Predetermination is foreign to Teilhard's thinking. If all that happens in evolution is a long strip-tease act, all evolution becomes meaningless. Why should there be such a delay in reaching the state of final perfection? This, together with the problem of the existence of evil in the world, would vitiate any attempt to build a theodicy, an understanding of the meaning of God's creative activity, which is in the center of Teilhard's whole thought. Evolution is meaningful only if it involves creativity and freedom. Extinction is comprehensible because evolution is, to use Teilhard's metaphor, "groping" in the dark, among dangers and pitfalls. Extinction is a consequence of becoming irrevocably adapted to environments which do not last.

Despite the dangers and pitfalls, evolution has been, on the whole, a success rather than a failure. It has achieved the two great transcendences, the origin of life and the origin of man. In this article, which has attempted to trace the directions in which Mendel's work has led evolutionary biology, it would be out of place to discuss Teilhard's extrapolations that the evolution will eventually reach the transcendences of the "mega-synthesis" and the "Omega." It is perhaps appropriate to conclude in Teilhard's words:

> The outcome of the world, the gates of the future, the entry into the super-human—these are not thrown open to a few of the privileged, nor to one chosen people to the exclusion of all others. They will open to an advance of *all together*, in a direction in which *all together* can join and find fulfillment in a spiritual renovation of the earth. . . .[2]

References

ANESAKI, M. 1963. *History of Japanese Religion* (Rutland & Tokyo, Ch. Tuttle Co.).

BIDNEY, D. 1953. *Theoretical Anthropology* (New York, Columbia Univ. Press).

CHETVERIKOV, S. S. 1926 (1961). "On Certain Aspects of the Evolutionary Process from the Standpoint of Modern Genetics. Translated by Malina Baker. *Proc. Amer. Philos. Soc. 105*: pp. 167–195.

DOBZHANSKY, TH. 1954. "Evolution as a Creative Process." *Proc. 9th International Congress Genetics, Caryologia, Suppl. 6*: pp. 435–449.

———. 1959. "Variation and Evolution." *Proc. Amer. Philos. Soc. 103*: pp. 252–263.

[2]Somewhat similar ideas were a part of the creed of the Tientai (Tendai) sect of Buddhism, which arose in China in the sixth century A.D. One of the tenets of this sect was that all human souls, and even all that exists, will eventually rise to the dignity of Buddha himself (*cf.* Anesaki, 1963).

————. 1960. "Evolution and Environment." In: S. Tax (ed.), *Evolution after Darwin 1*: pp. 403–428.

————. 1964. "Biology, Molecular and Organismic." *Amer. Zoologist 4*: pp. 443–452.

DOBZHANSKY, TH., and O. PAVLOVSKY. 1953. "Indeterminate Outcome of Certain Experiments of Drosophila Populations." *Evolution 7*: pp. 198–210.

DOBZHANSKY, TH., and N. SPASKY. 1962. "Genetic Drift and Natural Selection in Experimental Populations of *Drosophila pseudoobscura*." *Proc. Nat. Acad. Sci. 48*: pp. 148–156.

DUBOS, R. 1962. *The Torch of Life* (New York, Trident Press, Simon & Schuster).

FISHER, R. A. 1930. *The Genetical Theory of Natural Selection* (Oxford, Clarendon).

FROMM, E. 1959. "Value, Psychology, and Human Existence." In: A. H. Maslow (ed.), *New Knowledge in Human Values* (New York, Harper).

HALDANE, J. B. S. 1932. *The Causes of Evolution* (London, Longmans Green).

HALLOWELL, A. I. 1959. "Behavioral Evolution and the Emergence of the Self." In: *Evolution and Anthropology* (Washington, Anthrop. Soc.), pp. 36–60.

HESLOP-HARRISON, J. 1958. "Darwin as a Botanist." In: S. A. Barnett (ed.), *A Century of Darwin*, pp. 267–295.

PRESENT, I. I. 1964. "On the Essence of Life in Connection with Its Origin. (In Russian.) In: *O sushchnosti zhizni* (Moscow, Nauka).

SIMPSON, G. G. 1953. *The Major Features of Evolution* (New York, Columbia Univ. Press).

————. 1964a. *This View of Life* (New York, Harcourt Brace).

————. 1964b. "Organisms and Molecules in Evolution." *Science 146*: pp. 1535–1538.

SINNOTT, E. W. 1950. *Cell and Psyche* (Chapel Hill, Univ. North Carolina Press).

————. 1957. *Matter, Mind and Man* (New York, Harper).

STRICKBERGER, M. W. 1963. "Evolution of Fitness in Experimental Populations of *Drosophila pseudoobscura*." *Evolution 17*: pp. 40–55.

TEILHARD DE CHARDIN, P. 1959. *The Phenomenon of Man* (New York, Harper).

————. 1960. *The Divine Milieu* (New York, Harper).

————. 1964. *The Future of Man* (New York, Harper).

WALD, G. 1958. "Innovation in Biology." *Scient. Amer. 199*: pp. 100–113.

————. 1963. "Phylogeny and Ontogeny at the Molecular Level." In: A. I. Oparin (ed.), *Evolutionary Biochemistry* (London, Pergamon).

WRIGHT, S. 1931. "Evolution in Mendelian Populations." *Genetics 16*: pp. 97–159.

2

Problems in Primate Taxonomy

Molecules and Monkeys*

JOHN BUETTNER-JANUSCH

ROBERT L. HILL

(*Editor's Note*) The commonly accepted classification of the order of Primates is based on criteria of gross anatomy. Over the years the accumulating fossil evidence indicates that the hierarchy presented in that classification generally corresponds with the chronological sequence in which the taxa evolved. The question posed in this article by Buettner-Janusch and Hill is whether the molecular characteristics of the living taxa tell the same evolutionary story as indicated by the gross anatomical characteristics. The fundamental question is, however, do traits which are primary gene products, such as the amino acid sequences, have more or less significance than polygenic traits for taxonomic purposes when such a taxonomy is to indicate phylogenetic relationships? The approach by the authors is to take some of the molecular characteristics of the taxa and hold them up against the generally accepted classification of the primates. There are a number of complications. For example, the structural diversity of the hemoglobin molecule among primate groups depends in part, at least, on what part of the molecule is being examined. Some chains of this molecule are evidently quite "conservative"—they have differentiated less over time than others. Presumably there are functional correlates of the parts of the molecule which do vary among taxa, but as yet they are unknown. Gross anatomical differences, of course, lend themselves much more readily to functional interpretations although any statement about the selective advantages of such traits are just as highly speculative as such statements about some of the molecular differences.

*From *Science*, vol. 147, February 1965, pages 836–842. By permission of the authors and the publisher.

Buettner-Janusch and Hill emphasize that the degree of similarity among taxa, be it molecular or morphological, cannot be directly translated into the amount of time since their divergence. The authors believe that adaptation can override phylogenetic similarities. Moreover, adaptation at the molecular level may be quite independent of changes occurring at the gross level. Agreement among different kinds of classificatory sorting criteria need not always exist.

THE era of the molecule, the protein molecule, is upon us Anthropology, as it attempts to reconstruct the phylogeny of man and his fellow members of the order Primates, must take cognizance of molecules. It is unlikely that significant quantities of proteins will ever be extractable from fossil primates. But we can study the differences in many proteins of the living primates, a group of mammals that exhibit a remarkable degree of evolutionary stratification.

The respiratory protein hemoglobin is an excellent subject for a study of molecular evolution. The protein is easily obtainable in good yield. It has been extensively studied for many years, and much is known about it. The hemoglobin of one primate, *Homo sapiens*, has been intensively studied from genetic, biochemical, and molecular points of view. The formal genetics of many forms of human hemoglobin has been carefully worked out. Normal human hemoglobin A, designated Hb $\alpha_2^A \beta_2^A$, is a tetramer made up of two pairs of polypeptide chains called α and β (Figs. 1 and 2). The synthesis of the two chains is controlled by nonallelic genes. Various abnormal and variant human hemoglobins have been identified. The specific molecular differences among them have been characterized, and population frequencies have been determined for several of them. Thus an excellent model exists for research on hemoglobins of other primates (*1*).

Primate Phylogeny

We can place the living members of the order Primates in eight separate monophyletic taxa at various levels of the Linnaean hierarchy (Table I). We assign these eight taxa to four infraorders, two superfamilies, and two families. There are a number of ways in which the phylogeny of the Primates may be interpreted in the classification (2, 3). The phylogeny and classification we use are derived from Simpson's classic work on mammals and his subsequent discussions of primate systematics (4).

The Tupaiiformes, tree shrews of southeast Asia, are best placed with the Primates (5), even though they have many features which are intermediate between primate and insectivore. Often, in the past, they have been assigned to the Insectivora. The Tupaiiformes are of interest just because they appear to have characteristics intermediate between insectivores and primates.

The Lorisiformes of Asia and Africa and the Lemuriformes, unique to Madagascar, probably are the living representatives of an adaptive radiation that began in the late Paleocene or early Eocene. Though lemurs and lorises are often considered closely related, there are many good reasons for separating them at a fairly high level (6).

The Tarsiiformes are prosimians whose lineage is an ancient one, although one prominent monographer of the Primates wishes to classify them with the higher primates (7). They became a distinct phyletic group in the late Paleocene or very early Eocene.

The Cercopithecoidea are a major adaptive radiation that consists, today, of the monkeys of Asia and Africa. They are assumed to have a phyletic position intermediate between the prosimians and the apes. It is not unlikely that most modern cercopithecines are part of a relatively recent adaptive radiation, one that may just now be coming to an end. Some identifiable Cercopithecoidea are found in deposits of Oligocene age.

The Ceboidea developed in isolation in the New World with many structural and adaptive parallels to the primates of the Old World. Like the Malagasy lemurs, they are an example of the extent to which a primate stock may radiate and differentiate in isolation. They are a kind of evolutionary experiment and a side issue. They appear as a distinct group in Miocene deposits in South America.

The apes of Asia and Africa constitute the Pongidae—*Pan* (gorilla and chimpanzee), *Pongo* (orangutan), and *Hylobates* (gibbon and siamang) (3). Fossils of distinctly pongid aspect have been found in the late Oligocene deposits of Egypt (8).

The Hominidae became a separate phyletic line sometime in the Miocene (9). *Homo*, the single contemporary genus in this family, was fully differentiated in the early Pleistocene, and by that time the structural modification which led to the adaptive radiation of *Homo* was already being perfected.

(αT-1)
Val-Leu-Ser-Pro-Ala-Asp-Lys-Thr-Asn-Val-Lys-Ala-Ala-Try-Gly-Lys-Val-Gly-Ala-His-Ala-Gly-

(αT-2)   10   (αT-3)   (αT-4)   20

(αT-5)
Glu-Tyr-Gly-Ala-Glu-Ala-Leu-Glu-Arg-Met-Phe-Leu-Ser-Phe-Pro-Thr-Thr-Lys-Thr-Tyr-Phe-Pro-

30   (αT-6)

His-Phe-Asp-Leu-Ser-His-Gly-Ser-Ala-Gln-Val-Lys-Gly-His-Gly-Lys-Lys-Val-Ala-Asp-Ala-Leu-

50   (αT-7)   60   (αT-9)

Thr-Asn-Ala-Val-Ala-His-Val-Asp-Asp-Met-Pro-Asn-Ala-Leu-Ser-Ala-Leu-Ser-Asp-Leu-His-Ala-

70   80

His-Lys-Leu-Arg-Val-Asp-Pro-Val-Asn-Phe-Lys-Leu-Leu-Ser-His-Cys-Leu-Leu-Val-Thr-Leu-Ala-

90 (αT-10) (αT-11)   (αT-12)   110

Ala-His-Leu-Pro-Ala-Glu-Phe-Thr-Pro-Ala-Val-His-Ala-Ser-Leu-Asp-Lys-Phe-Leu-Ala-Ser-Val-

120   (αT-13) 130

Ser-Thr-Val-Leu-Thr-Ser-Lys-Tyr-Arg

(αT-14)

FIGURE 1. *The α chain of human hemoglobin A. The peptides obtained by digestion with trypsin are numbered αT-1, αT-2, and so on, according to nomenclature proposed by Gerald and Ingram (28).*

(βT-1)   (βT-2)   (βT-3) 20

β chain: Val-His-Leu-Thr-Pro-Glu-Glu-Lys-Ser-Ala-Val- Thr-Ala-Leu-Try-Gly-Lys-Val-Asn-Val-
γ chain: Gly-His-Phe-Thr-Glu-Glu-Asp-Lys-Ala-Thr-Ileu-Thr-Ser-Leu-Try-Gly-Lys-Val-Asn-Val-
Lemur: Thr-Leu-Ser-Ala-Glu-Glu-Asp-Ala-His-Val-Thr-Ser-Leu-Try-Gly-Lys-Val-Asn-Val-

                                    30 (βT-4)   40

β chain: Asp-Glu-Val-Gly-Gly-Glu-Ala-Leu-Gly-Arg-Leu-Val-Val- Tyr-Pro-Try-Thr-Gln-Arg-
γ chain: Glu-Asp-Ala-Gly-Gly-Glu-Thr-Leu-Gly-Arg-Leu-Leu-Val-Val- Tyr-Pro-Try-Thr-Gln-Arg-
Lemur: Glu-Lys-Val-Gly-Gly-Glu-Ala-Leu-Gly-Arg-Leu-Leu-Val-Val (Tyr,Pro,Try,Thr,Glu,Arg,

(βT-5)   50   (βT-6)

β chain: Phe-Phe-Glu-Ser-Phe-Gly-Asp-Leu-Ser-Thr-Pro-Asp-Ala-Val-Met-Gly-Asn-Pro-Lys-Val-
γ chain: Phe-Phe-Asp-Ser-Phe-Gly-Asn-Leu-Ser-Ser-Ala-Ser-Ala-Ileu- Met-Gly-Asn-Pro-Lys-Val-
Lemur: Phe,Phe,Glu,Ser,Phe,Gly,Asp) (Leu,Ser,Ser,Pro,Ser,Ala,Val,   Met,Gly,Asp,Pro,Lys,Val,

(βT-7)   (βT-9)   80

                                    70

β chain: Lys-Ala-His-Gly-Lys-Lys-Val-Leu-Gly-Ala-Phe-Ser-Asp-Gly-Leu-Ala-His-Leu-Asp-Asn-
γ chain: Lys-Ala-His-Gly-Lys-Lys-Val-Leu-Thr-Ser-Leu-Gly-Asp-Ala-Ileu-Lys-His-Leu-Asp-Asp-
Lemur: Lys,Ala,His,Gly,Lys,Lys,Val,Leu,Ser,Ala,Phe,Ser,Glu,Gly) (Leu,His,His,Leu,Asp,Asp,

FIGURE 2. *The β chain of human hemoglobin A, the γ chain of human hemoglobin F, and the partial sequence of β-like chain of Lemur fulvus hemoglobin. The tryptic peptides are indicated for the human β chain.*

(βT-10)   90   (βT-11)   100

β chain: Leu-Lys-Gly-Thr-Phe-Ala-Thr-Leu-Ser-Glu-His-Cys-Asp-Lys-Leu-His-Val-Asp-Pro-
γ chain: Leu-Lys-Gly-Thr-Phe-Ala-Gln-Leu-Ser-Glu-His-Cys-Asp-Lys-Leu-His-Val-Asp-Pro-
Lemur   Leu,Lys,Gly,Thr,Phe,Ala,Ala,Leu,Ser,Glu,Leu,His, Cys,Val,Ala,Leu,His, Val,Asp,Pro,

(βT-12)   110   120

β chain: Glu-Asn-Phe-Arg-Leu-Leu-Gly-Asn-Val-Leu-Val-Cys-Val-Leu-Ala-His-His-Phe-Gly-Lys-
γ chain: Glu-Asn-Phe-Lys-Leu-Leu-Gly-Asn-Val-Leu-Val-Thr-Val-Leu-Ala-Ileu-His-Phe-Gly-Lys-
Lemur: Glu,Asp,Phe,Lys,Leu,Leu,Gly,Asp,Ser,Leu,Ser,Asp,Val,Leu,Ala,Asp,His,Phe,Gly,Lys)...

(βT-13)   130   (βT-14)   140

β chain: Glu-Phe-Thr-Pro-Pro-Val-Gln-Ala-Ala-Tyr-Gln-Lys-Val-Val-Ala-Gly-Val-Ala-Asn-Ala-
γ chain: Glu-Phe-Thr-Pro-Glu-Val-Gln-Ala-Ser-Try-Gln-Lys-Met-Val-Thr-Gly-Val-Ala-Ser-Ala-
Lemur: ... Val-Val-Ala-Gly-Val(Ala,Asp)Ala,

(βT-15)

β chain: Leu-Ala-His-Lys-Tyr-His
γ chain: Leu-Ser-Ser-Arg-Tyr-His
Lemur: Leu,Ala,His,Lys,Tyr,His

FIGURE 2. (*Continued*)

Living primates constitute, in a crude way, a series of successively more advanced forms (*10*). They are an *échelle des êtres* in brief, and for this reason they are of great value for students of mammalian evolution. The evolutionary stratification of the living primates is the foundation for our study of hemoglobin. Hemoglobin for the studies reported here was obtained from representatives of the most primitive to representatives of the most advanced members of the order (Table 1). Unfortunately, we have not yet been able to beg, borrow, or steal a sample of *Tarsius* hemoglobin.

TABLE 1. *Classification of the order Primates, showing the eight major taxa and the representative genera used for studies on hemoglobin.*

CLASSIFICATION	GENUS	COMMON NAME
Suborder: Prosimii		
Infraorder:		
Tupaiiformes (I)	*Tupaia*	Tree shrew
Tarsiiformes (II)		
Lorisiformes (III)	*Galago*	Bush baby
Lorisiformes (III)	*Perodicticus*	Potto
Lemuriformes (IV)	*Lemur*	Lemur
Lemuriformes (IV)	*Propithecus*	Sifaka
Suborder: Anthropoidea		
Superfamily:		
Ceboidea (V)	*Saimiri*	Squirrel monkey
Ceboidea (V)	*Cacajao*	Uakari
Cercopithecoidea (VI)	*Papio*	Baboon
Cercopithecoidea (VI)	*Cercopithecus*	Guenon
Hominoidea		
Family:		
Pongidae (VII)	*Pongo*	Orangutan
Pongidae (VII)	*Hylobates*	Gibbon
Hominidae (VIII)	*Homo*	Man

It must be noted that there is an implicit assumption here. We assume that *Tupaia glis* has a more primitive hemoglobin than *Lemur fulvus* and that hemoglobin of *Hylobates lar* is more advanced than either. Though the various living primates *represent* Paleocene, Eocene, Oligocene, Miocene, Pliocene, and Pleistocene evolutionary developments, they are contemporary organisms. Each monophyletic lineage is the product of many genetic, adaptive, selective, and mutational events which have occurred since differentiation from the common stock. When we compare lemur to man we are comparing the contemporary products of about 55 million years of evolutionary divergence.

Materials and Methods

Hemoglobins from a number of non-human primates have been examined by various electrophoretic methods. Similarities to and differences from human hemoglobin have been reported by several investigators (11). We screened red cell hemolysates from a number of individuals of many primate species by the method of vertical starch-gel electrophoresis. A variety of patterns of migration of hemoglobin in such gels resulted (12). This screening enabled us to determine the so-called normal hemoglobin of each species. We were also able to demonstrate that hemoglobin polymorphism occurs in certain species (12).

We tested hemolysates from many species for the presence of alkali-resistant hemoglobin (13). The hemoglobin of all adult prosimian primates proved to have a large proportion of alkali-resistant pigment, as did the hemoglobin of the African elephant and the elephant shrews (Macroscelididae) of East Africa (14).

The normal hemoglobin of a species was further characterized by the technique of "fingerprinting" (15). Hemoglobin, globin, α chain, or β chain was digested with trypsin, and a "fingerprint" of the resultant digest was made on paper (16) or by means of column chromatography (17). Globins and α and β chains were prepared by methods previously described (18). Peptides were isolated after column chromatography of tryptic digests (19). The amino acid compositions of chains and peptides were determined by a method described elsewhere (20). Methods for determining NH_2-terminal amino acids and sequences of amino acids have also been described (21).

The α, β, and γ chains of Hb $\alpha_2^A \beta_2^A$ and Hb $\alpha_2^A \gamma_2^F$ are used as standards. A tryptic peptide from hemoglobin of a nonhuman primate is considered homologous to a human peptide if it migrates in the same way that the human peptide does on a paper fingerprint, if it is eluted with the same volume of buffer from ion-exchange columns, and if its amino acid composition is identical to that of the human peptide. Specific reactions with spray reagents that detect histidine, tyrosine, tryptophan, and arginine on paper fingerprints provide additional information.

Detailed studies of sequences have been made only for the hemoglobin of *Lemur fulvus*. The sequences of amino acids in other hemoglobins have been deduced, as described elsewhere (*16*). The final story of the evolution of primate hemoglobin must await complete elucidation of sequences of the polypeptide chains of hemoglobin from many species. However, the first chapter may now be written, based on less rigorous, less time-consuming, yet valid, methods.

Alpha- and Beta-Chain Evolution

The synthesis of the α and β chains of Hb $\alpha_2^A \beta_2^A$ are controlled by nonallelic genes. We assume that the homologous chains of hemoglobin of the other primates are similarily controlled. The α chains of primates seem to have evolved rather little, if we consider the small number of amino acid replacements found when these chains are compared with human α chains. The number of differences between the human α chain and α chains of various primates are listed in Table 2. The conservatism or the relative stability of the α chains is striking by comparison with the variability exhibited by the β-like chains of nonhuman primates. (Table 3). The α chains may have constraints placed on them. If a functioning hemoglobin is to be synthesized, then one of the two chains may have to remain stable. To put this another way, the β-like chain may be able to form functional hemoglobin in a variety of forms, but the α chain cannot do so. Our data suggest that the number of effective mutations in the β (or β-like) locus limits the number of effective mutations in the α locus. An effective mutation is one that has persisted and become the only form of the gene at the locus in question in a population of animals.

TABLE 2. *Differences (in terms of amino acid replacements) between the* α *chains of nonhuman primate hemoglobin and of human hemoglobin.*

PRIMATE	NUMBER OF PEPTIDES EXAMINED	NUMBER OF AMINO ACIDS	PROBABLE MINIMUM NUMBER OF REPLACEMENTS
Lemur fulvus	10	101	6
Propithecus	4	21	4
Lemur variegatus	4	24	3
Lemur catta	2	33	0
Galago	2	33	1
Perodicticus	3	37	0
Hylobates	5	53	0

The α chain of Hb $\alpha_2^A \beta^A$ must be able to form functional hemoglobin with β, γ, and δ chains. Now we also know, from the hemoglobins of nonhuman primates, that there are many other β-like or non-α chains synthesized. These must form functional proteins with the α-like chains.

The variability in the primate β-like chains is much more extensive that that of the α chains. We compared the probable sequences of non-α chains of various nonhuman primates with the β and γ chains of Hb $\alpha_2^A \beta_2^A$ and Hb $\alpha_2^A \gamma_2^F$ (Table 3). The comparison with γ chains was suggested by our earlier observation that hemoglobin from adult prosimian primates is resistant to alkaline denaturation (13), as is the fetal hemoglobin of man, Hb $\alpha_2^A \gamma_2^F$. Comparison of the total numbers of replacements is worth while, but evaluation of the significance of similarities and differences will have to wait until sequences of amino acids in various primate hemoglobins have been determined.

TABLE 3. *Differences (in terms of amino acid replacements) between β-like chains of nonhuman primate hemoglobin and β chain or γ chain of human hemoglobin A or F.*

PRIMATE	NUMBER OF PEPTIDES EXAMINED	NUMBER OF AMINO ACIDS	PROBABLE MINIMUM NUMBER OF REPLACEMENTS	
			RELATIVE TO β CHAIN	RELATIVE TO γ CHAIN
Lemur fulvus	12	134	23	36
Lemur variegatus	11	96	23	25
Galago	10	87	9	21
Perodicticus	5	49	8	9
Propithecus	3	30	4	10
Papio	6	64	3	18
Hylobates	7	65	0	18
Homo (γ chain)	15	146	39	0
Homo (β chain)	15	146	0	39

Partial sequences of β-like chains in hemoglobin of *Lemur fulvus* have been determined (21), and we can compare these sequences with homologous sequences of human β and γ chains. We find a high degree of homology among the three chains. The positions in the sequence at which β and γ chains differ from each other are also most frequently the positions at which the *L. fulvus* β-like chain differs from one or the other (Figure 2).

Invariant Sequences

Large segments of primate hemoglobin molecules appear to be invariant. Sequences which appear to be invariant are listed in Tables 4 and 5. These apparently immutable segments of the molecule suggest that replacements here disrupt the synthesis or function of hemoglobin. The obvious conclusion, to which many workers have jumped, is that the invariant segments are the functionally important part of the molecule. The segments in which effective mutations have occurred are sometimes believed to be less important functionally simply because of the mutability exhibited. However, an effective mutation, wherever it occurs, is preserved only because it plays some functional role in the life of an organism. Mutations in the invariant segments were not preserved by natural selection. But whether this is due to the disrupting character of *any* mutation in these segments is yet to be demonstrated.

TABLE 4. *Tryptic peptide sequences which are identical in* α *chains of primate hemoglobins.*

PEPTIDE*	PRIMATES IN WHICH SEQUENCES ARE PROBABLY IDENTICAL
αT-1	*Homo, Hylobates, Perodicticus, Lemur fulvus, L. variegatus*
αT-2	*Homo, Hylobates, Perodicticus, Lemur fulvus, L. catta*
αT-5	*Homo, Lemur fulvus, Propithecus*
αT-6	*Homo, Hylobates, Lemur fulvus*
αT-7	*Homo, Hylobates*
αT-9	*Homo, Hylobates, Perodicticus, Lemur catta, Galago*

*Peptides obtained by digestion with trypsin are numbered according to the nomenclature proposed by Gerald and Ingram (*28*).

The numerous identities in the primary structures of primate hemoglobins are every bit as important to an understanding of molecular evolution as are the differences. Since millions of mutations undoubtedly have occurred in the millions of animals that have made up any one of the evolutionary lineages we are studying, it is remarkable how few mutations have been passed by the censor of natural selection. The invariant sequences of hemoglobin are not the only such sequences that are known to exist in proteins of animals of various evolutionary grades. Cytochrome *c*, ACTH, and insulin are well-known examples (*22*). As we have pointed out, natural selection is the process by which mutations become effective in populations.

TABLE 5. *Tryptic peptide sequences which are identical in β chains of primate hemoglobins.*

PEPTIDE*	PRIMATES IN WHICH SEQUENCES ARE PROBABLY IDENTICAL
βT-1	*Homo, Hylobates*
βT-2	*Homo, Hylobates*
βT-3	*Homo, Hylobates, Papio, Perodicticus*
βT-4	*Homo, Homo* γT-4, *Hylobates, Papio, Perodicticus, Galago, Propithecus, Lemur fulvus, L. variegatus, L. catta*
βT-5	*Homo, Hylobates*
βT-6	*Homo, Homo* γT-6, *Hylobates, Papio, Perodicticus, Galago, Propithecus, Lemur fulvus, L. variegatus, L. catta*
βT-7	*Homo, Homo* γT-7, *Hylobates, Papio, Galago, Propithecus, Lemur fulvus, L. variegatus, L. catta*
βT-14	*Homo, Galago, Lemur fulvus*
βT-15	*Homo, Homo* γT-15, *Galago, Lemur fulvus, L. variegatus*

*Peptides obtained by digestion with trypsin are numbered according to the nomenclature proposed by Gerald and Ingram (*28*).

Resolution of primate hemoglobins by electrophoresis on starch gels revealed that several of the species which we are studying are apparently polymorphic with respect to hemoglobin. Several of these polymorphisms are being investigated in detail, particularly those found among gibbons and orangutans. Earlier work showed that one of the orangutan hemoglobins is apparently quite similar to the Norfolk type of human hemoglobin (*23*); the other seems very similar to human Hb $\alpha_2^A \beta_2^A$. No obvious differences were found among fingerprints of the two gibbon hemoglobins which proved to have different electrophoretic mobilities in starch gels.

Rates of Evolution

The calculation of evolutionary rates is a favorite pastime of evolutionary biologists, and we, too, can indulge ourselves. We shall use as data the number of replacements in the α- and β-like chains of *Lemur fulvus*. The standards are the α, β, and γ chains of Hb $\alpha_2^A \beta_2^A$ and *Hb* $\alpha_2^A \gamma_2^F$. Lemuriformes were a distinct evolutionary lineage sometime in the Eocene, therefore the maximum time which separates lemurs from men, with reference to their common ancestor, is about 55×10^6 years. When the α chain of *L. fulvus* is compared with the α chain of man, six replacements are found. Thus we obtain an average value of 9.1×10^6 years for the time it takes to fix an effective mutation in the α chain of the normal hemoglobin of a population of lemurs. The results are very different if we base our calculations on the non-α chains. Comparison of the β-like chain of *L. fulvus* with the human β chain shows differences at 23 positions. This gives us 2.4×10^6 years for the average time it takes to fix an effective mutation in the β-like chain of a population of *L. fulvus*. Another rate is obtained if the γ chain of Hb $\alpha_2^A \gamma_2^F$ is used as the referent. The β-like chain of *L. fulvus* differs from the human γ chain at 36 positions. If the γ chain represents the common ancestor, the average value for the number of years it takes to fix an effective mutation is 1.5×10^6. Therefore, if we assume that the α- and β-like chains of *L. fulvus* and, respectively, human α and human β or γ chains have a common ancestor, it is clear that the rate of point mutation is neither constant nor linear, at least for primate hemoglobins.

These calculations suggest that the one genetic locus evolves at a rate four times that at which the other evolves. It is reasonable to suggest that the two rates are not independent, for the synthesis of a functional hemoglobin molecule requires that the product of each locus, and α chain and a β chain, polymerize successfully. The calculations indicate that rates of evolution estimated from the number of changes in amino acid residues in the primary structure of a protein are meaningless. The rate at which hemoglobin changes— that is, the rate at which amino acid residues are replaced—is a function of the pressure of natural selection as well as of the rate at which random changes (mutations) in the genetic material occur. We do not have, at this time, sufficient information to put rates such as we have just calculated into a meaningful context.

Meaning of Amino Acid Substitutions

The demonstrated amino acid substitutions present us with a fascinating research problem. Just what are the advantages conferred on the animal by substituting, for example, threonine in lemurs for valine in humans at the NH_2-terminus of the β-like chain (*21*)? The suggestion that there are many neutral changes may make some sense chemically. The chemical role of some amino acids in polypeptide chains is probably not fully understood. Many of the amino acids are replaced by residues which seem to be their functional equivalents. A residue with a hydrophobic side chain, for example, may be replaced by another with a hydrophobic side chain, or an acidic residue may be replaced by another acidic residue, with no detectable change in function or activity of the protein. But whether these are chemically equivalent is really not the point at issue. The issue is, are they biologically equivalent or neutral? If they are, then we have indeed neutral traits and neutral genes—neutral from the standpoint of natural selection, that is. But if such a replacement is neutral, how has it become characteristic of the hemoglobin of the species?

The only mechanism by which a random mutation—and the original mutations are still assumed to be random—may become an effective mutation is through the action of natural selection. The animals that possess the mutated locus must have a reproductive advantage over the animals in the population that do not have the mutated locus. Eventually, if this advantage exists, the mutated locus will become the more frequent in a population. The only way a selectively neutral trait might become fixed would be through accidents of sampling from one generation to the next. This process is sometimes called genetic drift. Since there are relatively large numbers of effective mutations involved in the β-like chain alone, the probability of the repetition of fortuitous sampling accidents becomes incredibly small, and we must reject this hypothesis.

Measurement of Phylogenetic Distance

The finding of only a few differences in the amino acids of the hemoglobins of two primates should not be welcomed with too much enthusiasm by taxonomists. The fact that hemoglobin of gorilla (*Pan gorilla*) and human hemoglobin differ by only one amino acid residue does not change the systematics of the Primates (*24*). The gorilla still belongs to the family Pongidae, and man, to the family Hominidae. Hominidae is a taxon that is defined by its adaptive relationships and ecological situation, as reflected in the total morphology of its members. It is clear to us that phylogenetic distance is a concept that is confusingly applied.

The phylogenetic distance between two taxa is a function of two sets of events. First, phyletic branching is the basic event. When two taxa—say, the Pongidae and the Hominidae—have become distinct from each other, we say they have branched phyletically from a common stem. Demonstration of such phyletic branching appears in the fossil record. Second, all the genetic, adaptive, biological, and evolutionary events that occurred after branching are also part of whatever it is we mean by phylogenetic distance (*25*). Unfortunately, time is not a particularly useful parameter in measuring phylogenetic relationships. The Hominidae and the Pongidae became distinct from each other relatively recently, from the standpoint of evolutionary time spans. But the adaptive events that occurred in the hominid evolutionary lineage have been so many and of such a distinctive character that the phylogenetic distance between the living Hominidae and the living Pongidae is much greater than some might expect solely on the basis of the time that has elapsed since the two lineages diverged. Similarity in the primary structure of the hemoglobin of a species from each of the two lineages is not particularly significant as a means of distinguishing the lineages. It is, nonetheless, a most important datum in understanding the evolution of hemoglobin, and using it primarily for purposes of classification obscures this importance.

Phylogeny and Hemoglobins

The similarities and differences we have found among primate hemoglobins correspond in large part to the phylogeny which we presented earlier. The hemoglobins of members of the two suborders, the Anthropoidea and the Prosimii, differ from each other more than the hemoglobins of primates within each of these groups differ from each other. The evidence suggests that the hemoglobins of all the Anthropoidea are quite similar, including those of *Homo sapiens*. Hemoglobins of the Prosimii appear to vary among themselves far more than do hemoglobins of the Anthropoidea.

Hemoglobin of the baboon, *Papio*, is an exception. Clearly, this anthropoid hemoglobin differs from human hemoglobin a great deal more than does the hemoglobin of any other of the Anthropoidea examined to date. Peptide fingerprint patterns for *Papio* alone among the Anthropoidea show as many differences from human hemoglobin as patterns for some prosimians do.

It appears from the fingerprint patterns that the hemoglobin of *Tupaia glis* differs considerably from human hemoglobin. It differs more than the hemoglobin of most of the other nonhuman primates studied does, but probably not much more than that of some of the Lemuriformes. Fingerprints of *Tupaia* hemoglobin also differ greatly from the hemoglobin peptide patterns of certain Insectivora— *Rhynchocyon* and *Petrodromus*, elephant shrews of East Africa.

Hemoglobins of various Lemuriformes are more like each other than they are like human hemoglobin or hemoglobins of most other primates. There are many more similarities between the hemoglobins of Lorisiformes and Lemuriformes than there are between the hemoglobins of either of these Prosimii and hemoglobins of the other primates. These resemblances and differences are suggested by studies of amino acid composition, by end-group analysis, and by results of grosser methods, such as starch-gel electrophoresis and peptide mapping.

Hemoglobins of Ceboidea appear to resemble human hemoglobin rather closely. In this respect the Ceboidea are most interesting, for they are not closely related to man. They appear as a completely distinct lineage in Miocene deposits of South America. Their dentition separates them from all other living primates. They may be related to an Eocene fossil group, the Omomyidae, which is found in many parts of the world but not in South America. The data from peptide patterns and starch gels suggest that the Ceboidea have developed a hemoglobin quite similar to that of *Homo sapiens*.

We have relatively few data about hemoglobins of the Cercopithecoidea. Those we have suggest that—with the notable exception of *Papio*—these hemoglobins are quite similar to those of man.

The pongid hemoglobins are very much like those of man. The information available suggests that many pongid hemoglobins, if the sources were not known, might be mistaken for one of the many variant human hemoglobins.

Implications for Systematics

The data we have presented are best viewed from within a valid phylogeny of the Primates. The fact that this phylogeny (Table 1) is neither complete nor unchangeable does not discourage us from using it. We must be careful not to tamper with the classification on the basis of a single trait, such as hemoglobin. We keep our hands clean and our hearts pure and rigorously adhere to this particular phylogeny of the Primates. We have not suggested, or even dared to think of suggesting, that it be revised because primate hemoglobin molecules are difficult to interpret in the light of it. Any revision in the phylogeny of the Primates, and in the classification based on it, that has been suggested by one of us in the past has not been based upon hemoglobin research, nor will we suggest any revision on this basis in future publications. We promise not to become taxonomically unhinged if the hemoglobin of *Tarsius spectrum* eventually proves to be identical in structure with elephant hemoglobin. Nor would we suggest that there is a closer phylogenetic affinity between tarsiers and elephants than there is between tarsiers and man. The phylogeny upon which we base our work illuminates the evolutionary differentiation of hemoglobins among primates. The hemoglobin data, however, at this stage are not crucial for reorganizing phylogeny.

The molecular approach to systematics has been enthusiastically embraced by many investigators (26). This wave of enthusiasm has aroused considerable reaction from the evolutionists who use the paleontological and organismal approach to systematics (27). The exact determination of the differences in the primary structure of a protein from two organisms brings us closer to the genetic basis for similarities and differences than does the analysis of most morphological characters. We are, potentially, better able to characterize the genome of an organism, and of the population to which it belongs, than ever before. Eventually we should be able to study the specific biological effects of molecular changes such as we have described.

Organismal biologists are used to dealing with the effect of natural selection on a complex phenotype, the expression of most if not all of the genome of a population. They offer a counterargument—that the farther from the genes we go, the closer we get to the actual site of the action of selection (27). Thus, by implication, they reject the usefulness of the molecular approach to an understanding of the interaction between genome and environment.

The way in which selection acts upon a population is complex and often difficult to analyze in specific organismal and morphological terms, let alone molecular terms. Contemporary evolutionary theory views selection as a process that acts upon populations of organisms. This does not rule out, we believe, the possibility of viewing selection as operating within the nucleus of the cell as well. The population of organisms must be considered when we wish to explain the presence or absence of a genetic trait, even a single amino acid substitution in a hemoglobin polypeptide. We can view selection at a molecular level and ask how the changed molecule reacts to increase the chances for survival of the organisms in which it appears.

We know that it is the population of organisms which evolves, but do not molecules, metabolic pathways, tissues, and organ systems evolve as well? Certainly such systems evolve, though we should refer to their evolution in an organismal framework. When we study the hemoglobins of the Primates we are studying a molecular system within the context of a group of organisms which exhibit a unique degree of evolutionary stratification. Thus, we believe, we have an unbeatable combination for the study of *molecular* as well as *organismal* evolution.

References

1. V. M. INGRAM, *The Hemoglobins in Genetics and Evolution* (Columbia Univ. Press, New York, 1963); D. Rucknagel and J. V. Neel, in *Progress in Medical Genetics*, A. G. Steinberg, Ed. (Grune and Stratton, New York, 1961), vol. 1, p. 158.

2. G. M. ALLEN, *Bull. Museum Comp. Zool. Harvard 83*, 1 (1939); W. C. O. Hill, *Primates* (Interscience, New York, 1953), vol. 1.

3. G. G. SIMPSON, in *Classification and Human Evolution*, S. L. Washburn, Ed. (Aldine, Chicago, 1963), p. 1.

4. ———, *Bull. Am. Museum Nat. Hist. 85*, 1 (1945); *Ann. N.Y. Acad. Sci. 102*, 497 (1962).

5. W. E. LEGROS CLARK, *Proc. Zool. Soc. London 1*, 461 (1924); *ibid. 2*, 1053 (1924).

6. J. BUETTNER-JANUSCH, in *Evolutionary and Genetic Biology of Primates*, J. Buettner-Janusch, Ed. (Academic Press, New York, 1963), vol. 1, p. 1.

7. W. C. O. HILL, *Primates* (Interscience, New York, 1955), vol. 2, p. 1.

8. E. L. SIMONS, *Am. Museum Novitates No. 2051* (1961), p. 1.

9. ———, *Proc. Natl. Acad. Sci. U.S. 51*, 528 (1964).

10. W. E. LEGROS CLARK, *The Antecedents of Man* (Quadrangle, Chicago, 1960), p. 321.

11. G. F. JACOB and N. C. TAPPEN, *Nature 180*, 241 (1957); ———, *ibid. 181*, 197 (1958); G. H. Beaven and W. B. Gratzer, *ibid. 184*, 1730 (1959); N. N. Sen, K. C. Das, B. K. Aikat, *ibid. 186*, 977 (1960); J. Buettner-Janusch and V. Buettner-Janusch, *ibid. 197*, 1018 (1963).

12. J. BUETTNER-JANUSCH and V. BUETTNER-JANUSCH, in *Evolutionary and Genetic Biology of Primates*, J. Buettner-Janusch, Ed. (Academic Press, New York, 1964), vol. 2, p. 75.

13. J. BUETTNER-JANUSCH and J. B. TWICHELL, *Nature 192*, 669 (1961).

14. J. BUETTNER-JANUSCH and V. BUETTNER-JANUSCH, *Nature 199*, 918 (1963); J. Buettner-Janusch, V. Buettner-Janusch, J. B. Sale, *ibid. 201*, 510 (1964).

15. R. L. HILL, R. T. SWENSON, H. C. SCHWARTZ, *J. Biol. Chem. 235*, 3182 (1960).

16. R. L. HILL, J. BUETTNER-JANUSCH, V. BUETTNER-JANUSCH, *Proc. Natl. Acad. Sci. U.S. 50*, 885 (1963).

17. R. T. JONES, *Federation Proc. 23*, 173 (1964).

18. M. L. ANSON and A. E. MIRSKY, *J. Gen. Physiol. 13*, 469 (1930); S. Wilson and D. B. Smith, *Can. J. Biochem. Physiol. 37*, 405 (1959).

19. W. KONIGSBERG and R. J. HILL, *J. Biol. Chem. 237*, 2547 (1962).

20. R. L. HILL and J. BUETTNER-JANUSCH, *Federation Proc. 23*, 1236 (1964).

21. R. A. BRADSHAW, L. A. ROGERS, J. BUETTNER-JANUSCH, R. L. HILL, *Arch. Biochem.*, in press.

22. E. MARGOLIASH, *Proc. Natl. Acad. Sci. U.S. 50*, 672 (1963); T. H. Lee, A. B. Lerner, V. Buettner-Janusch, *J. Biol. Chem., 236*, 2970 (1961); C. B. Anfinsen, *The Molecular Basis of Evolution* (Wiley, New York, 1959), p. 154.

23. E. ZUCKERKANDL, R. T. JONES, L. PAULING, *Proc. Natl. Acad. Sci. U.S. 46*, 1349 (1960).

24. E. ZUCKERKANDL and W. A. SCHROEDER, *Nature 192*, 984 (1961).

25. E. MAYR, *Animal Species and Evolution* (Belknap, Cambridge, Mass., 1963).

26. E. ZUCKERKANDL, in *Classification and Human Evolution*, S. L. Washburn, Ed. (Aldine, Chicago, 1963), p. 243; M. Goodman, *ibid.*, p. 204; R. F. Doolittle and B. Blombäck, *Nature 202*, 147 (1964).

27. G. G. SIMPSON, *Science 146*, 1535 (1964).

28. P. GERALD and V. M. INGRAM, *J. Biol. Chem. 236*, 2155 (1961).

Organisms and Molecules in Evolution*

GEORGE GAYLORD SIMPSON

(*Editor's Note*) Among zoologists the counterpart of the physical anthropologist is the ecologist or the population biologist rather than the biochemist or molecular biologist. In part this is because even the most "biological" human biologist is not immune to the eventual necessity of considering relevant phenomena not characterized as natural science. It is also because physical anthropology has traditionally been concerned with phenotypic, rather than genetic aspects of man. This organismal and, more recently, populational approach to an understanding of human evolution can now, in most respects, be carried on as "scientifically" as the research of white-clad investigators working in laboratories. But is there any point at which the organismal and molecular approaches meet and complement each other? This is the concern of Simpson's article, and it's a very important one because mistaking points of emphasis for different and opposed basic viewpoints about nature can lead to artificial distrusts and misunderstandings which may impede scientific investigation. Physical anthropologists might pay particular attention because the traditional emphasis on gross anatomy, biometry, and descriptive morphology has led them up many a blind alley. On the other hand, the realization of this is no cause to abandon all the original questions, or to assume they will be answered in one fell swoop by jumping on the biomolecular bandwagon. Simpson suggests (and his own work is proof that it can be done) that it is possible to make the best of both the Cartesian and compositionist worlds by working within the framework of the synthetic theory of evolution, which requires the coordination of both kinds of approaches.

I T is universally recognized that molecules of biological importance may evolve—that is, they may change in the course of time as have the organisms in which they occur. Some molecules, like adenosine triphosphate, are so nearly universal and invariable as to suggest no evolutionary sequence, but many others surely have evolved, notably groups of proteins and, obviously, DNA. Before the importance of DNA was known, Florkin (*1*) had already discussed the systematics and evolution of various families of molecules. In such instances evolutionary interpretation of the biochemists' findings requires information from paleontologists and systematists, information especially on the time scale involved and the phylogeny and relationships of the species in which varying molecules are to be compared. An example is the hypothesis that serum proteins (*2*) or cytochromes (*3*) have changed in a regular if not linear manner with respect to time—that they have evolved by some sort of internal constant-rate mutational process and not in an irregular or a specifically adaptive way. In fact, when the data are replotted with what seem to be the most probable time coordinates they indicate that the hypothesis is incorrect or, at least, that these data do not support it. Williams now tells me that the hypothesis has been modified, but it exemplifies the clarifying confrontation of molecular and organismal data.

Other interesting examples of such confrontation arise from further studies of serum proteins, such as that by Goodman (*4*). Phylogenetic relationships of the animals concerned, primates in this case, are inferred from the apparent degrees of homology in their various serum proteins. The lineages thus inferred then permit conclusions as to the evolution of the proteins themselves. Similar inferential methods have been applied to the evolution of hemoglobins, also in primates, by Hill and the Buettner-Janusches (*5*). When phylogeny is inferred from the molecular data and molecular evolution is inferred in turn from that phylogeny, there is an element of circularity, which does not wholly invalidate the method but does warrant some reservations. A necessary cross-check is to arrange the molecular data in the framework of a phylogeny based entirely on nonmolecular evidence. It should be mentioned in passing that this, too, has sometimes led to semi-circular reasoning when molecule-based phylogeny has been compared with phylogeny with other bases: agreement between the two has been taken as the requisite validation of the molecular approach to phylogeny, but nonagreement has been taken as evidence of the greater reliability of the molecular method.

However, the most important reason for relating organismal and molecular evolution to each other is not simply the testing of hypotheses or the validation of methods. It is the balancing of points of view and the achievement of more complete explanations. Wald (6) has said that "living organisms are the greatly magnified expressions of the molecules that compose them." Anfinsen (7) believes that "we may almost define the life sciences as those concerned with the elucidation of the mechanisms by which molecules exert their specific actions in living cells." In fact there are many respectable and even eminent students of the life sciences who have no concern whatever with molecules or their actions. Concentration on one level of organization to the practical exclusion of others is often a necessity of specialized research, but nowadays almost everyone agrees that eventual understanding of relationships between levels is also necessary. Sonneborn (8) has emphasized the fact that molecular genetics could only have arisen through, and would now have little meaning apart from, "classical" or Mendelian organismal genetics. Weiss (9) has pointed out that there is a "cellular control of molecular activities" as well as a molecular control of cellular activities. There is also an organismal control of cellular activities, and, for that matter, a populational control of organismal activities. Indeed both Wald and Anfinsen, in the works from which one-sided aphorisms have been quoted, were concerned with relationships of molecules to higher organizational levels in evolution.

The sort of problem that can arise from a limited approach is exemplified in a recent article by Mora (10). He points out that living organisms have a teleological or purposive aspect which he proposes to label "urge." He finds that this aspect is inexplicable at the molecular level as hitherto studied. He proposes, but does not describe, a new approach, to be frankly permeated by teleology. Although he seems to think or hope that this may still be naturalistic, he does not clearly state what a naturalistic teleology might be. Now, this is precisely the problem with which organismal biologists have been coping for generations. Unknown, it would seem, to some biochemists, they have achieved a naturalistic (or, in a sense, materialistic) explanation of what is now often called [after Pittendrigh (11)] the teleonomic aspect of organisms. The teleonomic, or *apparently* teleological or purposive, characteristics of organisms are adaptations. They include "urge" itself in Mora's sense, its manifestations, and its results in the activities of individuals and the evolution of populations. Teleonomic adaptations arise in the course of evolution, and the factor governing their origin and maintenance is natural selection. That is surely as true at the molecular level as at any other. However, the ramifications of natural selection at various levels are far from simple.

Natural Selection

The process of natural selection, as now understood, is complex rather in its concrete working and its interactions than in its basis. That basis is simply differential reproduction correlated with genotypic constitution. If some individuals in a population have more surviving and breeding offspring than others, and if there is a consistent average difference, however small, in the genotypes of those who have more and those who have fewer, that is natural selection at work. The actual selection—that is, the determination of which individuals have more or fewer offspring that survive to breed in their turn—is an interaction between environment, in the broadest sense, and the population, in all its individuals throughout their complete ontogenies. Aspects of this process are discussed at length in recent works (see, for example, *12–14*) which supply many details not given here.

Natural selection requires, first, reproduction and, second, hereditary variation of such a kind as to influence the success of reproduction under existing circumstances. When those factors are present, natural selection *necessarily* occurs. In precellular evolution [a principal concern for Mora (*10*)] it necessarily began when there were replicating molecules that differed in the rate or efficiency of replication (see *15*). However, the pertinent unit is not the replicating molecule but the reproducing system. This was presumably a molecule at first but became a cell at the protistan level, and is a dynamic unicellular-to-multicellular ontogenetic individual at metaphytic and metazoan levels. Selection acts on the whole phenotype and can single out genes only to the extent that they have phenotypic effects separable both phenotypically and genetically from those of other genes. Although selection apparently does act in an analytically separable way on some particular molecules, it evidently does not do so as a rule. It usually acts on supramolecular phenotypic characters, on whole complexes of them, or indeed on all of them at once. Since most genes are pleiotropic and most characters are polygenic, it follows that selection usually is not concentrated on single genes, as might appear from the necessarily oversimplified models first formulated by population geneticists. Although the connection is not yet well understood, this presumably means also that it is unusual (it may even be impossible) for intermediary molecules such as enzymes and other proteins to be selected for or selected against independently of other molecules.

Effect of Selection on Particular Features

In considering the effect of selection on particular features of an organism, it is important to judge how far these are in one direction from the genes and in the other direction from the phenotypic characters directly subject to selection. Behavior is subject to particularly strong selection, and it is probably farthest removed from the genes and also most elaborately polygenic as a rule. Some single-gene determinants of behavior are known, but they are exceptional (see *16*). Proteins or, at least, intracellular enzymes are believed to be almost directly and uniquely determined by one or a few particular genes. The effect of selection will surely be influenced by the length of the functional chain from the genes to the character selected for or against. As a rule, with exceptions, the effect becomes more, not less, diffuse and less, not more, direct as the level of the gene is approached.

Zuckerkandl (*17*) has argued that a molecule like hemoglobin is preferable to most "structural," or more remotely phenotypic, characters for the determination of affinities because it is so near the genes, so nearly a direct reflection of part of the DNA code. It may be added that hemoglobin is so literally vital that natural selection may here act at a level near the gene. Those are advantages in certain respects, but they are accompanied by disadvantages, and the more distantly phenotypic approach also has advantages, as Zuckerkandl notes but possibly understresses. Zuckerkandl has shown that, "from the point of view of hemoglobin structure, it appears that gorilla is just an abnormal human, or man an abnormal gorilla, and the two species form actually one continuous population." From any point of view other than that properly specified, that is of course nonsense. What the comparison seems really to indicate is that in this case, at least, hemoglobin is a bad choice and has nothing to tell us about affinities, or indeed tells us a lie. (It does show that men and gorillas are rather closely related, but that has long and more accurately been known from traditional morphological comparisons.) Of course, as Zuckerkandl points out, we should use not just one kind of molecule but many, preferably proteins. However, if one can be misleading, so can many! (Let me add that Zuckerkandl's discussion of the phylogenetic interpretation of molecular data is invaluable and, unfortunately, almost unique.)

In some respects it is a drawback that hemoglobin, various enzymes, and some other proteins are so near to the genes in the functional chain. It means that each sample is genetically determined by, and therefore provides a sample of, only an extremely minute part of the whole genetic system—apparently only two genes in the case of hemoglobin and probably only one for many enzymes. The farther a character is from the genes, the more likely it is to sample a number of genes or a really significant part of the whole genetic system. The complexity of the genetic determination of a characteristic is a positive advantage, not a disadvantage, when the purpose is to determine affinities of whole organisms. Moreover, such characters are in almost all cases those which were in fact subject to selection. On an average, the farther we are from genes the nearer we are to the action of selection, and thus the better able we are to interpret the adaptive processes involved.

When, as is usual, selection is on the phenotype and well removed from the genotype, all that matters is that the genotype should in fact result in the selectively favored phenotype under the existing conditions of development. In this sense, or beyond that point, it really can be said that the genotype does not matter in adaptive evolution. There is ample evidence (much of it summed up in *14*, with references) that genotype-phenotype determination is not unique in either direction. Phenotypes that are apparently identical and that seem to be equal in the face of selection can have markedly different genotypes. There are also many systems—genetic, ontogenetic, and selectional—that tend to channel phenotypic development in the face of considerable change or variation in genes and hence, presumably, also in many families of macromolecules (*18*). I am arguing not that any one kind of evidence on evolution—genetic, molecular, phenotypic, or other—is superior but, on the contrary, that no one kind suffices in itself.

Special Problems

The evolutionary study of molecules has raised a number of special problems, not always seen in the same way by molecular and organismal biologists. The phenomenon that has caused most trouble in attempts to determine evolutionary affinities is convergence: the development of similar characteristics by organisms of different ancestry. Any addition of evidence would be most welcome, especially if it involved characters unlikely to converge. Here the molecular biologists do not agree; Wald (6), for example, says that convergence is much more likely at the molecular level, while Zuckerkandl (17) independently maintains that it is less likely. To me, as an organismal biologist, it seems that Wald is probably right. Convergence to the point of identity or of seriously confusing similarity would appear to be more likely in a single kind of molecule, even one as complicated as a protein, than in such phenotypic characters as are end results of the interactions of a very large number of such molecules. Anfinsen (7) cited an example (from the work of Sanger et al.) indicating from insulin composition that sperm whales are identical with pigs and quite different from sei whales! (19). To be sure, a sequence of only three amino acids is involved, and both differences and resemblances could be incidental without even true convergence, but the lesson is there. Fortunately, the fact that protein and morphological convergence may be independent of each other gives a double check if the evidence of both is available.

Another problem, discussed at some length by Anfinsen (7), arises from the evidence that proteins have parts that can vary greatly or even be removed altogether without seeming to affect function. There is also the concept of "dormant genes" [discussed by Zuckerkandl (17), among others, and in studies which he cites; see also Zuckerkandl and Pauling (20)]. This concept is, again, related to the hypothesis of regular, secular change in molecules, mentioned in the opening paragraph of this article. Essentially the same question has long been discussed by evolutionary biologists, in this form: Can a gene (or allele) be neutral with respect to selection? (Much of the discussion is summarized, with citations, in 14.) It is impossible to establish complete absence of exceptions, but so far every supposedly neutral gene that has been adequately investigated has turned out not to be neutral. There is a strong consensus that completely neutral genes or alleles must be very rare if they exist at all. To an evolutionary biologist it therefore seems highly improbable that proteins, supposedly fully determined by genes, should have nonfunctional parts, that dormant genes should exist over periods of generations, or that molecules should change in a regular but nonadaptive way.

This unsettled question could have far-reaching significance, for instance through the hypothesis [suggested but not fully supported by Anfinsen (7)] that the invariable or fully homologous parts of proteins in different animals are the functional, or at least the most significantly functional, parts. It would then seem to follow that the actual specific differences in proteins may be little or not at all adaptive, and this again seems unlikely to an organismal biologist. However, Anfinsen also points out (and the examples could be largely multiplied from other sources) that, for instance, serum proteins with no immunochemical similarity at all may be fully and identically functional. It is certainly not true as a generalization that molecular differences among species are commonly nonfunctional or nonadaptive, and indeed I think no molecular biologist would go to that extreme.

It is undoubtedly on questions related to adaptation that an evolutionary synthesis of molecular and organismal viewpoints and data will be most useful. I shall here give briefly two further examples from work by Wald (6, and earlier papers cited therein), not because I happen to disagree with his interpretations but because his brilliant studies provide such ideal data on the molecular basis of organismal adaptation. He shows that freshwater vertebrates generally have retinal pigments containing vitamin A_2, while marine and land vertebrates generally have A_1. He interprets this as a phylogenetic phenomenon, with A_2 in ancestral (true) fishes, supposedly freshwater forms, and A_1 developed in progressive phylogeny by marine and land descendants. He finds it inexplicable and almost an unnecessary complication that, for instance, reptiles, primitively having A_1, "revert" to A_2 when they adapt to fresh water. To an organismal biologist, the picture, including the apparent anomalies and supposed reversions, suggests interpretation in terms of adaptation, primarily, and phylogeny only secondarily. Many, but perhaps not quite all, of the observations would be explained if we assumed that A_2 is adaptive in freshwater forms and A_1, in land and saltwater forms—so much so that selection usually produced these adaptations rapidly and tended to erase purely phylogenetic effects. I have no idea what the difference in adaptation might be, but suggest that study from this point of view might clarify the molecular function involved.

A second example from Wald is his demonstration that tadpoles resemble fishes in a number of biochemical characteristics, whereas adult frogs have a biochemistry more like other land vertebrates. Amphibians were of course derived from fishes, and Wald interprets these changes as "the most striking instances we know of recapitulation." In my opinion there is no reason to invoke recapitulation and definite reason not to. As regards the species in question, it would appear that tadpoles are adapted to live in the water and adult frogs to live on land. In spite of some complications, this is the plausible explanation for nitrogen excretion: ammonia in water, urea out of it. Other changes may be less clearly adaptive but are likely, at least, to be adaptive. Some of the evidence, also given in part by Wald, is that when amphibians go from land to water, as some do, the changes tend to go in the opposite direction; they antirecapitulate!

The Adaptive System

Finally, let us turn (or return) to the structure of the whole adaptive system, its causations, and the place of molecules in it. The most basic of all molecules, in this context at least, is DNA. Its influence is exerted, in part if not altogether, through RNA. Recognizing the RNA as an agent of DNA in this sequence, we conclude that RNA is not the cause of the eventual action: synthesis of a protein. (One could raise some delicate semantic problems here, but I think the statement can stand as written for present purposes.) Then is the DNA the causative agent in a really explanatory sense? It carries, as we say, a message (another semantic problem!) and is indeed a messenger and an agent just as much as messenger RNA is. In following the chain back we reach a really significant point of causation not when we locate the message, which is in the DNA, but when we learn where the message came from to begin with, what composed it. Any message composed, so to speak, by the DNA itself would be in the language of mutation. But mutations are predominantly inadaptive, and the message, beyond doubt, is almost entirely adaptive. Mutations form what may be called letters or words, to continue the now somewhat shopworn metaphor, and in that way they supply materials that permit something new to be said and that limit what can be said. However, they certainly do not compose the message in any meaningful sense.

The message, or at very least the greater part of it, relates to interaction of organism and environment. The interaction involves the whole organism, and hence arises and expands from the molecular level. There must be some sort of feedback from the organism-environment interaction into DNA, and hence into the other molecules. There are, as is well known, innumerable feedback mechanisms at the molecular level itself, and many or most of these are responsive to interactions with the environment. The Neo-Lamarckians, before much was known about feedback or anything at all was known about molecular genetics, supposed that evolutionary feedback was of the same kind, within individuals and into the genetic system, whatever that might prove to be. Now, however, we do know about DNA and other essentials of the genetic system, and we know beyond serious doubt, even though it seems rather odd, that DNA is not subject to feedback within individuals. That is, as Pontecorvo (*21*) has put it, "the *structure* of the genetic material is not subject to regulatory change . . . although the *expression* of the genetic material . . . is subject to regulation—qualitative and quantitative—at all levels of organization. . . ."

Changes in individual expression—to put it figuratively, the way the message is read—do not affect the message itself. The necessary message-constructing feedback is not here but in a system of higher order: in the population and not the individual. It operates through natural selection, which operates in populations, just as populations are what really evolve. Thus, through a different approach we come again to natural selection and now see it as the most truly causative (although not the only) element in the adaptive system. Viewed in this way, it is the composer of the genetic message, and DNA, RNA, enzymes, and the other molecules in the system are successively its messengers.

References and Notes

1. M. FLORKIN, *Biochemical Evolution*, S. Morgulis, translator (Academic Press, New York, 1949).

2. C. A. WILLIAMS, JR., and C. T. WEMMYSS, JR., "Experimental and evolutionary significance of similarities among serum protein antigens of man and lower primates," *Ann. N.Y. Acad. Sci.* 94, 77 (1961).

3. E. MARGOLIASH, "Primary structure and evolution of cytochrome c," *Proc. Nat. Acad. Sci. U.S.* 50, 672 (1963).

4. M. GOODMAN, "Man's place in the phylogeny of the primates as reflected in serum proteins," in *Classification and Human Evolution*, S. L. Washburn, Ed. (Wenner-Gren Foundation, New York, 1963).

5. R. L. HILL, J. BUETTNER-JANUSCH, V. BUETTNER-JANUSCH, "Evolution of hemoglobin in primates," *Proc. Nat. Acad. Sci.* 50, 885 (1963).

6. O. WALD, "Phylogeny and ontogeny at the molecular level," in *Evolutionary Biochemistry*, A. I. Oparin, Ed. (Pergamon, London, 1963).

7. C. B. ANFINSEN, *The Molecular Basis of Evolution* (Wiley, New York, 1959).

8. T. M. SONNEBORN, "Implications of the new genetics for biology and man," *A.I.B.S. (Am. Inst. Biol. Sci.) Bull. 1963*, 22 (Apr. 1963).

9. P. WEISS, "From cell to molecule," in *The Molecular Control of Cellular Activity*, J. M. Allen, Ed. (McGraw-Hill, New York, 1961).

10. P. T. MORA, "Urge and molecular biology," *Nature 199*, 212 (1963).

11. C. S. PITTENDRIGH, "Adaptation, natural selection, and behavior," in *Behavior and Evolution*, A. Roe and G. G. Simpson, Eds. (Yale Univ. Press, New Haven, 1958).

12. V. GRANT, *The Origin of Adaptations* (Columbia Univ. Press, New York, 1963).

13. G. G. SIMPSON, *This View of Life* (Harcourt, Brace & World, New York, 1964).

14. E. MAYR, *Animal Species and Evolution* (Harvard Univ. Press, Cambridge, Mass., 1963).

15. H. F. BLUM, "On the origin and evolution of living machines," *Amer. Scientist 49*, 474 (1961).

16. E. CASPARI, "Genetic basis of behavior," in *Behavior and Evolution*, A. Roe and G. G. Simpson, Eds. (Yale Univ. Press, New Haven, 1958).

17. E. ZUCKERKANDL, "Perspectives in molecular anthropology," in *Classification and Human Evolution*, S. L. Washburn, Ed. (Wenner-Gren Foundation, New York, 1963).

18. These systems have been discussed from different points of view by I. M. Lerner [*Genetic Homeostasis* (Oliver and Boyd, Edinburgh, 1954)]. I. I. Schmalhausen [*Factors of Evolution: The Theory of Stabilizing Selection* (Blakiston, Philadelphia, 1949)]. C. H. Waddington [*The Strategy of the Genes* (Allen & Unwin, London, 1957)], and others.

19. As is all too common, the animals are not precisely specified. The pig is presumably the domesticated form of *Sus scrofa*. The sperm whale is *Physeter catodon*; the sei whale, *Balaenoptera borealis*. The two whales belong to different suborders of the same order. The pig belongs to a different order and cohort from the whales.

20. E. ZUCKERKANDL and L. PAULING, "Molecular disease, evolution and genetic heterogeneity," in *Horizons in Biochemistry*, M. Kasha and B. Pullman, Eds. (Academic Press, New York, 1962).

21. G. PONTECORVO, "Microbial genetics: retrospect and prospect," *Proc. Roy. Soc. London B158*, 1 (1963).

22. Drs. Ernst Mayr, George Wald, and Curtis Williams kindly read the manuscript and offered constructive suggestions; they do not necessarily endorse my opinions.

An Ape's Eye-View
of Human Evolution*

SHERWOOD L. WASHBURN

(*Editor's Note*) The layman observing the anthropologist observe the behavior of living non-human primates
in their natural habitat may jump to false conclusions.
He may surmise that the anthropologist is looking for
evidence of some sort of a primate basic instinct which
will ultimately explain man's behavior. (Indeed a lot
has been made of that recently by some non-anthro-
pologists.) Or he may conclude that the anthropologist
has deluded himself into thinking that when he is observing a baboon troop he is really looking at primitive
man. Yet there is some truth in *Time's* quip, "The
primatologist's a man who searches where mankind
began," and chief among anthropological primatolo-
gists is S. L. Washburn. He uses the comparative method
to determine in what areas of behavior man is most
similar and most different from other living primates
in order to discover the nature of the forces which
have operated on *Homo* from the time of his divergence
from the other primates to the present. Washburn has
often stressed the importance of establishing a "base-
line" as a prerequisite to valid comparisons. If comparisons between species are to be more than mere
analogies, it is of course essential that really comparable entities be established. In this article Washburn
details some of the problems that have arisen in this
quest.

*"An Ape's Eye View of Human Evolution," appears in the
symposium *The Origin of Man*, edited by Paul L. DeVore,
pages 89–96. Copyright 1965 by Wenner-Gren Foundation for
Anthropological Research, Inc. By permission of the author
and the publisher.

89

I have taken for the text of my sermon: "We apes did not live by teeth alone." Some years ago, Hallowell suggested that when we talk about the creatures that preceded man, we should talk in terms of proto-culture and reserve the term "culture" for *Homo sapiens*. If we look at the sequence of the past two million years, there are, perhaps, three major stages. There is a period of *Australopithecus*, both *africanus* and *robustus*; then, of *Homo erectus*; and, finally, that of *Homo sapiens*. And I suggest that the rules for interpreting behavior in each of these stages are very different. Hence, we do not want to confuse the rules for interpreting the behavior of *Homo sapiens* with those of the two earlier stages or of the Pongidae that went before that. And I suggest further that the relation of the brain to the behavior of these creatures is specific and definable, and I think we should be very much concerned with what lies behind the word "learning." It is a very general category and should be broken down into a series of specific things that apply very differently in the different stages of hominid and human behavior.

Now, if we look at man from an ape's point of view—and this is easy for somebody coming from Berkeley—we notice first that we are ourselves only slightly modified apes. We have the long arms, the chromosomes, and the biochemistry of apes, which should make it easy for us to see things through an ape's eyes. However, more seriously, I think the most recent studies of the behavior of contemporary monkeys and apes gives us a base line for our human problems that is quite different from the base line that we had just a few years ago. From an ape's point of view, some of the problems that we worry about aren't problems at all; while certain matters that we hardly consider pose serious problems to our hypothetical ape.

For example, if we look at the behavior of all the non-human primates, we find that these creatures are incredibly restricted in the area that they occupy. Only the gorilla and the baboon have ranges as great as fifteen square miles; while in the majority of the non-human primates, an animal spends virtually its entire life within two or three square miles—a tiny area. Here, then, are creatures with excellent vision who climb into trees and survey distant territories that somehow never become a matter of curiosity or importance to them and, consequently, never come into their experience. So one of the great problems of human history is to decide when the human way of considering territory and range diverged from the way of all non-human primates. We think it's such a simple thing to walk ten miles in a straight line, and we would be surprised to find a tribe that didn't know 300–400 square miles. But this is wholly unique if we look at it from the point of view of the non-human primates. And this is what I mean when I say that from an ape's eye-view, certain problems emerge 'that are hardly mentioned in the literature at present.

How, then, could we decide when our ancestors stopped viewing a tiny range as normal and began to act as we do? Obviously, this answer can only come from archaeology, and I would like to suggest that archaeologists consider the notion of range as something of major importance to be investigated. The things which, so to speak, put the bite on the ape's view of range would be those matters that made it important to expand. For example, any substantial amount of hunting in an area of only two or three square miles would simply drive the game out of the area. Any large amount of hunting implies following wounded animals and, hence, moving over relatively large areas. So I think that as soon as we find that hunting is definitely a part of the record, we have to assume that the creatures involved were occupying much larger ranges than is the case with monkeys and apes. The materials used in tools may also be used to make an estimate, however crude, of the long-past ranges. If we can show that a kind of stone found in an archaeological site has its nearest source ten or fifteen miles away, then it is clear just from this that these animals occupied a larger range than contemporary non-human primates.

Another kind of problem that has come up repeatedly in our discussions is the question as to whether we should be surprised to find two or three species coexisting in one locality. In this case, if we take the ape's point of view, we find that nothing could be of less concern to an ape than whether or not there are half a dozen species in his locality. When I was working with Dr. Schultz in Borneo some years ago, we found ten species of primates of several different genera living in one small area. We collected nine of them but didn't collect any *Homo*; although collecting *Homo* is an old custom in that area of North Borneo. The notion that it is so complicated to have two or three kinds of *Homo* or two or three kinds of primates in the same place comes from looking backward from the present rather than considering the situation of the majority of monkeys and apes. If one goes into any part of the Old World tropical rain forest, one finds a great variety of monkeys and apes together. And I am sure that this must have been equally true in the past, when these forests were much more extensive.

The point has been brought out in discussion here that it would take a lot of ecological separation to permit the coexistence of the large *Australopithecus robustus* and the smaller *africanus*. Yet this is in total contradiction to everything we know about non-human primates. It doesn't take much ecological separation to have in one small area in Uganda three kinds of *Cercopithecus* monkeys, two kinds of *Colobus* monkeys, one kind of mangabey, and two kinds of apes. There is not much separation in such a case, and it seems to be sufficient that the different species can rely on different parts of the habitat in times of crisis. And this, I repeat, is a perfectly normal situation among the non-human primates.

What, then, is remarkable about man in these regards? Well, first, that he occupies a huge range—even the most minimal human behavior requires a great deal of space. And, second, man is unusual among the primates in that, as I interpret the record, there was only one kind of man after the Middle Pleistocene. And the reason for this is his culture. He was an efficient hunter, too tough to have any competition from other members of his species. He was making fire and complicated stone tools and was killing large animals. There is a calculus we can apply to this. The more our ancestors became like us in the sense of efficient toolmaking, fighting, hunting, making fires, and so on, the less likely it became that there would be two species of man living at the same time. It is not especially surprising that there should have been, say, two species at the *Australopithecus* level of time. The remarkable thing is that from *Homo erectus* on there is only one species. I think that this is a measure of the effectiveness of human culture. If we look at the ground-living baboons and the cats, who are very effective in their own way, we find that it takes at least a dozen species of these creatures to occupy the area that one species of Middle Pleistocene man occupied. Therefore, the lack of speciation is a measure of the effectiveness of culture.

Let's see what the ape would think about population density. All through the anthropological literature one finds the idea that as man became more and more effective, his population density increased. Of course, this is completely contrary to the ape's view of human evolution. If we look at the distribution of small monkeys or of baboons in Africa or in Southeast Asia today, we see that their density runs a hundred times as high as that of men living under hunting conditions. DeVore says the density of baboons in the Amboseli Reserve is on the order of twenty-five per square mile. Or let's take just ten per square mile, which would be the distribution in Nairobi Park. Estimates on hunting peoples are on the order of one per ten square miles—one percent of the distribution of baboons! Now, baboons aren't very successful if we compare them numerically to other non-human primates. *Cercopithecus aethiops*, the vervets that Struhsaker has been studying, go well over one hundred per square mile. And in one place, he estimates four hundred per square mile as the distribution of one species of monkey, and there are several other species in the same area.

It is only in exceedingly recent times that the population density of human beings has approached that of the non-human primates, largely since the beginning of agriculture. The reason for this is that man's ecological niche, so to speak, was his effectiveness over a great many climatic situations. He was effective from South Africa to China to Europe, and there is no species of non-human primates that even approaches this kind of range. But in any one part of this range, he was less well adapted than the local primates in that particular area. As Dr. Dobzhansky pointed out, the ability to adapt to a wide variety of situations is a characteristic of man, but this doesn't necessarily imply great adaptation to a local situation.

For example, a great deal is written about man's adaptation to the savannah. I would like to point out that if we take baboon adaptation to the savannah or that of the *entellus* monkey to ground-living in India as a standard, man is extraordinarily poorly adapted to the savannah. The animals can do without water for a very long time. When a troop of baboons comes in from a really hot day on the plains, what do they do? A few of them drink but not very many; it just isn't very important to them. Man cannot eat most of the things on the savannah, so he needs the aid of cultural benefits to provide both food and water—something the baboons do not need at all. Man is remarkable, then in the variety of habitats that he can occupy through cultural means—even far back in his evolution —but not in terms either of population density or special adaptation.

A point that DeVore and I have mentioned several times that seems worth stressing in this regard is the matter of a home base, a place that animals can return to. The non-human primates have no such place. They come back to different places after being out on the plains all day, and this means that the troop must always stay together. If animals are isolated, they have no place to go and become subject to predation. So one problem for archaeology that is exceedingly important is to decide whether early sites represent places where the animals were staying for considerable periods of time or simply occupied occasionally for a night.

To return to the point with which I began, let's take a look now at the question of learning, taken this time from an ape's point of view. As men, we learn so easily the things that we are interested in that we totally underestimate the great problem of origin. We drop questions of origin out of our pursuits and forget that it is not so much a question of learning skills or language in a limited sense but, rather, how we got the structure which enables us to learn language or tool skills that should really be the focus of our attention. There is a biology, then, that goes along with the evolution of culture up until very recent times, and one cannot consider the evolution of man's tools and behavior without considering the evolution of the biology. If you look at the general record, you find something on the order of two million years, according to the potassium-argon dates, where you find the use of only very crude pebble tools. This is incredibly slow evolution, if we think of it in relation to the Middle Pleistocene. Then, in turn, if we think of the rate of tool evolution in the next few hundred thousand years—Acheulian and the like—it is also incredibly slow by comparison with the rate for *Homo sapiens*. We are so accustomed to thinking of agriculture, the industrial revolution, and other things that operate solely at the cultural level in very short time spans that we underestimate the problem of the genetic development of a behavioral basis for learning over long-term human evolution.

Let's consider tool-use for a moment, since it is the easiest of these problems. George Schaller has shown that orangs tear off limbs and throw them, at least in the direction of George Schaller. This matter of tearing off limbs and shaking them appears to be widely-distributed behavior among the monkeys and apes, as Wallace thought a long time ago. According to Jane Goodall's excellent accounts, chimps show a wide range of tool-using activities—sticks to get at termites, sticks of a different size to get at fire ants, leaves to clean the body or to get water, and rocks for throwing or, according to observations in West Africa, for breaking palm nuts. Here, then, is a wide variety of use of objects by a pongid, a use that is very different from that of any animals other than primates. Jane Lancaster first pointed out to me that the tool-use of most non-primates is something very specific, such as the use of stones by sea otters or the use of a thorn by a particular kind of bird. This is one kind of behavior that is lodged in experience and in the central nervous system of the animal; while the chimp uses a variety of objects for a number of different objectives.

I think that we will discover that the behavior of the gorilla is far more like that of the chimpanzee than appears from present accounts. I am not criticizing George Schaller's excellent monograph, but the problem here is the length of the study and the conditions under which the study was made. Schaller was with the gorillas for less than 500 hours, and by this time in her study Goodall hadn't seen termiting, drinking, hunting, or many of the other things in her study that we consider the most important. This is my point here concerning primate studies, and it is very discouraging—as when Irv DeVore pointed out that after 1,400 hours of observing baboons, we were completely wrong as regards their predation. This means that to get really accurate studies, they have to be long enough so that relatively infrequent kinds of behavior are well represented in the studies. And this requires about 2,000 hours, or about two or three years of work. Anyway, one reason I feel that the gorilla is going to be found to be really like the chimpanzee and should be classified in the same genus is, among many other comparisons, that the throwing behavior of gorillas in the zoos is exactly the same as that of chimps. This is not a general comparison but involves the precise way in which the gorilla holds things and the way he swings in throwing. And it's hard for me to believe that this behavior in all its details, so similar to that of the chimpanzee, occurs in the zoo but never in natural conditions.

If we return now to the general topic of the origin of tool-use in terms of human evolution, I'd like to stress two major different kinds of origin that have been brought out in papers by Hall, one of the top men in this field. One is the, so to speak, economic origin that we have already talked about here, and the other is the possible origin of tools in agonistic display. The chimpanzee throws rocks at creatures it is displaying against or they pull branches off trees and swing them, without hitting anything in either case. The gorillas do the same thing, so here are two species that use objects in agonistic display in such a way that they might eventually discover the effectiveness of hitting their target; even though this wouldn't represent an immediate economic return. I have always wondered how effective throwing and use of the club began. And I can imagine that if an animal was accustomed to relying on good big canine teeth for fighting and hunting, we would be very unhappy to substitute for those canines a club that was never used to hit the thing the animal was swatting at. In these apes, then, we have two different roots towards the development of tools, economic and agonistic. Again, there is no suggestion that these animals are close ancestors of ours. Whatever kind of phylogeny one wants to make of man, there are millions of years between anything like a human ancestor and the contemporary apes. There must have been millions of apes over millions of years using tools for economic and display purposes and, consequently, countless chances for the discovery of the potential effectiveness of these tools.

Tool origin seems to have taken a very long time, and if we look at the relation of tools to the brain, I think we can see why this is the case. I don't know why it should be so, but in anthropology we have stressed the cortex almost exclusively. I suppose this is because the cortex is particularly well-developed in man, but the cerebellum, which is concerned more with skill functions, is just as large as the cortex is. Our cerebellum is approximately three times the size of that of the great ape with large areas devoted to the thumb and the hand. And I think we should see in this difference in size and distribution the conclusion that the parts of the brain that are involved with skills must be greatly developed before tool-use will be effective. It is easy for us to learn manual skills, because our brains have evolved in accordance with these skills. But from an ape's point of view, the things that man does without effort—the detailed use of the fingers, and so on—are impossible and even inconceivable.

Another thing coming out of the work of Goodall and others that is contrary to what we usually think and say is the fact that the improvement of tools comes as early as does their use. The chimpanzee selecting something to termite with pulls off the side branches, tears off the leaves, and makes it the proper length. In other words, if the creature is intelligent enough to use tools in the first place, it doesn't just use whatever is lying around but selects something appropriate and then improves it. So, we can be pretty sure that improvement accompanied use way back before the introduction of any kind of stone tools or anything like the Oldowan Culture.

Now, I'd like to suggest that if something like tool-use is, so to speak, built into the brain, we have a variety of ways of comparing differences in the brain and differences in behavior and should be able to tighten down on this problem. The first index of whether something like manual skill is built into the brain can be found in the play of juveniles. Much of the social play of the non-human primates—rough chasing around and the like—is comparable to social play in young human beings. But there is a class of object-play, in which the young human takes tremendous pleasure in fooling around with objects, that has no counterpart in non-human primates. It's true that if you put a monkey or ape in a cage furnished with nothing but one or two objects, I suspect that out of total boredom it will investigate the objects and push them around slightly.

But this is very different from what young humans do with objects. One of the friends that met me at the airport had brought along a two-year-old, and I watched this kid fooling around. A stranger went over to a candy machine, stuck in some money, pushed a button, and got some candy. The kid immediately went over to the candy machine and pushed every point on it, obviously hoping to get a comparable reward. The non-human primates don't see this sort of combination and don't act this way at all. So, since manual dexterity is built into the brain and the biology of our species, it comes out in play in a very important way. And we can use the study of play to help us understand the background of contemporary human behavior.

In the language session, the same kind of thing was pointed out. Earl Count reminded us that the human infant, so to speak, plays with language in a way that non-human primates never do, and I believe this is entirely correct. Anyone who has watched and heard the behavior of children before speech realizes that they must have a built-in structure that leads to a quantity of babbling noises, which then can begin to form along the lines of the exceedingly simple rules outlined for us by Dr. Slobin. This is something else that simply never happens in the behavior of the other primates.

Another way of getting at these things is in terms of the ease of teaching animals. If an animal is biologically so constructed that something is easy for it to do, then we find that it's not very hard to teach it to do that sort of thing. And I think that it would be instructive to some people who talk a lot about learning to use tools to take a tame monkey and suffer through the problems of trying to teach the creature to do anything that we would regard as minimal effective use of tools. A couple of students were working on this last summer at Berkeley, and I must say that my admiration went out to the monkey for devising so many methods of obtaining the defined objectives without using the tools it was given. Unfortunately, the first tools given it were made of wood, and the monkey preferred the taste of the tools to that of the grapes that were supposed to be his reward. Seriously though, ease of learning—something that Dave Hamburg and I have discussed many times—is something built into an organism and represents things that have been favored by natural selection over the last many thousands of years. So, taken in this light, the pattern of ease of learning is a way that we can interpret the human long-past in detail—and I stress "in detail" as a perfectly feasible objective in this approach.

Again, I would like to draw a parallel with language and the point that Jane Lancaster made in the language session. You can't teach the non-human primates to name in any human sense, and the reason for this is that they do not have the structures in the central nervous system that are necessary for naming. They can learn that a certain color or shape will bring a reward, but they simply cannot learn naming. In terms of the origin of language, then, it is tremendously important to discover the beginnings of the ability to name and the factors that selected for a structural basis for naming during evolution. My own belief—and I think that Mrs. Lancaster would agree with this—is that the situation which originally led to naming was the making of tools. There may have been a couple of million years of making stone tools, far more complicated ones than any the chimpanzee makes, before the ability for naming was established.

In summary, I think that there are a number of tremendous problems that emerge almost for the first time when we look at human affairs from the standpoint of our knowledge of contemporary monkeys and apes. By reversing the usual perspective, we begin to wonder why language and manual skills and a broad concept of territory did not evolve in a very large number of primates over milions of years. I have used the word "tool," at least in speaking of Acheulian times and onwards, almost symbolically as something that stands for a very wide range of human abilities. And I think that if we look at the important things that humans can do and non-human primates can't do, we see that it amounts to much more than just language and tool skills. We can control our emotions, cooperate, learn, and plan to a degree that would be incomprehensible to any non-human primate. All these things depend on the human brain and are the structural results of human evolution, particularly during the past five or six hundred thousand years. And for this reason, behavioral genetics holds an important key to understanding human evolution. Huxley has said that man is closer to the apes than they are to the monkeys, but if we look at the major behavioral differences I have stressed, I think we'll find that man is truly very different from either.

3

Hominid Paleontology

A Biological Perspective of Language*

ERIC H. LENNEBERG

(*Editor's Note*) Even at the time of Linnaeus, the definition of man was couched in relative terms. Most human anatomical traits are not unique but simply relatively less ape-like. Upright posture, large cranial capacity, manual dexterity, etc., are but end points on a continuous scale of such characteristics within the living primates. Thus even before the days of modern systematics, a definition of man was sought more in the domain of behavior than in piecemeal morphological characteristics. Today some observers of primates in nature have come to the conclusion that even behaviorally the differences between man and non-human primates are also only a matter of degree. For example, it was found that some pongids use sticks as tools, communicate vocally, are socially organized, and even occasionally use stones as missiles. In other words, some non-human primates seemed more human than had been supposed. At least, that's what some investigators thought. The problem was what to make of all this taxonomically.

In the first place one would not expect to find continua existing across species boundaries. Species are closed biological systems. Gaps between them can only be filled by extinct fossil forms which are phylogenetically ancestral to the currently co-existing forms prior to their divergence from one another. Gaps between divergent species vary according to the different rates of evolution undergone by the two species. Man seems to be the most recently evolved primate, and his degree of divergence seems to have been particularly great. This means that sometime during the

*From *New Directions in the Study of Language*, edited by Eric H. Lenneberg, Massachusetts Institute of Technology Press, 1964. pp. 65–88. By permission of the author and the publisher.

Pleistocene he developed unique or new characteristics —the rate and direction of evolutionary remodeling was so great for the new species that differences that began as matters of degree evolved into differences in kind. Since species evolve as units, no gradations exist within *Homo sapiens* today that retain unequal evidences of a non-hominid ancestry. In other words, the species boundary is particularly distinct for man, which makes cross-species comparisons unusually hazardous. In the following article Lenneberg presents man's language capacity as a specific trait of his species. His argument, presented in genetic and evolutionary terms, emphasizes the importance of considering the existence of discontinuities when species differences are involved.

A T first it may seem as if biology had little to add to our knowledge of speech and language beyond the general and somewhat vague comparison of human communication with animal communication. I would like here to raise the question of whether there might not be biological endowments in man that make the human form of communication uniquely possible for our species.

The chief reasons for suspecting such specific biological propensities for our ability to acquire language are these:

1. *Anatomic and physiologic correlates.* There is increasing evidence that verbal behavior is related to a great number of morphological and functional specializations such as oropharyngeal morphology (DuBrul, 1958); cerebral dominance (Ajuriaguerra, 1957; Mountcastle, 1962); specialization of cerebrocortical topography; special coordination centers (or foci) for motor speech; specialized temporal pattern perception; special respiratory adjustment and tolerance for prolonged speech activities; and a long list of sensory and cognitive specializations prerequisite for language perception.[1]

2. *Developmental schedule.* The onset of speech is an extremely regular phenomenon, appearing at a certain time in the child's physical development and following a fixed sequence of events, as if all children followed the same general "strategy" from the time they begin to the period at which they have mastered the art of speaking (Lenneberg, 1964; Morley, 1957; Weir, 1962). The first

---

[1]More detailed treatment of this and the following point may be found in my book, *Biological Foundation of Language*, Wiley, New York, 1967.

things that are learned are principles—not items: principles of categorization and pattern perception. The first words refer to classes, not unique objects or events. The sounds of language and the configuration of words are at once perceived and reproduced according to principles; they are patterns in time, and they never function as randomly strung up items. From the beginning, very general principles of semantics and syntax are manifest. Even if the maturational scale as a whole is distorted through retarding disease, the order of developmental milestones, including onset of speech, remains invariable (Lenneberg, Nichols, and Rosenberger, 1964). Onset and accomplishment of language learning do not seem to be affected by cultural or linguistic variations.

3. *Difficulty in suppressing language.* The ability to learn language is so deeply rooted in man that children learn it even in the face of dramatic handicaps. Congenital blindness has no obvious effect on word acquisition even though there is only a small fraction of words whose referents can be defined tactually. Congenital deafness has a devastating effect on the vocal facilitation for speech, yet presentation of written material enables the child to acquire language through a graphic medium without undue difficulties. Children suffering from gross and criminal parental neglect, or who have parents who have no spoken language whatever, as in the case of adult congenitally deaf parents, may nevertheless learn to speak with only a minimal delay, if any, according to research now in progress.

4. *Language cannot be taught.* There is no evidence that any nonhuman form has the capacity to acquire even the most primitive stages of language development. The vocalization skills and the behavioral responses to verbal commands that we find in a few species can be shown to bear merely a superficial resemblance to human verbal behavior. In each case it can be demonstrated that their behavior is based on fundamentally different principles from those in humans. The difference is not merely a quantitative one but apparently a qualitative one (Lenneberg, 1962b). No one has demonstrated that a subhuman form can acquire the principles of speech perception in terms of phonemic analysis, of understanding the syntactic structure of a sentence, or of imparting the total semantic domain of any word, be it concrete or abstract.

5. *Language universals.* Although language families are so different, one from the other, that we cannot find any historical connection between them, every language, without exception, is based on the same *universal principles* of semantics, syntax, and phonology. All languages have words for relations, objects, feelings, and qualities,

and the semantic differences between these denotata are minimal from a biological point of view. According to a number of modern grammarians (Chomsky, 1957; Greenberg, 1963; Hartmann, 1961; Hjelmslev, 1953) working quite independently of each other, syntax of every language shows some basic, formal properties, or, in other words, is always of a peculiar algebraic type. Phonologically, all languages are based on a common principle of phonematization even though there are phonemic divergences.

Language universals are the more remarkable as the speakers live in vastly different types of cultures ranging from an essentially neolithic type to the highly complex cultural systems of Western civilization. Further, language and its complexity is independent of racial variation. It is an axiom in linguistics that any human being can learn any language in the world. Thus, even though there are differences in physical structure, the basic skills for the acquisition of language are as universal as bipedal gait.[2]

Owing to these considerations, it becomes plausible to hypothesize that language is a species-specific trait, based on a variety of biologically given mechanisms. Our task for the future is to discover and describe these mechanisms in greater detail than has been attempted so far.

This formulation poses three major problems which I shall now attempt to deal with:

1. Is uniqueness of behavior or form acceptable in the light of evolution?

2. Is there evidence for a genetic basis of language propensity?

3. Is language propensity a simple consequence of a general increase in "intellectual capacity," or must we assume some "language-specific" correlates?

Uniqueness of Species Characteristics

The discovery of a unique behavioral trait in a species need not mystify us, first, because we have been made aware by ethologists that speciation affects not only anatomy but also behavior, and that there are countless species with unique behavior patterns, and second,

[2]In an earlier paper (Lenneberg, 1961) I have defended the claim that universal features of language cannot be said to be either the most efficient or the most useful solution to acoustic communication except in a trivial sense: i.e., most useful for an organism that has the biological characteristics of man alone.

because uniqueness is to be expected from the evolutionary process itself.

There are two main processes in evolution: (1) cladogenesis, i.e., the process of branching out into newer and newer species; and (2) anagenesis or phyletic evolution, i.e., the process by which an entire species gradually undergoes change over time. If a given species fails to split up into isolated populations for a long period of time (or if only one of the newly resulting species survives), an animal with relatively unique traits will emerge. If the species has undergone anagenetic evolution, it will further deepen the gap between itself and its next of kin. According to Dobzhansky (1962), man's recent history is marked primarily by anagenesis; extinction of more closely related species has also taken place, as shown in Figure 1.

The fact that man communicates with man is not a unique zoological phenomenon. Most animals have inter- and intraspecies communication systems, and among mammals there is usually vocal

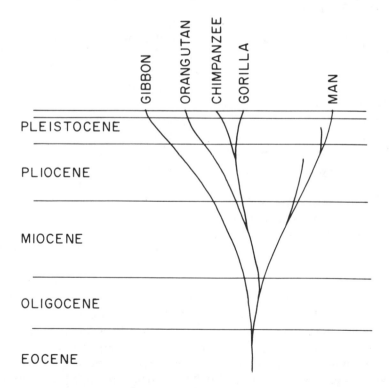

FIGURE 1. *Schema of the evolution of the* Hominoidea.

communication. However, the behavioral traits of animal communication cannot be ordered like a genetic tree and the phylogenetic relations among vertebrates, derived from comparative morphology, are not reflected in the taxonomy of their communication behavior. Many species have evolved highly specialized communication systems, such as the honeybee, many bird species, and dolphins. Neither these systems nor a dog's response to human commands represent primitive stages of human communication. Nor is there evidence that the communication of monkeys and apes constitutes a gradual approximation toward language. The empirically determined primitive beginnings of language in man (in the 18-months-old infant or in feeble-minded individuals) are behaviorally very different from the signals that animals emit for each other. Many animal communication systems are probably evolutionary offshoots, as is man's, and cross-species comparisons must be carried out with great caution.

Genetic Foundations

The genetic foundation of many types of behavior is widely recognized today (Fuller and Thompson, 1960; Hall, 1951). It is not assumed, however, that specific behavioral traits are directly produced by definite genes, but merely that propensities for certain behavior are inherited. This may be through changes in sensitivity thresholds or inherited perceptual, motor, or cognitive skills, such as changes in memory capacity (Rensch, 1954). Nevertheless, a unique or species-specific configuration of thresholds and skills may result through inherited propensities which make specific behavior uniquely possible. It is generally agreed that genes always affect a number of characters; this phenomenon is called *pleiotropism*. Pleiotropism is due to intramolecular rearrangements and may have in its wake disarrangements in the balance and harmony of embryological processes, particularly differentiation rates of tissues and growth gradients within the body. It is important to remember here that the developmental process is the unfolding of a continuously and precariously balanced affair where every single event is intimately related to a number of other events. Therefore, it is likely that genes often act on more than one property without interfering at the same time with the balance in other parts of the system. According to this view (Caspari, 1958), it is surprising that genetic changes are possible that are confined, phenotypically, to relatively circumscribed phenomena or, to put it differently, that, despite the frequent small changes that occur in the genotype, many characteristics of a species remain so completely stable.

Caspari explains the resistance of many characteristics to genetic change by postulating a gradient of "protection" against pleiotropic action. Thus, certain traits may be better established or more deeply rooted than others. Those that are well established tend to remain unaffected, even if genetic change has brought about thorough transfiguration of form and function in an individual. If, on the other hand, a given trait is not well protected, it is liable to change whenever there is any genetic disturbance interfering with the original state of balance. This resembles polygenic inheritance, i.e., many different gene actions contribute to bringing about a given condition. Fertility is an example of poor protection from pleiotropism in that it is very easily altered; most mutations are likely to affect it.

How do these concepts apply to language? The familial occurrence of language disabilities has been observed since the beginning of medicine. In recent years many reliable and careful studies have been published (Drew, 1956; Eustis, 1947; Gallagher, 1950; Hallgren, 1950; Luchsinger, 1959; Orton, 1930; Pfaendler, 1960), and the entire literature has been reviewed by Brewer (1963). On the basis of a carefully controlled and objective investigation of an entire family with congenital language disability (Fig. 2), Brewer con-

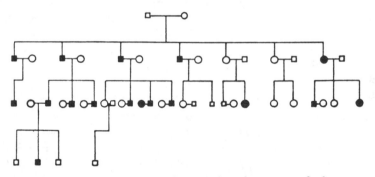

FIGURE 2. *Pedigree of a family with hereditary specific language disability. Circles are females; squares are males. Presence of trait is shown as solid symbols (Brewer, 1963).*

cludes that "specific language disability is a dominant, sex-influenced, or partially sex-linked trait with almost complete penetrance." In cases such as Brewer's there is never a total absence of language but merely a combination of certain deficits, including markedly delayed onset of speech, poor articulation persisting into the teens, poorly established hand preference, marked reading difficulties, either complete inability or marked difficulty for acquisition of second languages. Intelligence is usually not affected.

More direct evidence for the genetic basis of language comes from the work of Moorhead, Mellman, and Wenar (1961) who have made chromosome counts of a family in which a mother (Fig. 3) and four of her five children had a chromosomal abnormality associated with varying degrees of mental retardation and a striking failure of speech development. The father and a fifth sibling had a normal chromosome picture and were not affected behaviorally. Unfortunately, chromosome studies are too recent a development to have produced a large literature as yet. But it may be expected that in at least some families with specific language disability chromosome studies will eventually become available.

An important question that arises, especially from the Moorhead et al. study, is whether *any* chromosome abnormality is likely to lower intelligence and interfere with language. This is definitely not so. Some chromosome abnormalities are associated with somatic deficits without affecting intelligence, and other chromosome abnormalities affect intelligence but not necessarily language.

Although we have postulated that the propensity for language is the consequence of a pleiotropic effect, there is good reason to believe that the relevant genes are well "protected" from the pleiotropic effect of other genes; the propensity for language remains stable in the presence of a great variety of clearly genetic alterations. We have mentioned that the morphological diversification of the races does not affect it. Nor is it affected by the many traits that are apparently due to defects in genes and that are inherited in Mendelian fashion, such as hemophilia, Friedrich's ataxia, Huntington's chorea, etc. Thus the inheritance for the propensity of language deficits is a fairly independent trait.

On the other hand, there is an inherited error of metabolism producing a disease known as histidinemia which has in its wake a very high incidence of specific disturbance of language development in children, often without affecting their intelligence or other behavioral traits (Ghadimi, Partington, and Hunter, 1961, 1962; Auerbach et al., 1962).

This is the extent of our evidence to date. It poses the interesting question whether proof of language disturbance on a genetic basis is also evidence for the genetic basis of language *ability*. Perhaps so, but more work will have to be done before we can be relatively certain. In any event, evolution and genetics appear to be relevant to the general study of verbal behavior.

General or Specific Capacity

Nothing is gained by labeling the propensity for language as *biological* unless we can use this insight for new research directions—unless more specific correlates can be uncovered. At the present time we are merely able to pinpoint certain biological problems and thereby to reopen some questions about language that were falsely thought to have been answered. For instance, it is often assumed that the propensity for language is simply a reflection of man's great non-specific intelligence. And as evidence for a "phylogenetic increase in intelligence," man's brain-weight/body-weight ratio is cited

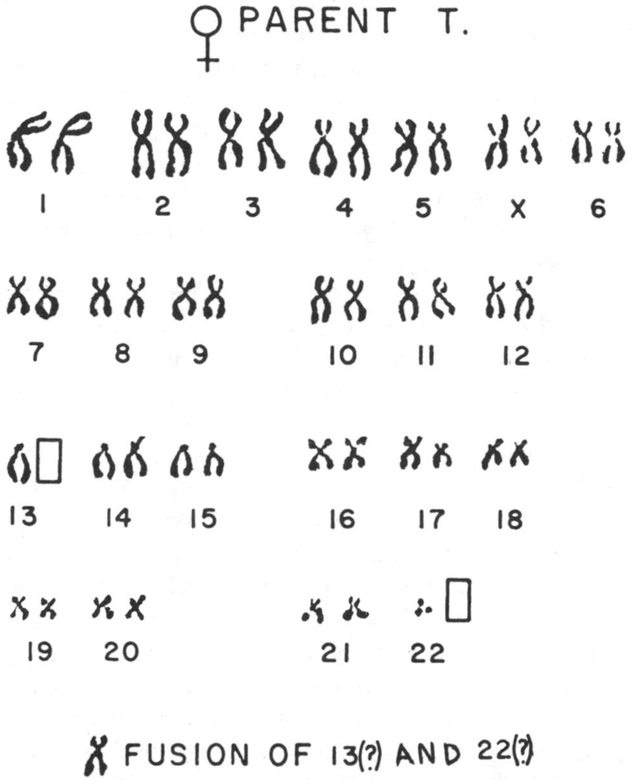

FIGURE 3. *Abnormal chromosome picture of woman with low intelligence and disproportionately poor speech and language. She gave birth to four children with similar chromosomal and clinical abnormalities. There is an unmatched chromosome which is interpreted as a fusion of missing chromosomes 13 and 22. Approximate enlargement 1200×. (Redrawn from Moorhead et al., 1961.)*

with the implication that the relative increase in neurons has made a certain level of intellect possible for language development. Both of these assumptions run into serious difficulties.

The definition and measurement of intelligence is difficult enough in our own species. When it comes to comparing different species, it is no longer permissible to talk about intelligence as if it were a single, clear-cut property that can be measured by a single objective instrument so as to yield quantities that are commensurable across species. Attempts have been made to compare across species such functions as memory span (Rensch, 1954), perceptual processes (Teuber, 1960), problem solving (Köhler, 1925), and others. In most of these instances, tasks are administered that are relatively easy for humans and more difficult for animals. On the other hand, tasks have been described in which various animals respond more quickly, with greater accuracy and, in a sense, more efficiently. Thus comparative psychology shows man to have a different mentation from other species and, obviously, a greater capacity to do things human. But we do not have objective and biologically meaningful proof that all mammals are endowed with a homogeneous and nonspecific amount of intelligence and that this amount increases with phylogenetic proximity to man.

Even if species could be compared in terms of general (surplus) intelligence and man could be shown to possess more of this quantity than any other creature, we still could not be certain that his ability for language is the result of, say, general inventiveness. Might it not be possible that language ability—instead of being the consequence of intelligence—is its cause? This has indeed been suggested by such thinkers as Hamann, Herder, W. v. Humboldt, Cassirer, and implied by Hughlings, Jackson, Wundt, Whorf, Penfield, and many others before and since them. This proposition, which has been criticized for a number of reasons (Black, 1959; Feuer, 1953; Greenberg, 1954; Lenneberg, 1953, 1954, 1962a; Révész, 1954), is important in one respect: it suggests that language might be of greater biological antiquity than the peculiar intellective processes of recent man. Nevertheless, I do not advocate the notion that language is the cause of intelligence because there is no way of verifying this hypothesis. Instead, I would like to propose a *tertium quid*, namely, that the ability to acquire language is a biological development that is relatively independent of that elusive property called intelligence. I see evidence for this view in the fact that children acquire language at a time when their power of reasoning is still poorly developed and that the ability to learn to understand and speak has a low correlation with measured IQ in man. Let me elaborate on this latter point.

In a recent study Lenneberg, Nichols, and Rosenberger (1964) studied the language development of 84 feeble-minded children raised by their own parents in a normal home environment. The basic results are represented diagrammatically in Fig. 4. IQ figures, as measured by standard instruments, deteriorate with chronological age in the mentally retarded, even though there is objective growth in mental age up to the early teens, after which time mental development is arrested.

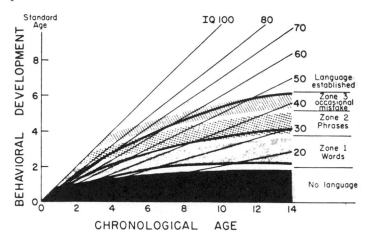

FIGURE 4. *Relationship between speech development and IQ. The curved lines show empirically determined "decay rates" of IQ in the mentally retarded. The shadings indicate language development. An individual whose IQ at a given age falls into the dark area at the bottom has no language. If he falls into the lighter areas, he is in one of three stages of language development and will develop further until his early teens, his progress depending upon both his IQ and his age. If he falls into the white area above, he is in full command of language. After age 12 to 13 speech development "freezes." (Data based on a follow-up study of 61 mongoloids and 23 children with other types of retarding disease.)*

Language begins in the same manner in retardates as in the normal population. We found that it is impossible to train a child with, say, mongolism to parrot a complicated sentence if he has not yet learned the underlying principles of *syntax*. However, the general principle underlying *naming* is grasped at once and immediately generalized. Naming behavior may be observed even in low-grade idiots; only individuals so retarded as to be deficient in stance, gait, and bowel control fail to attain this lowest stage of language acquisition. Incidentally, it is interesting to note that generalization of naming is beyond the capacity of gorilla and chimpanzee.[3] Children whose IQ is 50 at age 12 and about 30 at age 20 are completely in possession of language though their articulation may be poor and an occasional grammatical mistake may occur.

Thus, grossly defective intelligence need not implicate language; nor does the *absence* of language necessarily lower cognitive skills. For instance, congenitally deaf children have in many parts of the world virtually no language or speech before they receive instruction in school. When these preschoolers are given nonverbal tests of concept formation they score as high as their age peers who hear (Furth, 1961; Rosenstein, 1960; Oléron, 1957). From these examples it appears that language and intelligence are to some extent at least independent traits. In order to prove their complete independence it would be necessary to show that there are congenitally aphasic children whose nonverbal intelligence is unimpaired and who are also free from psychiatric disease. Many authorities believe that these cases exist, though in my experience I have not had occasion to examine such a patient. I have, however, studied one child (Lenneberg, 1962b) who had a congenital disability for articulation, who could not utter any intelligible word, but who did acquire the ability to understand language. Many other similar cases are familiar to me, constituting evidence that there is at least a highly particular motor skill in man which may be selectively impaired by both discrete lesions and inherited defect.

Let us now return to man's brain-weight/body-weight ratio. Because of our difficulty in defining the phenomenon of intelligence zoologically, we shall circumvent the problem of the relationship of brain size and intellective power. Let us ask directly whether a large brain is the morphological prerequisite for language learning. Would it be possible to learn to understand or to speak a natural language such as English with a brain the size of some non-speaking animal? The answer is *yes* but only if the individual is of the species *Homo sapiens*. This may sound like a contradiction in terms. Yet there is a clinical condition, first described by the German pathologist Virchow

---

[3]Viki, the chimpanzee raised by the Hayeses, could whisper "cup" when presented with a certain object by the Hayeses; but Mrs. Hayes describes how situation-bound the animal's naming behavior was. Room, time of day, examiner and acquaintance with object were all factors influencing the ability to understand and name correctly.

and named by him *nanocephalic dwarfism* (bird-headed dwarfs
in the English-speaking world) in which man appears reduced to
fairy-tale size. Seckel (1960) has recently described two such dwarfs
and has reviewed the scientific literature on thirteen others. He
ascribes the condition to a single-locus recessive gene for dwarfish
stature without affecting endocrine organs and function. Adult individuals attain a maximum height of 3 feet, and about half of the
described patients stand not much higher than 2½ feet at adult age;
the shortest adult mentioned measured 23 inches.

Nanocephalic dwarfs differ from other dwarfs in that they preserve the skeletal proportions of normal adults, as illustrated in
Figure 5; the fully mature have a brain-body weight ratio well
within the limits of a young teenager. Yet their head circumference

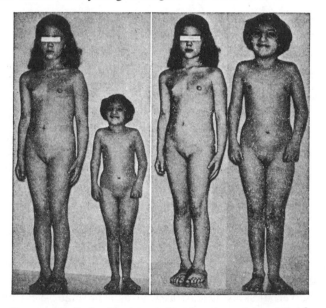

FIGURE 5. *Left: Nanocephalic dwarf next to normal
girl of same age (9 years); right: the dwarf's photograph enlarged to show that bodily proportions are
roughly similar to those of the normally developing
girl (from Seckel, 1960; reprinted with the permission
of S. Karger AG, Basel/New York).*

and estimated brain weight barely exceed those of a newborn infant,
as shown in Figure 6. On microscopic examination these brains
have an unremarkable histological appearance; both the size of
individual nerve cells and the density of their distribution is within

normal limits. Therefore we do not have here miniatured adult brains, but brains that differ very substantially from those of normal adults in the absolute number of cells. Intellectually, these dwarfs

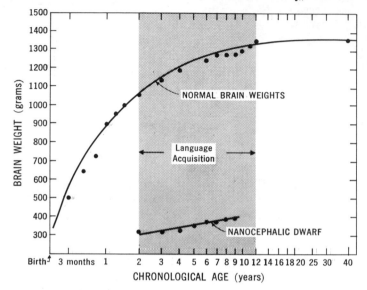

FIGURE 6. *Children's brain weights determined at autopsy plotted as a function of chronological age (based on data by Coppoletta and Wolbach, 1932). Bottom plot: various estimated weights based on repeated measurements of head circumference of patient shown in Fig. 5. The extrapolations were made by comparing autopsied children's head circumference with their brain weight.*

for the most part show some retardation, often not surpassing a mental age level of 5 to 6 years. All of them acquire the rudiments of language, including speaking and understanding, and the majority master the verbal skills at least as well as a normal 5-year-old child. From Table 1 it is apparent that neither the absolute nor relative weights of brains and bodies reveal the nature of the relationship between speech and its neurological correlates. Apparently the ability to speak is not dependent upon nonspecific increase in cell number or anything as general as brain-weight/body-weight ratios. Instead of postulating a quantitative parameter as the critical variable for the ability to acquire language, we should look toward much more specific modes of internal organization of neurophysiological processes. At present we do not know what they might be. But man's developmental and maturational history suggests that growth

TABLE 1.   *Brain Weights and Body Weights of*
Juvenile and Adult Hominoidea

	AGE	SPEECH FACULTY	BODY WEIGHT (KG)	BRAIN WEIGHT (KG)	RATIO
Man (m)	2½	beginning	13½	1.100	12.3
Man (m)	13½	yes	45	1.350	35
Man (m)	18	yes	64	1.350	47
Man (dwarf)	12	yes	13½	.400[a]	34
Chimpanzee (m)	3	no	13½	.400[b]	34
Chimpanzee (f)	adult	no	47	.450[b]	104
Rhesus	adult	no	3½	.090[c]	40

[a]Estimate based on Seckel (1960).
[b]Estimate based on Schultz (1941).
[c]Estimate based on Kroeber (1948).

processes and functional lateralization are involved (Lenneberg, in press), the physical nature of which remains to be discovered.

Conclusion

In the first part of this presentation I have argued that species-specific peculiarities are to be expected from the evolutionary processes themselves. Therefore, language specialization need not mystify us. In the second part I have tried to show that the basis for language capacity might well be transmitted genetically. In the last section I have rejected the notion that man's ability to speak is due to such general properties as an increase in intelligence or a relative increase in the weight of his brain. It seems, rather, as if language is due to as yet unknown species-specific biological capacities.

In conclusion I wish to emphasize that all these considerations serve to establish an hypothesis and to stimulate new directions for research on the nature of man. However, the facts presented do not constitute a theory. Let us hope they will lead to one in the future.

References

AJURIAGUERRA. J. DE. Language et dominance cerebrale. *J. franç. d'Oto-Rhino-Laryngol.*, 1957, 6, 489–499.

AUERBACH, V., DIGEORGE, A., BALDRIDGE, R., TOURTELLOTTE, C., and BRIGHAM, M. Histidinemia: A deficiency in histidase resulting in the urinary excretion of histidine and of imidazolepyruvic acid. *J. Pediatr.*, 1962, 60, 487–497.

BLACK, M. Linguistic relativity: The views of Benjamin Lee Whorf. *Phil. Rev.*, 1959, *68*, 228–238.

BREWER, W. F. Specific language disability: Review of the literature and a family study. Honors thesis, Harvard University, 1963.

CASPARI, E. Genetic basis of behavior. In A. Roe and G. G. Simpson (Editors), *Behavior and evolution*. New Haven: Yale University Press, 1958.

CHOMSKY, N. *Syntactic structures*. The Hague: Mouton, 1957.

COPPOLETTA, J. M., and WOLBACH, S. B. Body length and organ weights of infants and children. *Amer. J. Pathol.*, 1932, *9*, 55–70.

DOBZHANSKY, T. *Mankind evolving*. New Haven: Yale University Press, 1962.

DREW, A. L. A neurological appraisal of familial congenital word-blindness. *Brain*, 1956, *79*, 440–460.

DUBRUL, E. L. *Evolution of the speech apparatus*. Springfield, Ill.: Thomas, 1958.

EUSTIS, R. S. The primary etiology of the specific language disabilities. *J. Pediatr.*, 1947, *31*, 448–455.

FEUER, L. S. Sociological aspects of the relation between language and psychology. *Phil. Sci.*, 1953, *20*, 85–100.

FULLER, J. L., and THOMPSON, W. R. *Behavior genetics*. New York: John Wiley, 1960.

FURTH, H. The influence of language on the development of concept formation in deaf children. *J. abnorm. soc. Psychol.*, 1961, *63*, 386–389.

GALLAGHER, J. R. Specific language disability: A cause for scholastic failure. *New Engl. J. Med.*, 1950, *242*, 436–440.

GHADIMI, H., PARTINGTON, M., and HUNTER, A. A familial disturbance of histidine metabolism. *New Engl. J. Med.*, 1961, *265*, 221–224.

GHADIMI, J. R., PARTINGTON, M., and HUNTER, A. Inborn error of histidine metabolism. *Pediatrics*, 1962, *29*, 714–728.

GREENBERG, J. H. Concerning influences from linguistic to non-linguistic data. In Harry Hoijer (Editor), *Language in culture*. Chicago: University of Chicago Press, 1954.

GREENBERG, J. H. (Editor). *Universals of language*. Cambridge, Mass.: M.I.T. Press, 1963.

HALL, C. S. The genetics of behavior. In S. S. Stevens (Editor), *Handbook of experimental psychology*. New York: John Wiley, 1951.

HALLGREN, B. Specific dyslexia (congenital word-blindness). *Acta psychiatr. neurol. scand.*, 1950, Suppl. *65*.

HARTMANN, P. Allgemeinste Strukturgesetze. In *Sprache und Grammatik*. The Hague: Mouton, 1961.

HJELMSLEV, L. *Prolegomena to a theory of language.* Indiana University Publications in Anthropology and Linguistics, Memoir 7. Baltimore: Waverly Press, 1953.

KÖHLER, W. *The mentality of apes.* New York: Harcourt, Brace, 1925.

KROEBER, A. L. Anthropology. New York: Harcourt, Brace, 1948.

LENNEBERG, E. Cognition in ethnolinguistics. *Language,* 1953, *29,* 463–471.

————. A note on Cassirer's *Philosophy of Language. Phil. phenomenol. Res.,* 1954, *15,* 512–522.

————. Language, evolution and purposive behavior. In S. Diamond (Editor), *Culture in history.* New York: Columbia University Press, 1961.

————. The relationship of language to the formation of concepts. *Synthèse,* 1962a, *14,* No. 2/3, 103–109.

————. Understanding language without ability to speak: A case report. *J. abnorm. soc. Psychol.,* 1962b, *65,* 419–425.

————. Speech as a motor skill with special reference to non-aphasic disorders. In U. Bellugi and R. Brown (Editors), The acquisition of language. *Child Developm. Monogr.,* 1964, *29,* 115–126.

————. Speech development: Its anatomical and physiological concomitants. In V. E. Hall (Editor), *Speech, language and communication. Brain and Behavior* (in press).

LENNEBERG, E. H., NICHOLS, I. A., and ROSENBERGER, E. F. Primitive stages of language development in mongolism. *Proc. Assoc. Res. nerv. ment. Disease,* 1964, *42,* 119–137.

LUCHSINGER, R. Die Vererbung von Sprach und Stimmstoerungen. *Folia phoniatr.,* 1959, *11,* 7–64.

MOORHEAD, P. S., MELLMAN, W. J., and WENAR, C. A familial chromosome translocation associated with speech and mental retardation. *Amer. J. hum. Genet.,* 1961, *13,* 32–46.

MORLEY, M. *The development and disorders of speech in childhood.* Baltimore: William & Wilkins, 1957.

MOUNTCASTLE, V. B. (Editor). *Interhemispheric relations and cerebral dominance.* Baltimore: Johns Hopkins University Press, 1962.

OLÉRON, P. *Recherches sur le developpement mental des sourdesmuets.* Paris: Centre National de la Recherche Scientifique, 1957.

ORTON, S. T. Familial occurrence of disorders in the acquisition of language. *Eugenics,* 1930, *3,* No. 4, 140–147.

PFAENDLER, U. Les vices de la parole dans l'optique du généticien. *Akt. Probl. der Phoniatr. und Logopaed.,* 1960, *1,* 35–40.

RENSCH, B. *Neuere Probleme der Abstammungslehre.* Stuttgart, 1954.

RÉVÉSZ, G. Denken und Sprechen. In G. Révész (Editor), *Thinking and speaking: A symposium.* Amsterdam: North Holland, 1954.

ROSENSTEIN, J. Cognitive abilities of deaf children. *J. Speech Hearing Res.,* 1960, *3,* 108–119.

SCHULTZ, A. H. The relative size of the cranial capacity in primates. *Amer. J. Anthropol.*, 1941, *28*, 273–287.

SECKEL, H. P. G. *Birdheaded dwarfs: Studies in developmental anthropology including human proportions.* Springfield, Ill.: Thomas, 1960.

TEUBER, H.-L. Perception. In J. Field, H. W. Magoun, and V. E. Hall (Editors), *Handbook of physiology.* Section 1: Neurophysiology, Vol. III. Washington, D. C.: American Physiological Society, 1960.

WEIR, R. H. *Language in the crib.* The Hague: Mouton, 1962.

Science and Human Evolution*

BERNARD G. CAMPBELL

(*Editor's Note*) For quite some time now students of human evolution have found it difficult to do much more with the bones of fossil man than describe them. Attempts to interpret the material in functional terms are rare. Most fossil man studies are static and typological in their approach, with the result that cross-sectional studies on living taxa and studies of microevolution are perhaps better approaches to the understanding of primate evolution than fossil evidence can ever be. Nevertheless, a revival of interest in fossil man can be expected as we become more accustomed to thinking in populational, demographic, and ecological terms and as multivariate procedures become more common in the description of anatomical variables. This will hopefully be accompanied by a decline in the plethora of "trees" of hypothesized relationship and the large number of classifications passionately upheld but often devoid of modern taxonomic relevance. The message of Campbell's article is that the study of fossil man carried out in the context of the modern synthetic theory of evolution can provide scientifically valid information. While some will recognize this as yet another effort to rid anthropology of its traditional romance and color, others will be glad to pay the price.

> "Discovery is an art, demonstration makes the Science."
> ——CHARLES SINGER[1]

WHILE the scientific status of social anthropology has often been questioned, that of physical anthropology has not, and physical anthropologists would, in all probability, claim that their science, a branch of natural science, conforms to the methodology and traditions of science as a whole. Though the scientific method is perhaps

*From *Nature*, vol. 203, August, 1964, pages 448–451. By permission of the author and the publisher.

119

more immediately effective in the experimental sciences it is just as powerful a tool in those sciences which depend not so much on experiment as on observation. Palæontology is a branch of the natural sciences which is not subject to experimental investigation (though it may utilize results of experimental biology), and it seems therefore worth enquiring how scientific method can most effectively be used by students of human evolution. It is scientific method which makes science, not experimentation, not discovery; it is scientific method to which we owe modern knowledge and technology, on which scientific progress depends; and it is scientific method which makes scientific knowledge distinct from religious and historical knowledge—which makes it demonstrable and universal.

How does this method operate in palæontology? Most discoveries today are made as a result of a planned excavation, though this was not always the case. Important human fossils have been discovered by chance (Neanderthal, Gibraltar, Cro-Magnon, Mauer); today, knowledge of human evolution and geology enable predictions to be made about likely sites for excavation (such a prediction was made many years ago by Dr. L. S. B. Leakey about the Olduvai deposits, and it has since been amply justified). A rather vague hypothesis of this kind—often little more than a hunch—is a necessary prerequisite to palæontological investigation. After that, results depend not only on the skill of the investigator, but also on luck. (The well-organized and well-financed expedition to Java in 1906 under Mme Selenka returned without any further trace of Dubois's *Pithecanthropus.*) Deduction from a rather general hypothesis will give us a prediction which can act as a guide to palæontological investigation.

The fossils found can then be treated as the given facts or data of human evolution. On them are made observations—which are our attempts to describe them. On a series of these observations more exact hypotheses can be built by induction. These can then be tested by different means: by comparison with other well-founded hypotheses, and by further deduction and prediction. In this way we can move from rather vague general hypotheses to more precise ones. But at all times the power or truth of a hypothesis is its ability to predict, and nothing else. The predictions must be tested, and the result may be that the hypothesis will be corroborated, or it may need to be modified, or abandoned altogether.

In physics or chemistry, not only can experiments be devised to obtain data, but also observations can in some instances be made and interpreted without human interference—the subjective element is thus minimized. In biology this is less often possible, and in palæontology never. The science of palæontology is dependent on personal observations, and so by nature subject to subjective aberration. Even at the level of obtaining data, palæontologists face a number of difficulties: (1) data are limited and finite; (2) they are both difficult and expensive to obtain, and there is an element of luck in their discovery; (3) they are organic and therefore quite complex.

At the same time, in the observation of data, students of human evolution face special problems.

(1) In the first place, observations may be made at a number of different levels. Thus the form of the skull may be recorded in a descriptive manner with words such as dolichocephalic, platycephalic, tapeinocephalic, etc., or better still by measurement. Here the number of measurements and method of taking them are important. Beyond this, drawings, photographs, chemical analyses, spectrographical analyses, etc., may be made on the fossils. Quantitative data obtained in standard and recognized ways will be the least subjective and probably the most valuable. Owing to the limited amount of data at present available, however, it is essential that the maximum amount of observation be made on the fossil; every independent and descriptive measurement and every possible analysis must be carried out which is likely to prove of the smallest value. The quality of the observations will clearly affect the value of the hypothesis to be derived from them.

(2) A second difficulty which is closely related to this is that a number of different skills may be required in the observation of data. Basic anatomical knowledge is essential. Beyond this, genetic, taxonomic, mathematical, chemical, biochemical and physical skills may be required. In practice, the interpretation of fossil data, to be of greatest value to science, must be carried out, not by one man, but by a small team of workers with differing qualifications.

(3) A third difficulty is a special one for anthropologists. The relation of the material to its investigator is complex. Even in other fields of scientific research the investigator is subject to a host of prejudices. Wilfred Trotter[2] has written:

> The dispassionate intellect, the open mind, the unprejudiced observer, exist in an exact sense only in a sort of intellectualist folklore; states even approaching them cannot be reached without a moral and emotional effort most of us cannot and will not make.

How much more serious this problem is in anthropological research, when man investigates himself. Only a hundred years ago the theory of evolution caused a deep rift in man's mind. The idea of human evolution has still not been absorbed fully into our subconscious and a schism can be detected at many levels of thought and behaviour. The special relationship which we have with the material which we investigate affects our interpretation and observation of data in many ways. One of the most fascinating aspects of this problem is seen in the light of the investigator's world-view. At one extreme man sees himself as an animal which has achieved its humanity with struggle and which can be proud of its achievement. Such a man sees in his ancestry, not only a reminder of his own racial achievement, but also an explanation of his all too common failings in humanity. He may well prove to be tolerant and maintain his optimism in the face of human failure and cruelty which to another can only cause despair.

At the opposite extreme, an individual may see himself as fallen, or at least falling, far short of his potentialities and needs. He finds himself miserable, cruel and perhaps doomed, never to rise above the level of the super-intelligent animal which he is. Those who hold this view, though they may never realize it, may shun the idea of the animal in man and wish to confine his bestial ancestry to the most distant past. Such a man is all too conscious of the gulf between what is and what could be, of the best in man and of the worst. Man, he believes, can become a superman or a god, and his failure to progress is the cause of the deepest pessimism. Clearly these two views of the condition of man cannot fail to affect the frame of reference in which we study our origins (Figs. 1 and 2). Indeed, aberration resulting from the subjectivity of observation may be so serious as to render interpretation of fossil data of no value to science.

(4) A final difficulty which falls into this category is that discoveries in human palæontology receive world-wide publicity—the layman is intensely interested, and the investigator may find himself in the public eye. Publicity of this kind is not only ego-enhancing, but also compelling: the public will not only make a discoverer famous, but will also demand something in exchange. Once a discovery is signalled as great, the discoverer is obliged to maintain this image in his observation and interpretation of the material—the pressure again may be disastrous to that frail vessel which is the human mind. It has even happened that as a reaction to this pressure, a discoverer has completely rejected an early and quite valid interpretation for no good reason, and replaced it by a contrary form. This Dubois did, when towards the end of his life he revised his interpretation of the hominid *Pithecanthropus* find, and stated it

to be a giant gibbon. The history of human palæontology presents us with many examples of how not only opinion, but money too, has caused the discoverer to behave in a manner antithetical to science. (A notorious instance was the discovery and disposal of the Le Moustier skeleton, by Otto Hauser. The skeleton was lifted from the Dordogne in 1908 without the recording of any archæological data and sold to the Museum für Völkerkunde of Berlin for 125,000 gold francs. It was destroyed in the Second World War.)

The observation of data is followed by its classification, and the erection of a hypothesis on the basis of such data, together with other data and hypotheses; this new hypothesis brings to discrete observations some coherent meaning. It is at this stage that science begins—scientific investigation itself is an art, and a very skilled one; the erection and demonstration of hypotheses are the beginning of science and it is in this way that scientific method brings its unique kind of universal knowledge. The erection of a hypothesis follows a number of distinct steps.

(1) All observations relative to the matter under investigation must be assembled from different sources, published and unpublished. Those most reliable can be treated as primary or self-sufficient evidence; other data may be set aside and tested at a later stage.[3]

FIGURE 1. Zinjanthropus, *drawn by Maurice Wilson for Dr. K. P. Oakley.*

(2) One or more hypotheses can then be constructed which account for the maximum of reliable facts or evidence. It is, of course, by no means essential to devote time to the construction of hypotheses. Invaluable work has been done in anthropology of a purely descriptive nature, and in the absence of experiment, observation and description are the essential ground-work of palæontology. Charles Darwin gathered data for five years before he first formulated his hypothesis of evolution, and it was another twenty-two years between the formulation of this 'working hypothesis' in 1837 and its publication in 1859.

(3) The simplest hypothesis should be selected in the first place as a working hypothesis. This is the principle of Occam's Razor. The principle is particularly pertinent to studies of human evolution. As a result of the nature of the data there is no difficulty in the construction of unlimited hypotheses to account for them. Testing

FIGURE 2. Zinjanthropus, *drawn by Neave Parker for Dr. L. S. B. Leakey.* (*Copyright,* Illustrated London News and Sketch, Ltd.)

of complex hypotheses, which may suggest false predictions, has wasted much scientific endeavour. The most important point is that the hypothesis should not be otiose—it should contain no statement which is unnecessary to account for the observations on which it is based. On the other hand, the simple hypothesis will probably enable one to make more predictions, and will therefore be easier to test.

Occam wrote that "plurality is never to be posited without need." This suggests that in studies of human evolution the simplest coherent scheme which accounts for the reliable facts should be tested before a more complex (here probably polyphyletic) hypothesis. Adherence to this principle would speed the solution of many problems and ensure the most efficient use of scientific effort.

(4) Test the working hypothesis by comparison with other hypotheses and by deduction and prediction against further observations of a reliable nature (new discoveries, etc.).[11] Meanwhile, the probable or possible status of disputed fossils can be assessed. This testing process is one of the most vital stages in the method of science; but it is here that palæontology restricts the pace. Experiments in physics and chemistry can be specially devised to test hypotheses. All the palæontologist can do is to look for new facts, a lengthy process, or make further observations on known data. (It may be mentioned in passing that there is a very large amount of fossil material which has received very little attention and may prove of great value in the science of human evolution. Examples include the fossils from Steinheim, Jebel Kafzeh and Montmaurin.)

A logical corollary of the foregoing process involves the examination of any hypotheses or observations which do not support the hypothesis, together with an assessment of their validity. Such examination may result in a modification of . the hypothesis, as may the addition of new observations.

(5) Assuming that the hypothesis is able to account for the majority of the most reliable observations, the scientist should then publish it with a demonstration of its validity. This is the second essential stage in the method of science. The purpose of this publication is: (a) to communicate what is believed to be an advance in knowledge; (b) to make the hypothesis available for further testing by other workers.

If there is one characteristic which distinguishes science, it is that it must be universal—it is the "search for judgements to which universal assent may be obtained"[1]. This characteristic necessitates such publication. If judgements are to be universally accepted, their validity must be effectively demonstrated. As a rule, therefore, scientists refrain from publication of working hypotheses until such demonstration can be given. The publication of a hypothesis with insufficient evidence does, however, carry heuristic value, though if accompanied by expressions of certainty, it may result in unnecessary controversy, because it is, in fact, open to doubt.

Publication is necessary at other stages, however, besides that of the demonstrable hypothesis. First of all facts must be published. In the case of fossils, this means that they must be placed in a public museum for the observation of any suitably qualified person who may wish to examine them. Fossil bones should not be treated as personal property; to withhold scientific knowledge is anti-science. Secondly, personal observations should be made available for the benefit of those who are unable to examine the original fossil data themselves, or who are not qualified to do so. The maximum number of observations should be made by standardized techniques and should be widely published. The withholding of observational data can never be justified (measurements, analyses, etc.).

These remarks may not only help us to analyse the work of others, but they may make our own contribution to the science more valuable. From them emerges one important conclusion: the science of human evolution is fraught with so many difficulties that it is of the greatest importance that a strict and rigorous methodology is followed. Failure to do so leads us from difficulties to confusion and misunderstanding.

Nomenclature and Hypothesis

Harrison and Weiner[3] have pointed out that the economy principle of Occam's Razor "should be extended to the activity of naming new fossil finds." By "naming" they mean, of course, the designation of fossils with Latin names, which Simpson[4] terms *nomina*, to create new species. The reason for this may not at first be clear, but if the meaning of the sexual species concept is fully accepted, it follows that the creation of a *nomen* involves the erection of a hypothesis.

The word 'species' is as old as the Latin tongue, but has changed its meaning with time. Until the eighteenth century, a species was a real and discrete unit—a kind of animal created as such by God and showing only the smallest variation. Although Linnæus accepted this concept he later recognized that considerable variability existed within species, though he did not doubt their original purity and constancy. Darwin observed minutely the geographical variation of species, and when he arrived at his hypothesis of evolution he saw that the term 'species' was to become a convenient label, no longer signifying a discrete population. The concept of the species had lost its meaning.

Our understanding has now changed once more. The sciences of genetics and ecology combined during the early years of this century to nourish a new approach to systematics which developed during the 1930's. Today we recognize the species as a prime biological unit with objective criteria. The details of this important development are beyond the scope of this article and have been often described by Huxley[5], Mayr[6] and others. Suffice it to say that the use of a *nomen* as a 'label' for one or more fossils is no longer justified—as the concept of the species has developed, so the unit designated by the two Latin terms has come to assume a quite complex meaning.

The history of fossil discoveries contains very many instances in which fossils were named for purposes of convenience without an understanding of the modern species concept. Indeed, no scientist could be blamed greatly for this attitude before about 1935 because the modern species concept was until then in its infancy. The meaning of the term in fact did not worry palæo-anthropologists because fossil finds were so few and far between. However, a large number of *nomina* accumulated and have since had to be critically assessed. The resulting confusion has not greatly helped the investigation of human evolution.

But the modern species concept is complex, and has certainly not been understood by all those who have more recently named Hominid fossil species. It would be fair to say that in the field of systematics or taxonomy the concept is now generally accepted and understood, thanks to the brilliant work of Huxley, Mayr, Simpson, Dobzhansky and others. Outside this field the situation is less satisfactory. This is very troublesome for palæo-anthropology because fossil discoveries are usually made by either archæologists or geologists, and the fossils are usually described and published either by their finders or by anatomists. None of these skills is necessarily inclusive of taxonomic experience. The understanding of taxonomy usually reaches to a knowledge of the *Code of Zoological Nomenclature*, and of the hierarchical system of classification proposed by Linnæus, but the meanings to be associated with the different taxonomic levels are not understood. (In practice the ineffectual designation of *nomina* does still occur. Recent examples include *Homo sapiens shanidarensis* Senyurek, 1957; *Hemanthropus peii* von Koenigswald, 1957; *Homo homo* var *neanderthalensis* Blanc, 1961; *Sinanthropus lantianensis* Woo, 1964. The validity of all these is in doubt, and some of them are certainly *nomina nuda.*) The *nomina* are in fact still frequently treated as labels. I quote:

It always was and still is the custom to give generic and specific names to each new type without much concern for the kind of relationship to other types formerly known.

———Franz Weidenreich[12]

I think it will be more convenient to split the different varieties into different genera and species than to lump them.

———Robert Broom[13]

Since the names which we apply, *at any and every level in the taxonomic sequence* are inevitably arbitrary and artificial it does not, I believe, matter what we decide to do, provided only that the majority of those who are concerned in the classification, at any given time, are agreed as to how they will use the classification system. . . . All names and terms are after all, only 'arbitrary labels' which are made for the convenience of ourselves and our colleagues.

———Louis Leakey[14]

There is, of course, no objection to the use of names in any language as labels for either individual fossils or local populations (Simpson's N_1 and N_2 designations[7]) so long as they do not take the binomial Latin form. To avoid confusion such names should be explicitly stated to refer not to species, but to individuals or local populations.

The understanding of how the species concept can be applied to fossil finds must follow two stages. The first is to be clear about the meaning of a biological species or biospecies; these species can only be recognized at a given moment in time and are defined as "groups of naturally or potentially interbreeding natural populations, which are reproductively isolated from other such groups."[6] This concept of the biospecies is essential to the theory of evolution, since it is when two closely related groups of animals cease to interbreed that they become two species and henceforward can evolve in different directions to form eventually perhaps two entirely different families. But this concept of the biospecies can only be applied to a moment in time—it does not recognize the dimension of time.

A species in palæontology is an extension of this idea. It is a fundamentally different kind of unit and has been called a chrono-species or palæospecies. Such species can be recognized in two instances:

(1) in separate lineages (contemporaneous or not) between which significant interbreeding does not occur; (2) at successive stages in

one lineage but with intervening evolutionary change of such magnitude that populations differ about as much as do contemporaneous species.[4]

That is to say, that we must attempt to divide up each evolving lineage into temporal and morphological stages which show approximately the same amount of morphological variation in time as an average biospecies does in space. I have quoted Simpson[4] as a convenient reference; but this is not a new concept. It was already fully accepted by 1943[7] and was in use years earlier.

From an understanding of the concept of the palæospecies follows the realization that the creation of a new palæontological species involves the erection of a hypothesis. This unwritten hypothesis could be stated somewhat as follows:

> The species *A-us b-us* (of which specimen Reg. No. 1302 in the Natural History Museum, Timbuctu, is the holotype) is believed to have existed as a group of naturally interbreeding populations over a certain area . . . and with a variability typical of modern living biospecies, and also to have been evolved from, and to have evolved into, other species which are separated by the amount of morphological difference which is usually associated with a species in space at the present time. The species represents a stage in an evolving lineage and will no doubt prove to be divisible (if not already so) into a number of sub-species in both the dimensions of space and time. Furthermore, the species can be distinguished from its neighbouring species (in space and time) by the following characteristics, etc.

The *Code of Zoological Nomenclature* states that for a name to be valid it must be "accompanied by a statement that purports to give characters differentiating the taxon" (Article 13 (*a*) (i)). It is scarcely necessary to state that this implies that the taxon must be differentiated from its nearest neighbours in evolution. Mayr (1942) states: "The diagnosis should include a direct comparison with the nearest relative"[6]. It would scarcely be of value to list the characters common to the family in which the fossil falls to distinguish it from a related family; on the contrary, the diagnosis must be pertinent to its function—that is, to enable other discoveries to be assigned to one or other of two species. The *Code of Zoological Nomenclature* is not in a position to state whether such a diagnosis is effective, just as criminal laws can do little more than punish a breach of the legal code. They cannot instil virtue, and similarly the *Code of Zoological Nomenclature* itself cannot ensure the presentation of an effective diagnosis; but the methodology of science can, for *it is in the diagnosis that we find the demonstration*. It is here that the hypothesis of the new species must stand or fall; it is here that science will train its critical eye to discover the validity of the hypothesis. The diagnosis must support the hypothesis for the species to stand, not in law, but in reality. It is precisely here that publications of new species so often fail. (Many examples of this state of affairs could be quoted. The most topical, and one of the most important, concerns the creation of the taxon *Homo habilis*[8]. In their original publication the authors stated that *Telanthropus capensis* "may well prove, on closer comparative investigation, to belong to *Homo habilis*"; thus the effective demonstration of a novel taxon was negated[9]. The name is valid, but the species has not been effectively shown to have existed, as a distinct taxon.)

I have here attempted to suggest how an understanding and strict use of scientific method may help us to avoid some of the problems which arise in palæoanthropology. Not only will this make our endeavours more fruitful, but also in an anthropological science a proper methodology will obviate much argument and ill-feeling which has, from time to time, been reported in the Press. Scientific communications must be clear, and so far as possible open to no misunderstanding. Since improvement in method, and better presentation of observation and hypothesis are open to palæoanthropologists, it would be the height of folly to neglect them.

I thank Prof. Philip Tobias and Mr. John Wilson for their advice.

References and Notes

[1]Singer, C., *Encyclopaedia Britannica, 20*, 114 (1963).
[2]Trotter, W., *Collected Papers of Wilfred Trotter* (Oxford, 1941).
[3]Harrison, G. A., and Weiner, J. S., ref. 10, p. 77.
[4]Simpson, G. G., ref. 10, p. 1.
[5]Huxley, J. S., *The New Systematics* (Oxford, 1940).
[6]Mayr, E., *Amer. Nat., 74*, 249 (1940); *Systematics and the Origin of Species* (New York, 1942).
[7]Simpson, G. G., *Ann. New York Acad. Sci., 44*, 145 (1943).
[8]Leakey, L. S. B., Tobias, P. V., and Napier, J. R., *Nature, 202*, 7 (1964).
[9]Oakley, K. P., and Campbell, B. G., *Nature, 202*, 732 (1964).
[10]Washburn, S. L. (ed.), *Classification and Human Evolution* (Chicago, 1963).
[11]A thorough discussion of the process of testing and of the probability of hypotheses can be found in K. R. Popper, *The Logic of Scientific Discovery* (London, 1959).
[12]Weidenreich, F., *Apes, Giants and Man* (Chicago, 1946).
[13]Broom, R., *Amer. J. Phys. Anthrop., 8*, 13 (1950).
[14]Leakey, L. S. B., ref. 10, p. 32.

Some Fallacies in the Study
of Hominid Phylogeny*

ELWYN L. SIMONS

(*Editor's Note*) Anthropologists have traditionally left the pre-Pleistocene to the paleontologists. Simons makes it clear that important information about human phylogeny will come from Tertiary fossil finds. He emphasizes that there is good evidence that early hominoids ranged over Europe, Asia, and Africa in Miocene and Pliocene times, and that such a wide distribution does not necessitate the assumption of great speciation. In fact, unless there is definite evidence that two fossil forms could not interbreed due to ecological, geographical or temporal separation, morphological distinction is usually an insufficient species criterion. When a species that has a wide geographical distribution eventually evolves into a new successional species, the change occurs across the entire range. In other words, species don't usually, or ever, originate at a point in geographical space and at a point in time.

This article by Simons is a model of the use of fossil material for an understanding of evolution.

THE century-long search for documentation of the fossil record of man's ancestry, which was particularly stimulated by publication of Darwin's *Origin of Species* in 1859, has by now brought in relatively abundant evidence concerning the major stages of man's lineage during the Pleistocene epoch. Accelerated discovery during the past few years confirms the view that the mainstream of human evolution in Pleistocene times evidently passed through a species of *Australopithecus* and then through *Homo erectus* and men of Neanderthaloid type to the modern varieties of *Homo sapiens* (*1*). These comparatively new findings have shifted fundamental research

*From *Science*, vol. 141, September 1963, pages 879–889. By permission of the author and the publisher.

131

somewhat away from the *Australopithecus-Homo sapiens* lineage, which most students consider a plausible sequence, toward the problem of the nature and distribution of pre-*Australopithecus* hominids and hominoids (2). It is in this area that the new discoveries of the major stages in human phylogeny will come. Generally speaking, study of the Pleistocene section of human phylogeny has been carried out by anatomists and anthropologists, while the Miocene-Pliocene portion of the story has been investigated mainly by paleontologists. There have been, and perhaps there will continue to be, good reasons for this dichotomy. The study of Tertiary Mammals (including non-human Primates) requires a more extensive background in stratigraphy, in field methods, and particularly in comparative osteology and mammalian taxonomy than is often possessed by students of man. Another factor has slowed progress in this area—the idea, expressed by some vertebrate paleontologists, that the evolution of higher Primates, and of man in particular, is too controversial and confused a subject to be worth much serious attention. If this view remains common among those best equipped to interpret fossil species, such lack of interest will only prolong the controversy.

In spite of the fact that there are almost no members of the Dryopithecinae of Miocene-Pliocene age for which reasonably comprehensive osteological remains are known, the actual number of specimens of this period that have been discovered is considerable (about 550), and the geographic range of the specimens is extensive. Moreover, advances in geochronometric dating techniques (potassium-argon analysis in particular) now, or shortly, will enable us to make a far more accurate temporal arrangement of man's pre-Pleistocene relatives than we have had. Many of these relatives fall taxonomically within the pongid sub-family Dryopithecinae. Although the fossil record for most dryopithecines is scanty, restudy of this osteologically limited material has now become imperative, because it is adequate to clarify the evolutionary succession of pongids and hominids.

I wish to state initially that I have carefully examined the view that *Proconsul*, from the East African Miocene, should be placed in a different subfamily from Eurasian dryopithecines and have found it unconvincing. Actually, there is hardly any morphological basis for separating Dryopithecinae (*Dryopithecus, Proconsul, Sivapithecus*, and related genera) from Ponginae (*Pongo, Pan, Gorilla*). Through the proper application of modern taxonomic principles, even without recovery of specimens more complete than those we now have, much more can be said about evolutionary relationships among the so-called dryopithecines than has been said to date. Dobzhansky (*3*) recently summed up the pertinence of good taxonomy as it applies to fossil man. His point is equally relevant to the taxonomy of earlier hominoids.

> Does it really matter what Latin name one bestows on a fossil? Unfortunately it does. It flatters the discoverer's ego to have found a new hominid genus, or at least a new species, rather than a mere new race. But generic and specific names are not just arbitrary labels; they imply a biological status. Living men constitute a single species: *Homo sapiens*. Now, *Homo sapiens* can be descended from only one ancestral species living at any given time in the past. To be sure, some plant species arise from the hybridization of two ancestral species, followed by a doubling of the complement of chromosomes, but it is most unlikely that mankind could have arisen by such a process. It follows, then, that if two or several hominid species lived at a given time in the past, only one of them can possibly be our ancestor. All other species must be assumed to have died out without leaving descendants.

Undoubtedly a much more lucid picture of the Tertiary antecedents of man could be drawn on the basis of existing evidence were it not for the questionable nomenclatural practices of past years. Clearly, and regrettably, the taxonomic significance of the new systematics has been slower in gaining wide acceptance among anthropologists and paleontologists than among most biologists studying modern taxa. Of course, paleontologists have recognized for many years that the type individual of a fossil species is merely a specimen acquired through chance circumstances of fossilization and discovery from a population of variable organisms of which it may not even be a typical member. Types of fossil origin are thus chosen primarily as name-bearers for postulated species groups (*4*). Apparently it was less generally understood, until comparatively recently, that when one makes a specimen the type of a new species, or of a new genus and species, there is an obligation laid on the proposer of the new taxon to present a good deal of morphological or other evidence of probable genetic separation from any previously described species. This point applies particularly to Hominoidea, in which there is greater variability in dental pattern and relative tooth size than there is in many other mammal groups. Distinctions in dentition in a hominid specimen, sufficient to warrant designation of the specimen as the type for a new species, must be at least as great as the distinctions that occur between species of the closest living relatives of the fossil form.

Speciation

In order to understand what fossil species were and are, it is necessary to comprehend the processes of speciation and to be familiar with modern methods of species discrimination among living animals. Thus, in the case of the dryopithecines, in order to distinguish two fossil species of a given genus, one should be able to demonstrate that forms which are roughly contemporaneous show characters that fall outside the extreme range of morphological variability to be noted in comparable parts of all subspecies of present-day pongids, such as *Pan troglodytes* or *Gorilla gorilla*. High physical and dental variability in given species of man and apes has long been known (*5*), but it is clear that this has not been taken into account by the majority of past and recent describers of fossil hominoids. Beginning with Mayr (*6*) in 1950, or slightly earlier, several experienced taxonomists have drawn attention to the extreme oversplitting of the known varieties of Pleistocene hominids. Since the late 19th century this erroneous approach to taxonomy has produced approximately 30 genera and almost countless species. At the other extreme from this taxonomic prolixity stand such workers as Mayr and Dobzhansky, who, drawing on their knowledge of modern speciation, have adduced evidence for a single line of but a few species, successive through time, in this particular lineage (*7*). To alter their view it would only be necessary to demonstrate the occurrence of two distinguishable species of hominids in a single zone of one site, but, despite much discussion of possible contemporaneity, in my opinion such contemporaneity has not been satisfactorily established. There is fair morphological evidence that there were two species of *Australopithecus* (*A. africanus* and *A. robustus*), but their synchronous existence has not been confirmed by finds of both at the same level in one site. Although the concept of monophyletic hominid evolution during the Pleistocene is now widely accepted, certain fallacies continue to affect thinking on probable pre-Pleistocene forms in this subfamily.

In the discussion that follows I attempt to outline and to clarify some of these fallacies. Changes in the taxonomy of fossil hominoids are suggested, on the basis of my direct observation of relevant original materials in America, Europe, East Africa, and India during the past ten years (*8*). Among those acquainted with the traditional atmosphere of controversy that has surrounded the question of hominid origins there is often some reluctance to set forth an up-

to-date survey of the implications of recent research on the subject. Clearly, all the points made here cannot be extensively
supported by documentary evidence in this brief review. Nevertheless, it seems advisable to set some of the newer conclusions before
the public at this stage.

Oversplitting of Fossil Species

Apart from the widespread temptation to be the author of a new
species or genus, there are three primary causes of the oversubdi-
vision of many extinct taxa (in the case under consideration, fossil
Pongidae and Hominidae). These are, (i) uncertainties resulting
from incompleteness of the available fossils; (ii) doubts concerning
the identity and relative age of species (whether two or more given
"types" are time-successive or contemporaneous); and (iii) questions
relative to the possible, or probable, existence in the past of ecologic
barriers that could perhaps have brought about speciation between
populations widely separated geographically.

In view of these and other sources of uncertainty, taxonomists of
fossil Primates have generally sidestepped the question of reference
of new finds to previously established species, maintaining that it is
unwise to assign later discoveries to species named earlier when
finds are not strictly comparable or when they consist only of fragments of the whole skeleton; they frequently describe as separate
species specimens which appear to come from clearly different time
horizons; and they usually draw specific or generic distinctions when
materials are recovered from sites that are widely separated geographically, particularly if these sites are on different continents.
With continued advances in the dating of past faunas by geochemical
means, and with advances in paleogeography, it becomes increasingly possible to improve procedures and practices in the taxonomy
of extinct Primates, and to resolve many of the above-mentioned
problems.

GENERIC AND SPECIFIC DISTINCTIONS OF IMPERFECTLY KNOWN
FORMS. In the past it has sometimes happened that a taxonomist
proposing a new species or genus of fossil vertebrate has maintained
that, although no characteristics that would, of themselves, warrant
separation of the new fossil specimen (B) from a previously known
type (A) could be observed, the recovery of more complete osteological data would show the forms concerned to be different. This
sort of anticipation is poor scientific practice, and such an argument

should never be used in an effort to distinguish a new taxon unless (i) there is clear evidence of a marked separation in time between the previously described species A and the putative "new" form B, or (ii) there is definite geological evidence of geographic or ecologic separation—for example, evidence of a seaway or a desert—which would greatly reduce or eliminate the possibility of morphologically similar specimens A and B being members of one widespread, variable, but interbreeding, population. Some students would not grant even these two exceptions but believe that morphological distinctions must be demonstrated. Generally, some small distinction occurs as a result of individual variation and can be misused as evidence of species difference. Therefore it is best to rely mainly on differences which can be shown to be probable indicators of distinctly adapted, and consequently different, species.

Abundant data on Recent and late Tertiary mammals show that many of the larger species were, and are, distributed in more than one continent, particularly throughout Holarctica. Moreover, the belief that there were fairly close faunal ties between Africa and Eurasia during Miocene-Recent times has been confirmed by the recovery and description, during the past three years, of new samples of continental vertebrates of this period from Kenya, Tanganyika, and the Congo (9, 10). Several of the mammals in these localities show close morphological similarity to Eurasian forms, and while many African species of the period do not show extra-African ties, the types which the two land masses have in common do show that increased intercommunication was possible. The fact that some stocks did not range outside Africa cannot offset the clear evidence that many of the same genera and even of the same species occurred in both Eurasia and Africa at this time.

TAXONOMIC UNCERTAINTY DERIVING FROM TEMPORAL DIFFERENCES. Many hominoid species were proposed in the past mainly on the strength of a posited time separation from a nearly identical but presumably earlier (or later) "species." Most of the "species" designated on this basis should be reinvestigated in an effort to determine their true temporal position and taxonomic affinities. A "new look" is needed because of recent improvements in the potassium-argon method of dating, and in other geochemical dating methods (11, 12) which should ultimately enable students of past species to discuss them in terms of an absolute time scale. Like other kinds of scientific evidence, dates obtained by the potassium-argon method can of course be misapplied. For instance, it must be demonstrated that dated sediments come from (or bracket) the same zones as the faunas they are supposed to date. There are other well-known sources of error in geochemical dating, but in my experience the strongest criticisms of this method come from persons relatively unacquainted with the analytical techniques involved.

One example of the application of geochemical dating techniques to the study of fossil hominoids will suffice to show what wide application such information may have. Simons (*13*) has proposed that, on morphological grounds, the primitive gibbon-like genera *Pliopithecus* and *Limnopithecus* can no longer be considered distinguishable. Newly recovered materials of *Pliopithecus* [subgenus *Epipliopithecus*] from Miocene Vindobonian deposits of Europe are closely similar, both in dentition and in postcranial structure, to "*Limnopithecus*" from the Rusinga Island beds of Kenya, East Africa. The fauna associated with this East African primate was regarded, at the time of Hopwood's proposal that a genus "*Limnopithecus*" be established, as being of earliest Miocene age and, therefore, older than the European *Pliopithecus* materials. In his fullest discussion of the generic characteristics of "*Limnopithecus*," Hopwood (*14*) was able to list only a few slight features of distinction between the tooth rows, then known, of *Pliopithecus* and of "*Limnopithecus*." These are dental variations of a degree which have repeatedly been shown to occur even within members of one small population of such living pongids as *Pongo pygmaeus* and *Gorilla gorilla*. Hopwood further bolstered establishment of his new genus by remarking that additional bases for distinguishing the genera concerned "are the various ages of the deposits in which they are found and their widely separated localities." But he did comment, "apart from convenience neither reason [for placing the African species in a new genus] is particularly sound. . . ." The point I stress here is that taxonomic separations such as Hopwood proposed are not "convenient," for they create complexity where it does not exist.

Recently, Evernden and his associates (*12*) have reported a date of 14.9 ± 1.5 million years obtained by the potassium-argon technique from biotite samples of tufaceous sediments in the Rusinga Island series. Admittedly this is only a single datum, but if this sample is truly satisfactory for dating by the potassium-argon method, and if it does come from the same horizons as the "*Proconsul* fauna," it shows that the fauna which contains "*Limnopithecus*" *legetet* and "*L.*" *macinnesi* could be contemporary with the European Vindobonian materials. Nevertheless, more dating of this fauna will be necessary before we have proof that it is as young as this.

If this younger age becomes established, species of *"Limnopithecus"* may well fall entirely within the known temporal distribution of European members of *Pliopithecus*. Evernden and his coworkers also state that the evidences from relative faunal dating suggest a middle or late, rather than an early, Miocene age for the Rusinga fossils. In my opinion this view is supported by close similarities between three other Rusinga primate species (which I discuss later) and forms which occur in the Siwalik deposits of India, of probable middle or late Miocene age.

Finally, it should be stressed that Hopwood did exhibit considerable foresight in recognizing the basic unsoundness of attempting to reinforce a taxonomic separation by the argument of possible (but not proved) temporal difference. The foregoing example, and others which could be noted, show the danger of using the temporal argument when separating closely similar fossil specimens taxonomically. Moreover, it has been demonstrated that many extant mammalian genera have time ranges greater than the entire Miocene epoch, as estimated at present. Numerous instances of genera with long time ranges could be adduced. For instance, the perissodactyl genera *Tapirus* and *Dicerorhinus* in all probability extend back to the early Miocene or late Oligocene, about 25×10^6 years ago; members of some genera of carnivores (*Ursus, Bassariscus, Lutra, Felis,* and others) have all been described from deposits of late Miocene or early Pliocene age (10 to 15×10^6 years ago). Of course, we do not know that any hominoid genera survived as long as the genera in these categories, but most hominoid genera probably endured for at least 3 to 7 million years without much change of form. Consequently, even if it were known that European and East African *Pliopithecus* differed in absolute age by 4 or 5 million years, taxonomic separation at the generic level could not safely be based on this fact alone.

MIGRATION, PALEOGEOGRAPHY, AND PAST RESTRICTIONS OF SPECIES RANGES. One of the most widespread assumptions in the study of the antecedents of man is that at some early period (Miocene, Pliocene, or "Villafranchian," depending on the author concerned) the species ancestral to *Homo sapiens* was restricted to a comparatively small geographic area. This restriction is taken by many scientists to account for the supposed "failure" to find pre-Pleistocene human forerunners. Such an assumption may be referred to as the "Garden of Eden illusion." Insofar as this widespread view is held as a scientific theory by some persons interested in the evolutionary history of man, it appears to be based on analogy with the restricted ranges of various recent mammal species, particularly, in this case, of higher Primates with limited distributions, such as orangutan (*Pongo pygmaeus*) or mountain gorilla (*Gorilla g. beringei*).

Place of Man's Origin

Some people believe that the place of hominid or human origin has not been discovered; conjectures, by others, as to its location have followed shifting vogues. Thus, when the first materials of "*Meganthropus*" were recovered in Java from levels lower stratigraphically than those at which "*Pithecanthropus*" remains were recovered, many students favored the view that differentiation of the ancestral stock of mankind occurred in Southeast Asia. Later, with the realization that *Australopithecus* finds from the Transvaal were hominid remains, a case was made for initial hominid differentiation in South Africa (*15*). Now, new additions to our knowledge of early Hominidae, made in East Africa by Leakey and his associates, have shifted attention northward to that quadrant of the African continent.

It should be obvious that the oldest *known* localities of occurrence of human tools, or of given species of higher Primates, are probably not the first places where these technical developments or species arose. In order to report with confidence the exact regions of origin of the human species and of earliest cultural items, we would need 100 times the archeological and paleontological evidence that we now have, with absolute dates for all sites.

There are a number of possible reasons for the persistence of the "Garden of Eden" concept among scientists, but here I mention only a few of the misconceptions through which this point of view appears to have been initiated and sustained. Students who believe that ancestral species occurred in restricted areas may have in mind four well-known kinds of diffusion from local centers: (i) spreading of cultural items from specific places of invention; (ii) wandering of tribes, both historic and prehistoric, over great distances; (iii) spreading of advantageous gene mutations from individuals or local populations outward throughout an entire species population; and (iv) intercontinental faunal migrations across land bridges at various times in the past.

All these, and other, similar concepts, while pertinent in their own right, do not in my opinion validate the illusion that, through time, each species, as a unit, wanders widely from one region to another. Such a picture is particularly inaccurate in the case of Late Tertiary land-mammal species, such as species among the dryopithecines, whose main area of distribution was the tropical and warm-temperate portion of the Old World. Of course, given sufficient time, species ranges, particularly among the large Mammalia, do expand and contract, and do occasionally shift from one continent to another in response to environmental change. Nevertheless, movement of subpopulations is much greater than the range shifts of an entire species. Even within an evolving species lineage, time-successive species apparently do not appear from one of several populations of the antecedent species; in general, all populations of a single species tend to evolve together, the species changing as a whole because, as the environment changes, newly advantageous genes originating in various sections of the group spread through the species. Of course, if these streams of gene flow are broken for sufficiently long periods, speciation will ultimately occur. A single species, however, *is* a single species just because gene flow throughout all its members is (or recently has been) taking place.

Range of Large Mammal Species

Now, in applying these ideas to the evolution of large mammals in the Miocene-Recent period, primarily to mammals of the tropical and warm-temperate regions of Palearctica, certain points extremely relevant to the interpretation of dryopithecine evolution emerge. The first of these is illustrated in Fig. 9, which shows a hypothetical model of the range of a large mammal species-series at three periods in the earth's history. The diagram is given as an abstraction because limitations in the distribution of sites yielding fossil land mammals (limitations that result from erosion of sediments or from non-deposition) are such that exact species ranges for past forms cannot now be drawn (and probably never can be). Nevertheless, this is the sort of distribution which recovered fossils indicate was characteristic, during the period with which we are concerned, of certain species of groups such as elephants, hyenas, the big cats, and ruminants. In this context it should be pointed out that the early supposition that many surviving species of large mammals have diminished ranges owing primarily to climatic fluctuations during the Pleistocene and to the activity of human hunters has, by now, been abundantly confirmed. Two examples, taken from dozens, illustrate this point. The lion, *Felis leo*, is now extinct in Eurasia except for a few small surviving populations in India. However, 15,000 to 20,000 years ago, *Felis leo* occurred widely in Europe

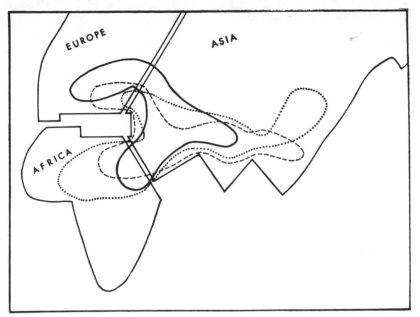

FIGURE 1. *Three species ranges, successive through time, of a hypothetical lineage of a large mammal, as they might have appeared in (dashed lines) the late Miocene, (dotted lines) the early Pliocene, and (solid lines) the late Pliocene.*

and the Near East and was, presumably, then abundant in the Indian subcontinent and perhaps even further east. Ewer (*16*) has reported fossil remains closely resembling *Felis tigris* (but from a mammal slightly larger than the largest of modern tigers) from Olduvai Gorge in Tanganyika. Today, of course, the tiger exists only in Asia.

In the sort of species succession through time that is diagramed in Figure 1, it is not possible to say where the paleontological "species" came from—the population during, for example, the late Pliocene did not come *from* any one place and, strictly speaking, does not have a known place of origin. As nearly as can at present be determined, from the literature and from direct study of the relevant fossils in East Africa and in India in Miocene-Pliocene times, Eurasia and Africa had over 35 genera of land mammals in common. These included insectivores, anthracotheres, rodents, ruminants, monkeys, apes, hyracoids, hyenas, felids, mastodonts, deinotheres, and several other groups of mammals. Members of over 15 additional mammalian genera that now occur in Africa but have not yet been found in fossil sites on that continent have been found in Pliocene deposits of the Indian Siwalik Hills (*17, 18*). This total

141

figure of half-a-hundred genera stands in spite of the early tendency to separate, at the generic level, African mammals from allied forms found elsewhere, just because they are of African provenance. Nevertheless, there are some distinct differences in African and Eurasian faunas of Miocene and Pliocene times.

Although numerous groups do appear to have been prevented from crossing between the two areas, there is now evidence that certain mammal species had no difficulty in getting across whatever partial ecological barriers may have existed between the two regions in Pliocene times. One of these is the proboscidean species *Trilophodon angustidens*, which has been found as far east as Baluchistan, occurs in the Kenya Miocene, and has recently been reported by Hooijer from the Congo (*10*). There are enough such occurrences to indicate to me that there was reasonably free faunal interchange between these two major regions of the Old World at some time in the Miocene. I see no reason why certain species of dryopithecines or early hominids, or both, could not have participated in this interchange.

Nevertheless, one may ask whether higher Primates ever had range distributions as extensive as those of such later Tertiary Mammalia as I have mentioned. Clearly, the range distribution of most present-day great apes is a restricted or relief distribution, but the fossil record of the pongids for the Miocene through the Villafranchian, as it now stands, is ample indication that certain varieties of these animals had much wider range distributions formerly than they have now. This also appears to be true for many animals of the later Pleistocene. For instance, *Pongo pygmaeus*, now restricted to the islands of Borneo and Sumatra, was then present in South China, and if the Siwalik Pliocene fossils reported by Pilgrim (*19*) are truly ancestors of this species, it probably had, at an earlier date, an extended range through the Malay Peninsula and Burma into India. Probable antecedents of the gibbons (*Pliopithecus*) are known from several scattered localities throughout Europe and northern and eastern Africa; at one time they must have been distributed (in suitable habitats) between these areas and the present range of members of this genus, in Southeast Asia. Evidently the ranges of modern species of great apes have dwindled greatly as a result of environmental changes in the relatively recent past. Among such changes was shrinking of the type of forest cover that was necessary for their existence. In certain populations, such as those of *Pongo* in South Asia, extermination or restriction of isolated enclaves on offshore islands surely came about as a result of hunting by human beings.

One of the varieties of primates least affected by these types of constriction are the present-day species of the genus *Macaca*. Distribution of members of this genus (Fig. 2) illustrates the extremes of geographic range which members of a single stock of a prehominoid grade of partly arboreal primates have been able to achieve. It need not be assumed that man's ancestors had limited species range until they became terrestrial bipeds. In late-Pliocene and Villafranchian times, *Macaca* was nearly twice as widespread

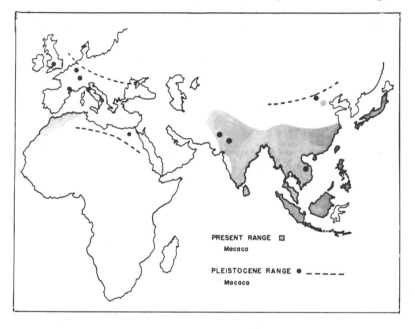

FIGURE 2. *Recent and fossil distribution of the species of* Macaca.

geographically as it is today. An acceptable evolutionary interpretation of this distribution would be that the ancestors of present-day *Macaca* reached the present extremes of their range (Japan, Gibraltar, and so on) when continental shelves were exposed during one of the Pleistocene glaciations, and that the far-flung present-day populations are descendants of perhaps no more than one widespread species that existed 1 to 3 million years ago. Of course, this species could have been already differentiating into genetically diverse populations (subspecies), with only moderate gene exchange between them, before and while the total range of the species was approaching its greatest extent. But it seems more probable that such species distinctions as exist in *Macaca* came about through relatively recent cessation of gene flow between various populations within the entire genus range (*20*). This would be particularly the case for populations isolated on islands since the last glaciation, or separated by late disappearance of suitable habitat, as between the western population of North Africa and its eastern allies. Members of *Macaca* appear to have been able to achieve such broad distribution mainly because its species have been ecologically plastic. Some varieties, such as the Japanese monkey, have remained relatively arboreal, while others, like the Barbary ape of Gibraltar, are almost entirely terrestrial. Conceivably, from the late Miocene on, the earliest hominids were at least as capable of extending their range as the species of *Macaca* evidently were at a somewhat later date.

Thus, it can no longer be argued with confidence that the reason no pre-Pleistocene forerunners of man have been discovered is that these prehominids lived only in a limited geographical area of the Old World, and in a region (perhaps of tropical forests) which has yielded no fossil remains. It is now quite clear that the early hominoids as we know them from fossil remains ranged widely in the Old World in Miocene and Pliocene times. In Fig. 3 the scattered occurrences of the hominoid genera are connected by straight lines, forming rough approximations to range diagrams. Particulars of the sites and species upon which Fig. 3 is based can be found in

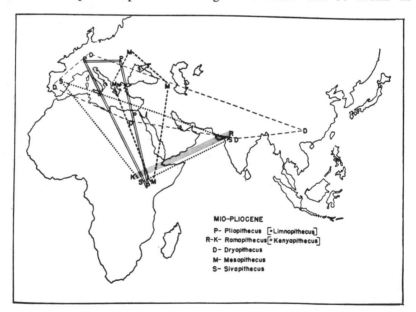

MIO–PLIOCENE

P- Pliopithecus [•Limnopithecus]
R-K- Ramapithecus[= Kenyapithecus]
D- Dryopithecus
M- Mesopithecus
S- Sivapithecus

FIGURE 3. *Occurence and range distribution of some Miocene-Pliocene* Hominoidea.

Piveteau (*21*). In spite of three contrary factors—the rarity of fossil Primates, the enthusiasm of certain taxonomists for subdividing at the generic level, and failure to discover fossil-bearing localities in relevant areas—each of several "generic" units among Anthropoidea of this period have now been reported from at least two Old World continents, and some have been discovered in all three. That ancestors of man are not included among these extensive materials is, in my opinion, no longer an easily defended viewpoint. Moreover, the idea is equally controverted on morphological grounds. Some dryopithecines do show hominid features. The argument that human antecedents lived during pre-Pleistocene times in a restricted area which remains undiscovered has another rather unlikely consequence. This assumption implies that apes and even some monkeys (*Dryopithecus, Pliopithecus, Macaca*), although largely or partly arboreal, were able to spread their range widely, while the forerunners of man were somehow unable to do this. We are here concerned with a stock which, by the early Pliocene, was probably experimenting with terrestrial living and bipedal locomotion. If, at this time, man's predecessors were not able to distribute themselves as readily as their contemporaries among the monkeys and apes could, then it becomes necessary to conclude that man's evolutionary emergence from his pre-human past was truly explosive. This conclusion becomes all the more necessary if we assume that our supposedly poorly distributed antecedents suddenly outdistanced their more "primitive" contemporaries in the matter of species-range extension.

Species Distinctions

It should be noted that, although the particular specimens assigned by one or more competent authorities to the genera indicated in Fig. 3 are adequately known for purposes of generic placement, students cannot tell definitely whether the specimens assigned to a genus were members of the same or of different species. The common practice has been to regard European, Asian, and African finds of later Tertiary fossil Mammalia as belonging to different species, presumably in part because of the tacit assumption that ecologic barriers would, in nearly all cases, have prevented members of a species from reaching all three areas. Nevertheless, since these fossil forms are known primarily from fragmentary dentitions, it remains as difficult to prove that members of populations discovered in different continents represent distinct species as to demonstrate that they are members of the same species. Consequently, it will not be possible to test the validity of species distinctions among many such extinct mammals until much greater numbers of fossils of particular groups are known. In the case of these fossil "apes", for instance, when enough material has been recovered, statistical methods may be used in making species distinctions.

In connection with Fig. 3, it should also be pointed out that leading taxonomists of fossils differ as to the generic assignment of some of the species represented. For instance, after initial assignment of certain Spanish dryopithecine remains to the genus *Sivapithecus* (*22*) (an assignment followed here), this material was later referred elsewhere. On the other hand, Lewis (*23*) believes that materials currently assigned to *Dryopithecus* from the Miocene of Czechoslovakia should be placed in the genus *Sivapithecus*.

Consequently, I doubt that it has been established that *Sivapithecus* does not occur in Europe. Conversely, Fig. 3 does not indicate a range extension of *Pliopithecus* into Southeast Asia, but it seems entirely possible that the very fragmentary type of "*Hylopithecus*" from the Siwalik "series" may represent a primitive gibbon, perhaps assignable to *Pliopithecus*. With reference to this specimen, it seems instructive to quote what must be one of the most amazing passages in the history of bad taxonomic practice. This remark occurs as a conclusion to the description of the type species of "*Hylopithecus*" (*24*): "In preference to leaving the tooth now described without a generic name and so increasing the difficulty of reference I am giving it the name of *Hylopithecus*, although I am conscious that my material is quite insufficient for diagnosis."

Origin of the Hominidae

In 1910 Pilgrim was ready to state that Hominidae are descended from *Sivapithecus* (*25*). Later, in 1922, W. K. Gregory observed (*26*) "that man is a late Tertiary offshoot of the *Dryopithecus-Sivapithecus* group. . . ." Discoveries of hominoids during the half century which have elapsed since Pilgrim's writing have reinforced his viewpoint. Entirely apart from morphological considerations, such conclusions gain strength in the light of the taxonomic procedures and zoogeographic examples that I have discussed. It is curious that, in spite of numerous suitably cautious demonstrations in paleontological papers that the origins of man lay among the dryopithecines, it is still widely held by experts that next to nothing of definite value is known about the pre-Pleistocene forerunners of man (*27*). One is reminded of a possibly apocryphal comment said to have been made in 1860 by the wife of the Bishop of Worcester. On learning from her husband that T. H. Huxley had then recently argued that man had ape-like ancestors, she observed (28): "Descended from apes! My dear, let us hope that it is not true, but if it is let us pray that it will not become generally known." Although the fact of human evolution is no longer doubted, the phyletic sequence before the Pleistocene has never been elucidated during the more than 100 years which separate us from the pronouncements of T. H. Huxley.

Briefly, the following relevant facts as to the origin of the family of man are known. Fossil "apes" of the *Dryopithecus-Sivapithecus* type have now been recovered from deposits distributed throughout a vast area of warm-climate regions of the Old World, including sites in Spain, France, central Europe, Turkey, Georgia, the U.S.S.R., Egypt, Kenya, Uganda, Pakistan, India, and China. Without undertaking a taxonomic revision of these forms at this juncture, but assuming for the moment that all these occurrences do in fact pertain to dryopithecines, I must point out that far too many genera have been proposed for them (29). Some of the genera which have been named are *Ankarapithecus, Austriacopithecus, Bramapithecus, Griphopithecus, Dryopithecus, Hylopithecus, Indopithecus, Kenyapithecus, Neopithecus, Paidopithex, Proconsul, Paleosimia, Ramapithecus, Rhenopithecus, Sivapithecus, Sugrivapithecus,* and *Udabnopithecus* (21, 30).

Such a large number of distinct genera implies an extensive adaptive radiation of sudden appearance in the early or middle Miocene, but in the case of the dryopithecines this diversification probably occurred more on paper than in reality. Direct study of nearly all of the original specimens of these Primates suggests to me that the dryopithecines should probably be assigned to only three or four distinct genera, perhaps even fewer.

Species of four of these "genera" (*Dryopithecus, Sivapithecus, Proconsul,* and *Ramapithecus*) are now fairly well known. To date, however, no student has adequately dealt with the possibility that not even all of these genera may be separable from each other. This is an important issue, for it now appears that the direct hominid lineage passed through members of at least two of these taxa.

Starting with the more *Australopithecus*-like of these forms and working backward through time, we can now draw some fairly clear inferences about the evolutionary appearance of Hominidae. *Ramapithecus brevirostris*, of probable early Pliocene (Pontian) age, from the Nagri zone of the Siwalik Hills of India, has long been known to possess several characters in the upper dentition and maxilla which significantly approach the dental conformation of Pleistocene species of tool-making man. Briefly, these characters, which distinguish the forms from typical pongids and suggest hominid ties, are a parabolic (not U-shaped) dental arcade, an arched palate, a canine fossa, low-crowned cheek teeth, small incisors and canines, a low degree of prognathism, and a short face. Separately, almost all of these features can be found among pongids, but their occurrence in combination in *R. brevirostris* is a strong indication of hominid ties. Recently, Leakey has described a new East African primate specimen, *"Kenyapithecus wickeri,"* probably from about the same period or a little earlier, which is exactly like *R. brevirostris* in these and other features. In fact, in my opinion, not one *significant* character of difference exists between the two specimens (both are maxillae). This being so, the new form from Kenya should be assigned tentatively to *R. brevirostris*, at least until such a time as further material provides a basis for demonstrating that the two are different species. The conclusion that these two specimens are at least of the same genus has recently been supported by Frisch, who has also studied them directly *(31)*. Perhaps the most extraordinary thing about Leakey's Fort Ternan, Kenya, specimen is its extreme similarity to the type specimen of *R. brevirostris*—an important and very significant fact that "generic" splitting only obscures. Greater differences than are to be noted here typically occur among members of a single-family social group within nearly all species of present-day hominoids. These two specimens indicate to me a considerable probability that in early Pliocene or latest Miocene times, or both, a single species of progressive (?) dryopithecine ranged all the way from northern India to East Africa, and perhaps farther. Personal examination of the specimens concerned also indicates that a third individual of this species, from the Nagri zone of the Siwalik Hills, in the Haritalyangar area, is represented by Pilgrim's specimen No. D185—the right maxilla of *"Dryopithecus punjabicus"*— in the Indian Museum, Calcutta. This specimen agrees with the other two in significant details of dental morphology, and in the possession of a much-reduced rostrum and an extremely short canine root (alveolus). These three specimens of *Ramapithecus* strongly reinforce each other in indicating a valid species group. Moreover, all three specimens come from a stratigraphic level higher than that at which most of the more generalized dryopithecine remains are found.

The transitional nature of these specimens of itself raises the question of arbitrariness in separating the families Pongidae and Hominidae—a problem which has also been posed recently in connection with another event, the discovery of close biochemical similarities between man and the apes, in particular the African apes (32). Nevertheless, there do seem to be fairly good reasons for continuing to view the Pongidae and the Hominidae as distinct enough to be considered separate families. What I want to stress is the fact that the transitional nature of the *Ramapithecus* materials is such that they cannot be placed with finality in either group. Personally I do not see that it very much matters whether members of this genus be regarded as advanced pongids or as primitive hominids, but perhaps considerations of morphology slightly favor placement among the hominids. There is certainly no need to produce a new, higher category for such links—an alternative which has sometimes been resorted to in the past when a fossil taxon was determined to be roughly intermediate between two others.

Two Series of Dryopithecines

To date, the most extensive series of dryopithecines come from two main areas, the Rusinga Island and Fort Ternan beds of Kenya and the Siwalik Hills of India and Pakistan. A primary difficulty in understanding the actual significance of these two series of Primates arises from the fact that the Indian dryopithecines were studied and described primarily in the period between 1910 and 1937, while the dryopithecines of Kenya have been dealt with mainly since 1951. No one has ever published the results of extensive comparative study of the two sets of materials. Lewis, in the most recent taxonomic treatment of the Siwalik "apes," in 1937, reduced the number of genera to four (*Bramapithecus, Ramapithecus, Sivapithecus, Sugrivapithecus*), with ten contained species (33). Members of the first two of these genera he regarded as more manlike than members of the other two; *Sivapithecus* and *Sugrivapithecus* he regarded as being closer to the present-day great apes. Unfortunately, there was a lack of associations between upper and lower dentitions in the Siwalik material, and knowledge of some of these genera—such as *Bramapithecus*, known only from jaw fragments containing the last two molars—was very limited. There were no whole or nearly complete dentitions in which to study the range of variability. This situation has now changed, because of the recovery in Africa (1948–1962) of relatively complete portions of skulls, maxillae, and mandibles of several individual dryopithecines, together with postcranial bones and, in some cases, associated upper and lower jaws. Comparison of these two series of data indicate the following problems.

(1) In both the Kenyan and the Indian sites (in the lower part of the section, in particular) is found a large form with large snout, protruding incisors, slicing anterior premolars, and rather high-crowned teeth. In the East African material the lingual molar cingula are more pronounced, but otherwise, characters of dentition, snout, and jaw do not differ significantly. Mainly, these Miocene varieties have been called *Sivapithecus indicus* (Siwaliks), and *Proconsul major* (Rusinga). May it not be that these two sets of fossils represent a single species that ranged fairly widely, and perhaps over a long period, but which in known populations (even from far-flung portions of its range) is not particularly variable? This large-snouted type of ape is temporally distributed from early or middle Miocene (Rusinga; Chinji, in the Siwaliks) to latest Miocene or early Pliocene (Fort Ternan; Nagri, in the Siwaliks), as is evidenced by a very large upper canine recovered at Fort Ternan, at the same level as *"Kenyapithecus,"* reported by Leakey (9); perhaps by other teeth found at Fort Ternan, that have not been described; and by several discoveries in the Nagri Zone. Differences in the molar-crown patterns of the two populations are about as great within each area as between the two groups. A few successive species may be indicated by this material, or only a single species may be involved. This species could well be ancestral to the gorilla and chimpanzee. Ancestors of the African apes certainly need not always have been restricted to that continent.

(2) A second primate form common to the Kenya and Indian areas in the Miocene is represented by the *Sivapithecus africanus* material (Kenya) and the "species" *Sivapithecus sivalensis* (India). In this group the teeth, particularly the canines, are relatively smaller than in *"S." indicus*, and lingual cingula on upper molars apparently occur less frequently. The possibility remains high that other East African and Siwalik species, of the 15 accepted as valid in the more recent literature, will fall into synonymy with these two species as new data are recovered, or as a result of a fuller comparative study now in progress. The main distinction in dentition (and almost the only difference in known parts) between some *Sivapithecus* and modern *Pongo* is the higher degree of crenulation of the crowns of cheek teeth in *Pongo*. Several specimens of Indian *Sivapithecus* show rather crenulate molar crowns, and this may be assumed to indicate something about the origin of the orangutan. Such crenula-

tions are particularly developed in the upper molar described by Pilgrim as "*Paleosimia*," which may be a valid genus. In view of these crenulate teeth, it appears probable that a species that differentiated toward the Bornean great ape is represented in the Siwalik material, but this form has not been fully distinguished in taxonomic work to date. The probability that *Proconsul* cannot be separated generically from *Dryopithecus* is worth mentioning here. Both these genera, if indeed they are two rather than one, appear to be restricted to the Miocene. *Sivapithecus* apparently crosses the Mio-Pliocene boundary but is not easily separated from *Ramapithecus*, a conclusion indicated by Leakey's report on the East African materials (*9*) and by my own studies on the Indian dryopithecines.

Conclusion

In concluding it seems advisable to make several observations as to the current state of knowledge of the origins of advanced hominoids.

The fossil hominoids of the Miocene of Kenya do not now appear to belong to the early part of that epoch, as had been previously believed, but may be of middle or, less probably, late Miocene age. Similarities between hominoids of the Miocene in India and Kenya, together with resemblances in other members of the two faunas, suggest that the Chinji Zone of the Siwaliks may be middle or late Miocene, as originally suggested by several early workers (see *18*). At this time the "radiation" which produced the great apes of today and man seems barely to have begun. The possible occurrence of *Dryopithecus* in early Miocene equivalents of Egypt requires further investigation (*34*). There is now nearly universal agreement among those most competent to judge that *Oreopithecus* does not stand in the ancestral line of later pongids and hominids, although it is related to them (*35*). In view of these conclusions, the origins of man and of the great apes of Africa and Borneo are seen to lie directly among the dryopithecines. This conclusion supports the extensive discussions of Gregory as to the significance for human phylogeny of the *Dryopithecus* molar pattern and LeGros Clark's analysis of the morphological evidences favoring the occurrence of secondary canine reduction in the ancestry of Hominidae (*36*).

There is now adequate fossil evidence to indicate, (i) that, from about middle Miocene times, a few widely distributed species of the larger hominoids were present in both Eurasia and Africa and that successive differentiation of these species, through time, has occurred, with little branching or radiation; (ii) that the primary center of speciation among these animals was outside of Europe; (iii) that some dryopithecines in known parts entirely close the slight morphological gap between Hominidae and Pongidae; and (iv) that, if reports as to localities of *Australopithecus* (*37*) by several serious students be accepted, the data now show that this earliest generally accepted antecedent of man was widely distributed in tropical regions of the Old World in the early Pleistocene (Fig. 4). Present archeological evidence does suggest that the use of tools may have occurred

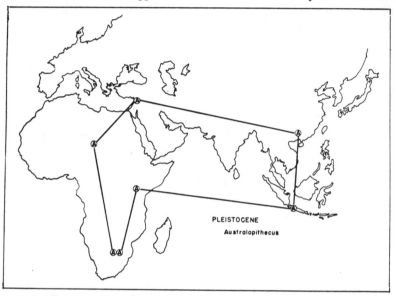

FIGURE 4. *Reported range of* Australopithecus *species.*

first in Africa, but this is not the same as to suppose that the initial species of man differentiated there, unless man be defined solely as a tool-manufacturing primate. To date, the latter supposition is an inference primarily supported by negative evidence—namely, the scanty recovery of australopithecines and of pebble tools in Southeast Asia and China. It must be remembered that one creditable occurrence is all that is needed to demonstrate the early presence of *Australopithecus* in the East. Such an occurrence apparently has now been confirmed by von Koenigswald, through his description of about a dozen teeth, assigned by him to a new genus, "*Hemianthropus,*" in materials recovered from Chinese drugstores (*37*). In my opinion these teeth are from members of the Australopithecinae assignable to the subgenus *Paranthropus,* but Woo (*38*) suggests that some of these teeth could belong to *Gigantopithecus* (*39*).

References and Notes

1. W. E. LeGros Clark, *Proc. Am. Phil. Soc. 103*, 159 (1959).

2. A few taxonomic terms used in this article may require definition for the general reader: Dryopithecinae, a subfamily of pongids which includes several species of Miocene-Pliocene "apes"; Hominidae, the family of man and his immediate forerunners; Hominoidea (hominoids), a superfamily which includes the great apes and man, living and fossil, but excludes monkeys; Pongidae, the family of the fossil and living great apes. The term "Primates" is capitalized when the order Primates, as a major mammalian subdivision, is intended; "primates" (not capitalized) means some, but not all, members of this order.

3. T. Dobzhansky, *Sci. Am. 208*, 169 (1963).

4. G. G. Simpson, *Am. J. Sci. 40*, 413 (1940).

5. A. Remane, *Arch. Naturgeschichte 87*, 1 (1922); A. Remane, in *Primatologia*, Hofer, Schultz, Starck, Eds. (1960), vol. 3, p. 637; W. K. Gregory and M. Hellman, *Anthropol. Papers Am. Museum Nat. Hist. 28*, 1 (1926); A. Schultz, *Am. J. Phys. Anthropol. 2*, 1 (1944).

6. E. Mayr, *Cold Spring Harbor Symp. Quant. Biol. 15*, 109 (1950).

7. ———, *Am. Naturalist 74*, 249 (1940); T. Dobzhansky, *Am. J. Phys. Anthropol. 2*, 251 (1944).

8. My conclusions are documented at greater length in a monographic analysis of dryopithecines now in preparation.

9. L. S. B. Leakey, *Ann. Mag. Nat. Hist. 13*, 689 (1962).

10. D. A. Hooijer, *Ann. Musee Roy. Afrique Central, Tervuren*, in press.

11. K. P. Oakley, *Advan. Sci. 18*, 415 (1962).

12. J. F. Evernden, D. E. Savage, G. H. Curtis, G. T. James, *Am. J. Sci.*, in press.

13. E. L. Simons, *Genetic and Evolutionary Biology of the Primates* (Academic Press, New York, in press), chap. 2.

14. A. T. Hopwood, *J. Linnean Soc. Zool. 38*, 31 (1933).

15. D. M. S. Watson, *Am. Scientist 41*, 427 (1953).

16. R. F. Ewer, *Advan. Sci. 18*, 490 (1962).

17. A. T. Hopwood and J. P. Hollyfield, *Fossil Mammals of Africa, Brit. Museum (Nat. Hist.) 8*, 1 (1954).

18. E. H. Colbert, *Trans. Am. Phil. Soc. 26*, 376 (1935).

19. G. E. Pilgrim, *Records Geol. Surv. India 45*, 1 (1915).

20. Although several present-day species of *Macaca* surely must be valid—that is, genetically isolated—it is of some interest to observe

that most of these living "species" of the genus *Macaca* have not been shown by cross-breeding experiments to be distinct species [see A. P. Gray, *Mammalian Hybrids* (Commonwealth Bureau of Animal Breeding and Genetics, Edinburgh, 1953)].

21. J. Piveteau, *Traite Paleontol.* 7, 167 (1957).

22. J. F. DE V. COMELLA and M. C. PAIRO, *Bol. Inst. Geol. Espan. 91*, 1 (1947).

23. Personal communication, and Yale Peabody Museum records.

24. G. E. PILGRIM, *Mem. Geol. Surv. Ind. 14*, 12 (1927).

25. ———, *Records Geol. Surv. Ind. 40*, 63 (1910).

26. W. K. GREGORY, *Origin and Evolution of the Human Dentition* (Williams and Wilkins, Baltimore, 1922), vol. 1, p. 548.

27. F. C. HOWELL, *Science 130*, 831 (1959).

28. M. F. ASHLEY MONTAGU, in T. H. Huxley, *Man's Place in Nature* (Univ. of Michigan Press, new ed., 1959), intro.

29. I am currently engaged in a taxonomic revision of Dryopithecinae, based on direct study of nearly all known European, African, and Indian materials.

30. W. K. GREGORY, M. HELLMAN, G. E. LEWIS, *Carnegie Inst. Wash. Publ. 495* (1938), p. 1; E. L. Simons, *Postilla 57*, 1 (1961).

31. J. E. FRISCH, *Anthropol. Anz. 25*, 298 (1962).

32. E. ZUCKERKANDL, R. T. JONES, L. PAULING, *Proc. Natl. Acad. Sci. U.S. 46*, 1349 (1960); M. Goodman, *Ann. N.Y. Acad. Sci. 102*, 219 (1962).

33. G. E. LEWIS, *Am. J. Sci. 34*, 139 (1937).

34. R. FORTEAU, *Ministry of Finance, Survey Department, Cairo* (1920), vol. 1.

35. W. L. STRAUS, JR., *Clin. Orthopaed. 25*, 9 (1962).

36. W. E. LeGROS CLARK, *The Fossil Evidence for Human Evolution* (Univ. of Chicago Press, Chicago, Ill., 1955).

37. In addition to major finds in Olduvai Gorge, Tanganyika, and the Transvaal, South Africa, the reported assignments of fossils to the Australopithecinae and specifically to *Australopithecus* (subgenera *Australopithecus* and *Paranthropus*) are as follows. (i) Stekelis *et al., Bull. Res. Council Israel Sect. G 9*, 175 (1960), teeth found in association with a Villafranchian fauna at Tell Ubeidiya, Jordan Valley, Israel; (ii) Y. Coppen, *Compt. Rend. 252*, 3851 (1961), *Australopithecus* cranial fragment found near Largeau, Lake Chad, North Africa; J. T. Robinson, *Am. J. Phys. Anthropol. 11* (1953), transfer of Javan *"Meganthropus"* to *Australopithecus* (subgenus *Paranthropus*); G. H. R. von Koenigswald, *Koninkl. Ned. Akad. Wetenschap. Proc. B60*, 153 (1957), description of *Australopithecus* (= *Hemianthropus*) *peli*, from China.

38. J.-K. WOO, *Palaeontol. Sinica 146*, 1 (1962).

Five Steps to Man*

JOHN NAPIER

Just Another 'Man-Ape'?**

BERNARD CAMPBELL

(*Editor's Note*) The next two articles by Napier and Campbell, both recognized experts on human evolution, provide an insight into the difficulties encountered by students of human taxonomy. Napier believes that the fossil evidence indicates a divergence of hominid species. He finds that the morphological and functional characteristics of the fossils identified as *Homo habilis* and *Australopithecus* warrant such a distinction. He finds additional support for the distinction by reasoning that modern man would not have been descended directly from the Australopithecines because the morphological differences are too great and the time for such anagenic evolution too short. Therefore, we should expect to find a divergence from the *Australopithecines* to *Homo* somewhere in the Lower Pleistocene. Campbell, on the other hand, believes the distinction has been made too hastily before the necessary comparisons were performed. He also believes that instead of hypothesizing a divergence it is more reasonable to consider the new *H. habilis* fossil as a transitional form, not warranting species designation, between *Australopithecus* and man.

In addition to the controversy over the position of a new hominid fossil, each article presents important taxonomic concepts with Napier discussing "grades", and Campbell, bio- and chrono-species.

*From *Discovery*, now incorporated in *Science Journal*, vol. 25, June 1964, pages 34–36. By permission of the author and the publisher.

**From *Discovery*, now incorporated in *Science Journal*, vol. 25, June 1964, pages 37–38. By permission of the publisher.

Five Steps to Man

JOHN NAPIER

THE naming and classification of any new human or near-human fossil is bound to promote controversy, particularly when a transitional form is involved. Officially, taxomic designations must be derived solely from the physical characteristics of those parts of the fossil that have been recovered; this precludes the introduction of certain accessory evidence, such as that of ecology and culture, which in forms transitional between the non-human and human grades is particularly crucial.

A number of other factors which provide a ready source of disagreement must also be taken into account. Firstly, fossils are representatives of populations, and populations are the units of evolution. Early human material tends to be fragmentary and therefore, in practice, the diagnosis of a new population is usually based on parts of a few individuals. Within the population there undoubtedly will have been considerable individual variation and, when only one or two individuals are known, there is, of course, no means of telling whether they are typical examples of their kind or whether they represent extreme variations. Secondly, at a time of rapid evolutionary diversification, some of these variations may well overlap those of a separate population, even one which lived at the same time. *Homo habilis* appears to have occupied broadly the same niche in time and space as the near-men known to us as the Australopithecines, and because of the close ancestral relationship of the hominine and australopithecine groups (*see* Figure 1) the two forms share many physical characteristics. It would seem, however, that they differed radically in their way of life. These considerations combine to make the naming and classification of *Homo habilis* somewhat contentious.

It is no longer meaningful to think of man's evolution in terms of a series of direct ancestors—a concept which is usually expressed graphically in terms of a 'tree' and which tends to give a false impression of simplicity. Rather it is necessary to appreciate that it was populations, not individuals, that were evolving, that they were widely distributed in space and time, and that from them there emerged a population which represented a new grade of evolution. This new grade, if distinct enough, will eventually result in a new biospecies which, by definition, will be reproductively isolated from all other species. Figure 1 attempts to illustrate this approach; it shows the expanding nature of evolution and the approximate location of known fossils according to their age, and their affinities to other species. Such a scheme does not call for direct linkage between individuals and thus avoids over-indulgence in the idea of "missing links".

The ancestral apes, represented by the Pongines in the diagram, diverged approximately 20 million years ago from the stock that ultimately gave rise to man. From then on within the Hominidae (Hominids or man-like forms) two separate major groups arose: the Australopithecines and the Hominines. The Australopithecines are an important group of near-men known best from fossils found in South Africa. They are of great significance to the story of human evolution because, as we shall see, they provide us with a very good idea of what the ancestors of *Homo habilis* must have been like. Ultimately the Australopithecines died out leaving no known descendants.

The evidence from Olduvai—where an australopithecine *Zinjanthropus* was discovered by Dr. L. S. B. Leakey in 1959—is that these near-men were living at the same time as *Homo habilis* or true man. This co-existence has been the subject of much concern among anthropologists who have doubted that early man would have permitted another group so similar to himself, to have existed side by side with him. The situation however is entirely comparable to the successful co-existence of pygmies on the one hand, and gorillas and chimpanzees on the other, in certain tracts of the Congo Forest.

The evolution of modern man can be considered in terms of five grades: (1) Early pre-human; (2) Late pre-human; (3) Early human; (4) Late human; and (5) Modern human.

EARLY PRE-HUMAN. As might be expected the first grade of hominine evolution is still largely unknown. The two most likely contenders are, firstly, *Kenyapithecus* from Fort Ternan in Kenya known from part of the jaw and teeth only; the provisional age of this fossil is about 12 million years. Secondly, *Ramapithecus* from Northern India. Dr. Elwyn Simons of Yale University has recently re-studied the upper jaw of this form and found it to show many hominid-like features. It seems possible that these creatures may be closely related, and together represent the earliest known stage of evolution on the human line.

LATE PRE-HUMAN. This grade is represented by the Australopithecines. They were clearly less like modern man than *Homo habilis*,

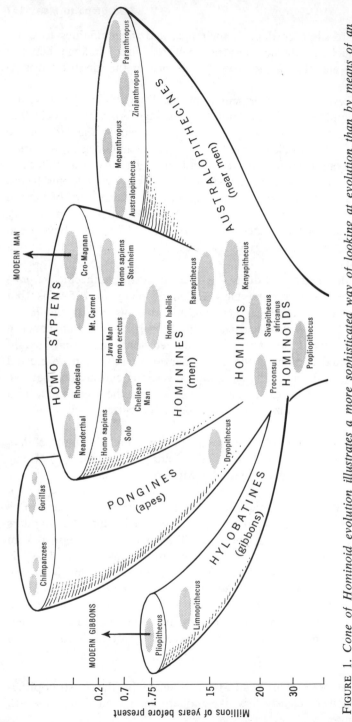

FIGURE 1. *Cone of Hominoid evolution illustrates a more sophisticated way of looking at evolution than by means of an evolutionary 'tree.' It stresses that fossil finds should be regarded as representatives of populations which were widely dispersed in time and space. It also eliminates the need to draw direct ancestral links between the different fossils. Nearness of their characteristics to those of modern man are expressed by their closeness—horizontally and vertically—to line leading to modern populations.*

and although there is some doubt about their dating they were certainly still living one million years ago. Several specimens of the pelvis are known, and they show that these creatures were very close to the human threshold in terms of walking ability. However, Dr. S. L. Washburn of the University of California has recently suggested that the Australopithecines were not capable of walking in the sense that modern man walks, but they may well have been capable of running. Strangely enough, running requires considerably less subtle adaptations of the pelvis than does walking.

Large numbers of australopithecine remains have been found but so far there is no unequivocal evidence that they made stone tools, an important non-physical characteristic of man. The possibility remains, however, for a number of stone tools have been found in the same deposits as australopithecine teeth at the Sterkfontein Extension Site in South Africa. Nevertheless many people hold the view that these tools are not the work of Australopithecines but are likely to have been made by some higher form—probably of the genus *Homo*—that is known to have existed at this time level at nearby Swartkrans. Although Australopithecines probably did not *make stone tools* they may well have *used stones as tools*—a nice distinction, but an important one. The brains of the Australopithecines were quite advanced, and their teeth were man-like in their general form but not in their size; the molars were exceptionally large, a fact which is reflected in the size of the bone buttresses and flanges on their skull and facial skeletons.

The known Australopithecines are too late in time to be ancestral to *Homo habilis* or to modern man (*see* Figure 1). They are also too specialized. The use of Australopithecines as 'models' for the late pre-human grade is justified by the belief that the ancestors of the Australopithecines were also ancestors of *Homo habilis*.

EARLY HUMAN. The first importance of *Homo habilis*, the representative of this third grade, is that it appears to have crossed the threshold between human and pre-human grades to become the earliest true man. Potassium-argon dating indicates that he was living in East Africa as early as two million years ago. From the evidence of his fossil foot—which lacks only the back of the heel and toes and is therefore relatively easy to reconstruct—his height can be estimated to have been in the region of four feet. He was not particularly muscular, had fairly large jaws and a brain capacity greater than that of the Australopithecines, but smaller than that of Java Man (*Homo erectus*), and, of course much smaller than that of modern man. In their absolute dimensions and in their relative proportions the teeth are closer to those of modern man than to those of the Australopithecines, which usually have disproportionately large molars. The hands are decidedly not those of an ape, nor are they typically those of a modern man; they are perhaps surprisingly less "advanced" than one might expect from the study of the foot. It appears that *Homo habilis* was not capable of opposing thumb and forefinger in the characteristic precision, or pen-holding, grip of modern man, due principally, I believe, to a relatively short thumb. The hand, however, does have one notable human characteristic: the tips of the fingers and thumb were broad and stout and surmounted by flat nails. I have suggested that such a hand would be capable of making the stone tools found in Bed I at Olduvai. It seems reasonable to conclude that *Homo habilis* did, in fact, make the stone tools found on the site. The alternative possibility is that they were made by *Zinjanthropus*, the so-called Nutcracker Man, whose remains are found at the same level of the site. *Zinjanthropus* is a primitive member of the australopithecine stock and is therefore much less likely to have been adept as a toolmaker. The idea that the tools could have been made by a third, and yet undiscovered species, is unacceptable on the principle of Occam's razor.

The foot of *Homo habilis* is very close to that of modern man: it has many of his special characteristics, such as a big toe in line with the other toes, and a transverse and longitudinal arch system. However, it had not yet attained the structural perfection and—one is therefore inclined to deduce—the function of the modern foot.

HOMO HABILIS is known to us from a number of finds comprising parts of seven individuals extending from the bottom of Bed I at Olduvai well up into Bed II, and covering a time span of one million years. On many of these levels are found the remains of mammals, rodents, tortoises, birds and fish—the scavenging and hunting detritus of *Homo habilis*. At the bottom of Bed I were a number of large stones arranged in a semi-circular form, some piled on top of one another. Dr. Leakey and other observers regard these as the remains of a primitive shelter or windbreak.

So far, we know of *Homo habilis* only from Olduvai, but the French discovery in 1962 of part of a skull from Lake Chad in N. Africa may possibly represent another population that should be included in the early human grade.

LATE HUMAN. The fourth grade of human evolution is represented by the Java, Pekin, Ternifine, and possible Heidelberg, men collectively referred to as the species *Homo erectus*. These forms were relatively big brained, with heavy jaws and, as their name implies, were fully erect in posture. The later representatives of the species were moderately advanced toolmakers: Pekin Man constructed the classic choppers of the Choukoutien industry, but Ternifine Man from North Africa and Heidelberg Man from Germany were involved in the hand-axe industry which never spread further east than India. Pekin Man also knew the use of fire.

MODERN HUMAN. By about 250,000 years ago the earliest type of modern man (*Homo sapiens*) had come into being. He is known to us from two fragmentary skulls found at Swanscombe in Kent and Steinheim in Germany. From then on the fossil record becomes more abundant, and relationships correspondingly more complex and controversial. Towards the end of the last glaciation—about 30,000 years ago—there suddenly appeared, possibly from the East, the first representatives of modern man in the form of Cro-Magnon. With the coming of Cro-Magnons no more Neanderthalers are found and the later fossil remains become indistinguishable from those of present day skeletons.

This stratification of human evolution into grades makes it clear that *Homo habilis* represents a major step in the story of human advancement. He bridges the gap between the Australopithecines, which had not required human status, and *Homo erectus* who clearly had. The anatomical facts concerning *Homo habilis* are these:

1. He had a brain with a cranial capacity of 680 cc.
2. He had a skull which in its curvatures is more man-like than that of the Australopithecines.
3. He had a lower jaw, admittedly chinless, which contained teeth that in their relative proportions are more man-like than those of the Australopithecines.
4. He had a hand which, though not 'human' in the modern sense was functionally able and was characterized by flat tips to the fingers and thumb.
5. He had a collar-bone, which was entirely modern in its principle features.
6. He had a foot in which the big toe was arranged as in modern man, and in which the arch system of the modern human foot was present.

In addition to these diagnostic features, there are certain accessory items of evidence that are circumstantial. His fossil remains were associated with "living-floors" on which are found:

(i)   Stone tools that are unequivocally artifacts;

(ii)   Bones of large mammals which have been cracked open to extract the marrow, and which presumably provide evidence of scavenging;

(iii) Small mammal, reptile and fish remains that suggest a moderate amount of simple hunting;

(iv)   Structures of piled stones which can best be explained at present as windbreaks or shelters.

There is thus a forcible argument for regarding *Homo habilis* as having crossed the threshold between the pre-human and human grades. Exactly what his precise relationship was to *Homo erectus* and *Homo sapiens* is still not clear—nor indeed the relationship of these two forms to each other. Whatever the final answer—and it is highly unlikely that there ever will be a *final* answer—there is no doubt that the human phase of evolution passed through a number of grades of anatomical and cultural improvement. As far as our present knowledge goes these grades are exemplified by *Homo habilis—Homo erectus—Homo sapiens*.

Just Another 'Man-Ape'?

BERNARD CAMPBELL

I DO not think that any student of human evolution would fail to agree that Dr. L. S. B. Leakey's work over the last thirty years at Olduvai Gorge has brought to light the finest prehistoric site on earth. It is the most remarkable achievement in every way. Not only has Olduvai yielded a number of fragments of prehistoric man which fully justify the term "missing link", but they lie in a stratified deposit which is geologically and archaeologically sensational. It covers a long time span, it is undisturbed, and is as rich in fossils as any prehistorian could wish.

It is my conviction that by his remarkable perseverance, and passionate devotion to archaeology and natural history, Louis Leakey has given mankind a very precious gift—a unique record of the past. Not one amongst us is not grateful to him and the immense value of his discoveries is unquestionable. Their interpretation, however, is open to criticism.

The creation of the new species *Homo habilis* can be criticized on both general theoretical grounds and in matters of detail. While the method of naming and classifying fossil species is not altogether satisfactory, conventions do exist and must be followed until they are superseded. Today we know that species evolve and that all are related by a continuous series of organisms in past time, which intergrade imperceptibly. Only at a given moment in time can different species be recognized. These species are called "biological species" and are defined as groups of organisms potentially able to interbreed but reproductively isolated from each other. The concept of the biological species or biospecies is essential to the theory of evolution, since it is when two closely related groups of animals cease to interbreed that they become two species and henceforward can evolve in different directions to form, eventually perhaps, two entirely different families of organisms. But this concept of the biospecies can only be applied to a moment in time—it does not recognize the dimension of time. How then is the student of evolution, the palaeontologist, to name the evolving lineages of organisms which show slight morphological change through the ages?

The acknowledged aim of palaeontologists is to divide up each evolving lineage into temporal stages which show approximately the same amount of morphological variation *in time* as an average biospecies does *in space*. Such variation can be recognized by an experienced taxonomist and applied to fossil series.

We can therefore look at a fossil series and divide it into sections, properly called "chronospecies" or "palaeospecies". Their morphological range *in time* will be equivalent to that of a living species *in space* (*see* Figure 1). In the case of the Hominidae, this process has given a lineage which has been divided, up to the present, as I have shown in Figure 2A. Dr. and Mrs. Leakey have discovered fossils which seem to lie near the boundary between *Homo erectus* and *Australopithecus*. It was to be expected that such forms would be found sooner or later, and one could have predicted that there would be a lengthy discussion as to which genus they would fall into. What we did not suppose was that the discoverer and his colleagues would create a new species to contain them. Our first criticism of this new species therefore is that if it is presumed to lie in the lineage between *Homo erectus* and *Australopithecus* (*see* Figure 2B), there is not enough "morphological space" between the two to accommodate it.

The creation of *Homo habilis* might, however, be justified if it is believed—as Dr. Leakey has suggested in the *New York Times*—that only this new form leads to modern man and that *Homo erectus* is a side branch which became extinct (*see* Figure 2C). In this case we have sufficient "morphological space" in the lineage and the hypothesis deserves consideration. However, such a hypothesis would require evidence more compelling than that available at present. It would have to show firstly that the two species *H. habilis* and *H. erectus* were contemporary, and secondly that they were morphologically and genetically discontinuous, that is, were good biospecies. No such evidence exists at present: the hypothesis cannot stand. The same comments apply to the alternative hypothesis suggested by Figure 2D.

The second general criticism which has been levelled against the publications of Dr. Leakey and his colleagues is that it is laid down in the International Code of Zoological Nomenclature that new species should be compared with closely related species before they are created. That is, new species must be shown to be clearly distinguishable from their nearest neighbours in evolution. This of course is common sense and is designed to prevent two names being given to one species—a situation which occurs all too often. To the zoologist's astonishment, he reads in *Nature* (April 4) that Dr. Leakey and his colleagues have not yet compared the new finds with what by general agreement are the most closely related forms, that is, those known as *Telanthropus capensis* from South Africa, which are now generally classified as a subspecies of *Australopithecus africanus*. Not only is this explicitly stated, but it is even suggested

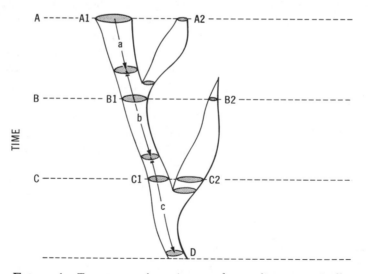

FIGURE 1. *Two types of species are shown diagrammatically above. Three sets of biospecies are represented by discs at times* A, B *and* C. *Chronospecies—evolving over a long period of time—are labelled* a, b *and* c *along an evolving lineage,* D *to* A.

that these two groups of fossils may belong to the same species. If this is so, the creation of a new species is not justified.

Whether or not the new finds represent the same species as *Telanthropus capensis*—and it is highly probable that they do, as Leakey and his colleagues admit—it is still arguable as to whether these finds should be placed in the genus *Homo* or the genus *Australopithecus*. There is no doubt at all that they lie near the border of the two. The only way to resolve this problem is to compare them precisely with the known members of each genus which lie nearest to them. Not only must the brain size of one specimen be compared—as Professor Tobias has done in *Nature*—but every known feature of all specimens must be taken into account and a detailed comparison must be made. This has not been done.

For example, we read in *Nature* that the cranial capacity or brain size lies between that of *Homo erectus* and *Australopithecus*, but this statement gives no clue as to generic status. Not only can the precise mean cranial capacity never be known on the basis of the available evidence, but it has not even been estimated on the basis of both crania—only in the case of the largest and most incomplete.

Evidence from the general form of the skull is not considered, and the shape of the frontal bone—a most significant feature—is

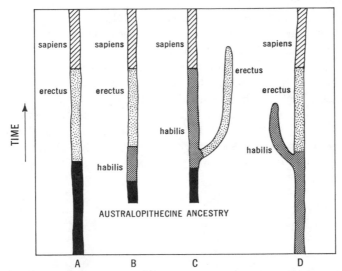

FIGURE 2. *Four alternative schemes of man's evolution. A represents scheme before the reports on* Homo habilis *were published. B, C and D show three suggestions of how the new fossil might be fitted in—but there are no good reasons for rejecting them.*

totally neglected, although parts of a frontal bone exist. Some characters of the teeth are mentioned, and there is no doubt that the elongated form of the premolars and molars is a most *Homo*-like feature, but much more exact information is required about these all-important dental characters. Variation in size (especially stature) is normal within a species—compare the "giant" and pigmy races of man living today in Central Africa. The fact therefore that the mandible is smaller (how much?) than that of *Australopithecus* is not significant in this context. At the same time the hand and foot bones are stated to be more or less like those of *Homo sapiens*, but are not compared with those of *Australopithecus*, even though some comparative material is available.

An interesting basis by which the threshold between *Homo* and *Australopithecus* could be identified has been proposed by Dr. Napier in the preceding article. He suggests that the line must be drawn between the toolmakers and the non-toolmakers. However, stone tools are found in association with *Australopithecus* at Olduvai and at Sterkfontein in South Africa. We cannot assume without evidence that these tools were made by another species living contemporaneously—to do so would wantonly complicate our hypothesis. At the same time, we cannot rule out the possibility that even if some *Australopithecines* did not make tools of stone, they made them of wood and bone—substances softer and easier to work.

We must therefore conclude that the archaeological evidence and published accounts of these new fossil discoveries are not sufficiently detailed to justify the creation of a new species of man (genus *Homo*). It is in the tradition of science that when a hypothesis is promoted with evidence, that evidence should itself justify the hypothesis. Until such evidence is finally published, those of us who are onlookers are unable to examine the fossils for ourselves in a museum. Dr. Leakey and his colleagues are not alchemists and they must not expect us to accept their pronouncements in awed silence, unless they effectively demonstrate them to be justified.

Where and When
Did Man Become Wise?*

DON R. BROTHWELL

(*Editor's Note*) Recent research on fossil man has been concerned almost exclusively with evolution of the genus before and during the Basal Pleistocene. New dating techniques and particularly new fossil finds from that period are responsible for this emphasis. Meanwhile little research effort has been devoted to the fossils that can be undeniably assigned to the genus *Homo* and that date since the Lower Pleistocene. Even review articles are scarce in this area. The situation has been somewhat relieved by some Paleolithic archaeologists who, without having made new fossil man finds, have developed a biological-cultural approach to their data which tells us a great deal about the dynamics of Pleistocene human populations. Such information takes on increasing importance as it becomes apparent that there is still insufficient evidence upon which to decide whether there were different species of *Homo* coexisting in the Pleistocene. Whether divergent species of the genus coexisted allopatrically and/or sympatrically is still totally obscure, but, as Brothwell points out in this article, the age of modern man is probably far greater than has been commonly believed. This implies that races of all species are much older than has been generally assumed, although the incredible rate of raciation necessary to produce the present situation in man, if as a bonafide species he appeared as recently as 35,000 years ago, has always been a major stumbling block. Moreover, there has been general dissatisfaction with the effort to stuff every single Pleistocene homid fossil into a chronospecies consisting of ill-defined grade-like slots called *H. erectus,* and *H. sapiens.*

*From *Discovery,* now incorporated in *Science Journal,* vol. 24, June 1963, pages 10–14. By permission of the author and the publisher.

167

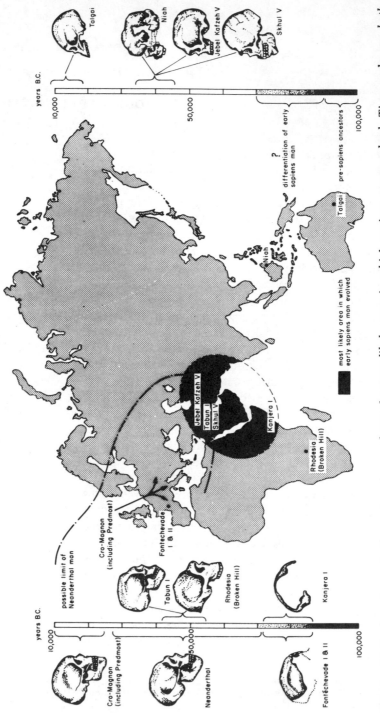

FIGURE 1. Darkened area in the center of map shows the most likely area in which sapiens man evolved. Time scales on both sides date most of the Upper Pleistocene skulls and place the origin of Homo sapiens at about 80,000 B.C.

SOME biologists and anthropologists have attempted to split man into more than one species. There is, nevertheless, general agreement that all modern varieties should be regarded as one—*Homo sapiens*, or 'man the wise.' This species represents what is as yet the most advanced degree of evolution in terms of brain development—involving the ability to learn and to transmit information, and a capacity for 'original thought.' Moreover the various attempts that have been made to discredit Negroes, Australian aborigines and certain other human groups, alleging that they have an inferior mental capacity, have no sound scientific basis.

It would appear that man's present mental ability was established many thousands of years ago. But when and where did he attain his status as *sapiens* man?

Determining the beginnings of *H. sapiens* is no easy task—it is just as difficult as bridging the evolutionary gap from fossil ape to man. Although it is necessary to think in terms of a definite change from non-sapiens to *sapiens* man, obviously no clear division can be made. As in the majority of evolutionary changes, the time interval before a noticeable change between the ancestral and evolved group can be detected must be thought of in terms of thousands of years at least. At present it is still debatable which 10,000 years or so was particularly significant for the appearance of *H. sapiens*. Differences of opinion place his arrival between upwards of 60,000 years and only 30,000 years ago, but recent views and new discoveries are throwing much more light on this problem.

The Criteria for 'Wisdom'

In reviewing early *sapiens* man, we must rely almost completely upon fragments of skull—but at least these remains are from one of the most significant areas of the body. Within the geologically short period of two million years the primate (hominid) stem leading to modern man has increased its brain size by approximately 1,000 c.c., so that we now have a brain three times as large as that estimated for our unspecialised late Pliocene/early Pleistocene ancestors. The 'cranial capacity' of a fossil skull is certainly of value in differentiating the earlier phases of human evolution. But during the final 100,000 years the very divergent forms in the Upper Pleistocene period, in particular Rhodesian, Neanderthal and 'Cro-Magnon' man, all have brain capacities well within the range for modern man and in some cases the capacities even exceed those generally found today.

Because of the limited information which can be obtained from the external structure of the brain (as revealed by an internal cast of the brain box), attention has been directed towards the positioning and general form of the brain, particularly in the frontal region. Also details of skull change, especially at the frontal bone and face, are valuable differentiating features. It is, of course, one matter to see changes taking place in a fossil series, primate or otherwise, but it is far from an easy matter to know which features are the most significant and so deserve more 'taxonomic weight' than others.

Bearing this in mind, which fossils may be regarded as contestants for the earliest phases of evolving *Homo sapiens*?

Neanderthal man, the heavy faced, fairly large brained variety of man who spread through Europe, into North Africa, and advanced eastwards at least as far as Uzbekistan in Russia between about 70,000 and 30,000 B.C., was originally considered by some to represent one of modern man's ancestors. But in view of the time period he occupied, and some noticeable skeletal specialisations— such as a very heavy brow ridge—there is increasing opinion that he represents a 'residual,' and to some extent specialised, variety of man, independent for much of his evolution from the developing *H. sapiens* group.

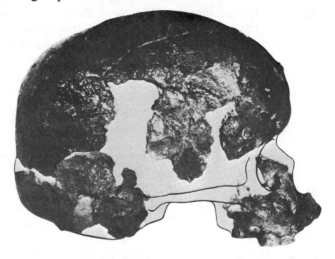

FIGURE 2. *This skull was found in the great Niah Cave in Sarawak and is probably some 40,000 years old. This suggests that modern man had reached south-east Asia at a time when the more robust Neanderthalers still occupied most of Europe.*

Fontéchevade

The earliest fossil skulls which show a clear division from the Neanderthal form were found at Fontéchevade, Charente, in 1947. The Fontéchevade skull fragments (*see Fig. 1*), recently described in detail by Professor H. V. Vallois of Paris, would appear to date from the Riss-Wurm Interglacial period, and are certainly more than 70,000 years old. The largest skull fragment (No. II) consists of most of the top of the skull vault, but with a little extension down at the brow region. Although the cranial bones were markedly thick, post-mortem pressure had shattered the bones, and accurate restoration has not so far been possible. It would appear, however, from the shape of the frontal area and the positioning of the small area of frontal sinus which remains, that there was a high vault with a fairly vertical forehead. This latter feature is confirmed by the other fragment (No. I) which consists of an area of frontal bone above the nose. If Vallois is correct in saying that this person was a fully adult female, then there can be no doubt that prior to the main spread of Neanderthal man in Europe a group had existed which had the distinctive features of *sapiens* man—certainly as far as the features of the frontal bone are concerned.

An East African Jigsaw

At the site of Kanjera in Kenya, remains of four skulls were discovered in 1932, and in three of them the absence of heavy brows is noticeable. A new reconstruction by Dr. Bernard Campbell of the most complete specimen is shown in Figure 5—the forehead is clearly vertical but, alas, still looks like an unfinished jigsaw puzzle. There has been much controversy over the date of these fragments, but recent uranium determinations by Dr. Kenneth Oakley support the view that this type of man must have lived in the late Middle or early Upper Pleistocene period. It is thus possible that both in France and East Africa we have *sapiens* man established at least 60 or 70 thousand years ago.

Evidence from Borneo

There now seems little doubt that, by 40,000 years ago, not only had *H. sapiens* become fully differentiated into the varieties we know so well in the Upper Palaeolithic of Europe, but also sufficient time had elapsed for *sapiens* man to have spread into such distant points as south-east Asia. Pioneer work being undertaken in Borneo by Tom Harrisson, Curator of Sarawak Museum, has confirmed this beyond doubt. He has recently undertaken the systematic excavation of the great Niah Cave, Sarawak, resulting in the discovery of numerous skeletons. In February, 1958, at a level which yielded a radiocarbon date for charcoal of 40,000 years, part of a human skull was found. It seems probable that the skull is contemporary with these charcoal remains. This skull, alas somewhat broken and in parts defective, belonged to an ancient Niah individual no more than 17 years of age, as revealed by the degree of dental development and the condition of the 'synchondrosis' at the base of the skull. But the skull shows no close affinities with the Neanderthal group. Moreover, in comparison with the Palaeolithic Talgai skull (*see Fig. 1*) from Australia (which also belonged to a youth of about the same age), it is slenderly built. The Niah skull vault appears smaller, the face less rugged and the jaw and mouth protrude less than those of the Talgai youth. Moreover, the forehead is vertical, whereas the Australian specimen (even allowing for post-mortem crushing and deformity) appears to be robust-browed and with a receding forehead. It seems reasonable to assume from the Borneo evidence that true *sapiens* man had migrated well into south-east Asia by 40,000 years ago, and furthermore the slender structure of the Niah skull suggests that these early *sapiens* varieties need not all have been robust forms.

The Caves of Mount Carmel

Until recently, it was generally thought that the human remains from the Mount Carmel (Jordan) sites of Mugharet et Tabun and Mugharet et Skhul were more or less contemporary. But the noticeable differences between these skeletons, in spite of their proximity to one another and apparent contemporaneity, have given rise to much speculation. Do the Mount Carmel people represent the first evidence of a *sapiens* divergence from a Neanderthal-type stock some 45,000 years ago; or do they provide a unique example of intermixing between a Neanderthal and an early Upper Palaeolithic type of man? A recent reconsideration of the faunal remains from these sites, by Eric Higgs of Cambridge, now suggests that the two cave peoples are by no means contemporary, and that the Skhul people may have been quite a few thousand years more recent.

This re-analysis has helped to emphasise that it is quite unnecessary to speculate on the possibility of hybrids or primitive *sapiens* types diverging from a Palestinian Neanderthaloid stock. It can now be suggested with more confidence that by about 40,000 years ago, and certainly no more recently than 35,000 years ago, a robust early *sapiens* variety was occupying at least some parts of south-west Asia. (Further supporting evidence is the material from Jebel Kafzeh— still unpublished in detail—and one skull from that site is shown in Figure 1.) The robust skull form of these people certainly continued into later Upper Palaeolithic times, as exemplified by the Aurignacian Predmost III skull (*see Fig. 1*).

Thus we have remains from four widely divergent sites in the Old World to vouch for the considerable antiquity of *sapiens*-type man. Whether we should designate the species 'wise' is a matter for taxonomic hair splitting. I think this must be done on morphological evidence rather than on cultural attainment, and on the former grounds I think 'wise' is right. If the dating is correct for the Kanjera and Fontéchevade fossils, then *sapiens* man had already moved into—

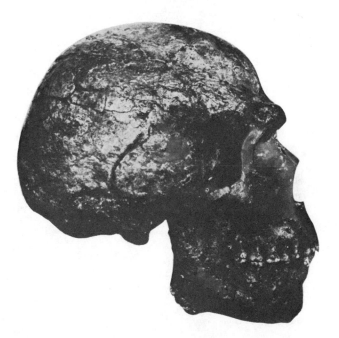

FIGURE 3. *Skhul V specimen from Mount Carmel in Palestine—as reconstructed by Dr. C. E. Snow—shows that a robust early sapiens variety was present in south-west Asia by about 40,000 B.C. This type continued into Upper Palaeolithic times.*

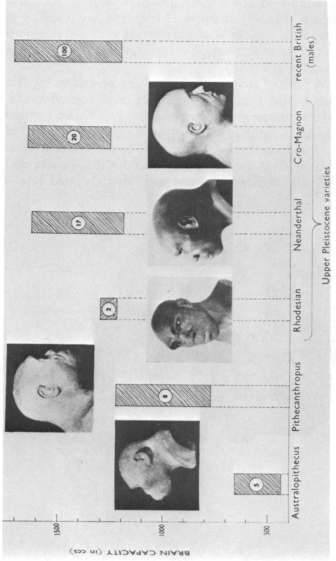

FIGURE 4. *The increase in brain size from the earliest hominids to recent man. Modern range had been attained by Upper Pleistocene times, even though there was considerable physical variation at that time—as shown by reconstructions of the head form of Rhodesian, Neanderthal and Cro-Magnon man. The length of the vertical bars shows variation within the group, and the numbers on the bars show the number of skulls from which the measurements of brain size were made.*

but not necessarily stayed in—Europe and Africa by 60,000 B.C., and by 40,000 years ago he had spread right into south-eastern Asia. Considering the apparent rates of evolution seen in earlier hominids and some large mammals, it seems very unlikely that the *sapiens* divergence from a more robust *Homo* species could have occurred in less than 20,000 years. Our own species thus seems likely to be more than 80,000 years old at the very minimum (*see Fig. 1*), though, of course, physical change at least comparable with the extremes of variation to be found in modern races must be expected *within* the species during this long time span.

Pinpointing Man's Origins

Where was the place of origin? This is no easy question to answer in view of the paucity of evidence. Clearly we must look for an area climatically favourable but sufficiently isolated for the 'directives' of evolution to exert an influence upon the potential *sapiens* population. From the occurrence of very robust and morphologically primitive men in the Upper Pleistocene of south-eastern Asia (Java) and the

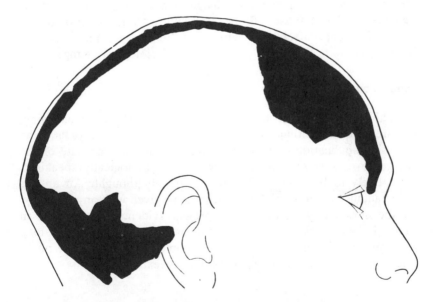

FIGURE 5. *A new reconstruction by Dr. Bernard Campbell of one of the skulls from Kanjera in Kenya. Forehead is clearly 'vertical' and there is a notable absence of heavy brow ridges. This is part of the evidence for existence of sapiens man in East Africa (one of his possible places of origin) by at least 70,000 years ago.*

lower part of Africa (Rhodesia and Cape Province), it seems reasonable to eliminate these areas. What Middle Pleistocene fossils are known are very fragmentary and fail to indicate a possible area of initial *sapiens* development. Bearing in mind, however, that the Neanderthal group would appear to have evolved principally in Europe, it seems reasonable to suggest that *sapiens* man diverged either in a part of south-western Asia (Persia, Turkistan, Afghanistan, Baluchistan) or somewhere in north-east Africa. This is blatant speculation, but I feel that the evidence so far certainly points in this direction.

To what extent can changes in artifact forms be correlated with the physical evolution of man? This is a controversial topic at present, but there is no doubt in my mind that little if any weight can be given to such correlations, at least in the latter half of the Pleistocene. The differentiation of *sapiens* and Neanderthal lines of man was *not* based on superior or inferior flint technology, but on a mosaic of biological factors (mutation, selective pressures, genetic drift). In other words, the Mousterian industries must not be correlated purely with one physical type, Neanderthal man. Clearly, if we place Fontéchevade, Skhul, Kanjera and Niah man in the *sapiens* category, even though they represent Stone Age cultures much inferior to the advanced Upper Palaeolithic cultures of Europe, we must concede that artifact change noticeably lagged behind biological change.

Conclusions

Ideas about the evolution of our own form of mankind are changing, and are sure to continue to do so with further discoveries and the increasing application of modern dating techniques. The date of the emergence of *sapiens* man as known today (biologically speaking) seems likely to be much earlier than generally thought. An answer to the tantalising question of *where* cannot be given with any certainty, but the most likely region on the present evidence is as shown in Figure 1. Our species would appear to have had a surprisingly long life, even though for the most part a humble one. Perhaps we might reflect on this before bringing it rapidly to extinction.

4

Races: Past and Present

Racial Taxonomies from an
Evolutionary Perspective*

FRANCIS E. JOHNSTON

(*Editor's Note*) How old are the racial differences in
man? Did the populational variation we find in man
today exist prior to the full evolution of *Homo sapiens*?
Johnston believes the *H. erectus—H. sapiens* transition
to have been anagenic. The two species are chrono-
species and any line between them must be arbitrary.
Thus there is the possibility that some or even all of the
populations of the Pleistocene have contributed to the
variation now found in man. *Homo* was evidently
widespread geographically all during the Pleistocene and
variation from one area to another would be expected.
On the other hand, there is no reason to suppose that
there was any permanency of specific population differences over time. Due to the action of drift, selection
and migration, the nature of these differences was and
still is constantly changing. Efforts to raciate fossil man
are therefore futile, although attempts are occasionally
made to describe variation in fossils in terms of differences between existing geographical races.

ONE of the thorniest problems with which physical anthropologists
have attempted to come to grips has been the question of racial
origins, and particularly the origins of those groups accepted by the
majority as extant races. The hypotheses proposed present the student
with a continuum; at one end is the view that the present racial
boundaries are quite recent (Washburn 1963); at the other is the
theory (the modern restatement is by Coon 1962) that these varieties
existed before the evolutionary emergence of *Homo sapiens*. The
lively, to say the least, discussions that have occurred as a result of
Coon's thesis, contrasted with the horror among systematists that

*From *American Anthropologist*, vol. 66, August, 1964, pages 822–827. By
permission of the author and the publisher.

infra-specific characters could have arisen before specific, has prompted this examination of the issues, and particularly the semantics involved, in an attempt to ascertain if the ends of the continuum are truly mutually exclusive, or if they both possess elements of mutual scientific value.

Any discussion of racial taxonomy is initially at a disadvantage due to the lack of agreement about what a race really is. There are even those (Montagu 1962; Livingstone 1962) who deny the existence of such taxa, but they are in the minority. However, even authorities who agree that the category race is a valid one, are not unanimous in its delimitation. It should be noted that a race is not necessarily a subspecies. As defined by Mayr (1963:348) subspecies are considered to be *aggregates of local populations* which inhabit a segment of the geographic range of the species. On the other hand, with the acceptance of the Mendelian population as the unit of evolutionary change (Thieme 1952), it is clear that these groups, operating as minimum breeding units which display genetically-effective endogamy, become natural taxonomic categories and are accepted by many (e.g., Hulse 1962) as valid races. The differentiation of these two levels has long been a matter of record (Garn and Coon 1955) and, in truth, most modern racial classifications (Coon, Garn, and Birdsell 1950; Garn 1961) regardless of terminology, are combinations of the above approaches; even though geographical races (the physical anthropologist's equivalent of the systematist's subspecies) are enumerated and defined, the inability to fit certain small populations into this scheme results in the retention of at least some Mendelian populations as distinct racial entities.

It is now accepted that what we call racial variation is the observable result of a series of adaptations, largely through natural selection, to varying kinds of environmental stress. It is commonly accepted (Washburn 1963) that almost every observable characteristic has, at some time, been subjected to selective pressure which has led to the impressive amount of polymorphism so evident in human populations. It is notable that the only exception to this, save the action of genetic drift under specific conditions, would be the phenomenon of genetic linkage to a trait under subject to selection. The phenotypic results of this adaptative process have been often described (e.g. Garn 1959; Newman 1961). Variation is also introduced by means of plastic responses (Kaplan 1954; Hulse 1960), but it is, in general, taxonomically useless due to its temporary nature reflecting phenotypic, rather than genotypic, alteration.

On the other hand, those characteristics which are useful within the genus *Homo* for differentiating species are not so much the ones traditionally associated with selective processes, but rather with anagenesis. Rensch (1960), the coiner of this term, discusses aspects of anagenetic evolution which can be summarized in three major trends: increased functional complexity, increased plasticity, and increased propensity for future modification. Since all living men are members of a single species, and since, at any one time level among the genus *Homo* only one species has existed, evolution in this taxon has proceeded only by means of anagenesis; local adaptation has failed to result in speciation, and different kinds of traits are taxonomically relevant at species and infra-specific levels.

Thus, there are characters which are relevant at the level of the species and above. Between the Primate families, these characters are basically anagenetic. Le Gros Clark (1960) points out that the Primates form an ascending scale representing a series of evolutionary events occurring within this order. Due to the nature of the evolutionary process in the case of *Homo*, the single most important trait that can be observed osteologically is brain size; all other morphological details show considerable overlap. The nature of anagenetic change and the continuous distribution of the morphological variables makes it impossible to draw a line between *erectus* and *sapiens* in anything other than purely arbitrary terms (this is brought out, at a theoretical level, in Sylvester-Bradley [1956]). Though the argument for species-level differences between Java Man and Cro-Magnon are at least admissible, the establishment of a time line dividing them is an exercise in futility. In fact, Thomas (1956) states that even the naming of paleospecies (segments of evolutionary lineages) is "unnecessary and impracticable" since they merge into each other.

It would seem, therefore, that arguments concerning the placement of a particular population, or population aggregate, into such a paleospecies is likewise an exercise in futility. Again recalling the nature of anagenesis, the slow modification of one species in a more organized direction, it is pointless to argue whether there was a Negro race within the species *erectus*, when neither *erectus* nor *sapiens* has reality in terms of beginning or end. Likewise, any properly scientific implications which arise out of one race evolving into a new species faster than another fail to exist, simply because there is no evolutionary threshold between the two species. This concept forms the basis for the synthetic theory of evolution (Mayr 1963), and to proceed contrary to it is to move away from the deeper insight it has provided physical anthropologists.

The second class of taxonomic characters which is utilized within the genus *Homo* is that which forms the basis for separation into races. It can be argued that these adaptive changes operate largely independently of those differentiating species; thus Bergman's rule can be applied to many mammalian orders quite successfully. Traits of this nature reflect largely environmentally-related modifications, are as reversible as the environment, and may vary in their rates of change. The more genetic loci involved, the greater the likelihood of selection as the evolutionary mechanism (Newman 1961). Gene flow, drift, and mutation also exist as additional mechanisms for differentiation at this level.

Characters of taxonomic importance at this level, within a particular species, arise not out of gene quality, but as a result of gene quantity. The biological nature of a species resulting in reproductive isolation from other species, implies qualitative differentiation in the genetic material; at the infra-species level distinguishing characters appear only through the existence of different gene frequencies at a given locus between populations. The genes are the same; they merely occur differentially.

Since the genetic material is similar between groups of a species, and since the importance lies in inter-population differences in frequency, attention obviously becomes centered on the definition of the populations themselves. We may hypothesize that, among proto-hominids, or even the earliest humans, geographic factors assumed prime importance; this resulted in the environmental isolation (differing in degree of permeability) of groups and the establishment. of Mendelian populations. With the culturally-bestowed abilities to overcome some of these geographic barriers, and the increased efficiency to be gained from collective pursuits, accelerating rapidly with the dawn of food-production, cultural factors assumed more and more importance, and many more Mendelian populations became socially defined than before.

However, despite the rise in the number of cultural isolates, populations co-existing within a broad geographical area which exhibited no sharp climatic breaks were all subject to the selective pressures of that environment. The long term result, provided the climate persisted a sufficiently long time, was the evolutionary modification of all of the populations in a generally similar direction. Climatic gradients would result in adaptive gradients, and reflected in morphological gradients.

Since, in the broadest sense, a race is a collection of geographically-delimited Mendelian populations, the existence of definable geographical barriers is a necessary prerequisite to a racial taxonomy. These barriers under ideal situations satisfy two conditions: *first*, they provide interference to gene flow sufficient enough to interrupt population continuity across them; *second*, they result in enough of an environmental gap to cause an adaptive (and, hence, a morphological, or genetic) gap. Under such circumstances, a geographical race may be defined. Even if climatic changes were to occur within such an area through time, a geographic race could be said to persist providing the barriers themselves remained.

Applying this to the evolution of the genus *Homo*, it becomes obvious that the existence of a particular barrier from the Lower Pleistocene (or even longer) onward would result in the existence of a geographic race within its confines. Thus, the oceans have provided an excellent barrier for the entire period of man's evolutionary history, as have the mountain ranges of central Asia. Even the Sahara Desert, though varying in its appearance to the point where it could have been broken by savannas and lakes, nevertheless presented obstacles to gene flow as far back as the Paleozoic (Monod 1963:210).

It, therefore, is not surprising to discover morphological differences within the geographically diverse *Homo erectus*. Likewise, when Coon (1962) advances a racial classification of a geographic nature, it is not surprising that he hypothesizes some of the same races in *erectus* as we accept today in *sapiens*. Though the morphological evidence may be less than convincing, the ecological evidence would seem to bear out his contention, at least this far. The fact that he chooses names which, today, have the connotation of a set of morphological and serological characters is probably inappropriate; however, we may agree that, for example, since east Asia has existed as a geographic area throughout the Pleistocene, an Asian geographic race has also existed.

If Coon's thesis has some features which we can accept, it has others which are untenable from a number of aspects. If any classification is to approach the observed phenomena, it must, as much as possible, reflect natural conditions and mechanisms. Modern racial taxonomies, acknowledging the existence of local populations do this; Coon has not attempted it. Part of it may rest in a geographical orientation; or it may relate to the desire to work within an evolutionary framework with the paucity of material available. At any rate if we accept Thomas' (1956) statement that it is practically impossible to differentiate contemporaneous species in the fossil record, then it becomes even more difficult to differentiate infra-specific categories. The delineation of fossil Mendelian populations is a virtual impossibility. Any attempt to do so comes dangerously close to, and even invades the forbidden realms of, outmoded typology. Without the ability to investigate the breeding structure, a racial taxonomy is almost meaningless.

However, postulates concerning the origins of some races in prehistoric times can be made from an examination of the morphological *and* the geological records. In his attempt to be as broadly synthetic as possible, Coon has overlooked some important changes. For example, there is every reason to believe, from the morphological as well as the geological evidence (Howell 1952) that conditions which existed in the final Alpine glaciation resulted in the creation of the Neanderthal geographic race. As a legitimate taxon, this is as justifiable as any other, if we attempt to give our system time depth. Their inclusion within the European geographical race by Coon may, under the terms of his definition, be technically correct, but obscures several facts about past racial events. One could easily extrapolate this to some time about 30,000 years hence, when the South African Bushmen would not be listed by Coon as a major race due to their assimilation. In addition, though we have mentioned the geographical unity of east Asia, this was interrupted during the Pleistocene to the extent that the American Indian geographical race came into being. Though this aggregate lacks the antiquity of others, it is as legitimate a taxon as any.

The failure of any traditional racial classification to include the Neanderthals suggests what is perhaps the central idea of this paper: to classify races with an evolutionary framework is an impossible task. The process of evolution is identified with the concept of slow, continuous, dynamic change and resists any efforts at vertical classification. A racial taxonomy is an attempt to organize existing interpopulation variability in such a way that it will be both biologically meaningful and systematically useful. Both of these criteria are sacrificed in a diachronic taxonomy. A racial classification recognizes the existence of certain local populations that defy categorization and give to it the changing character it must have. However, the extent to which we are able to define and isolate a segment of an infra-specific evolutionary sequence is no greater than our abilities to do the same at the species level, unless our taxonomy is to become merely an exercise in typology.

This does not imply that a geographic area should not exist in time depth. However, its utility is concerned with analyses of the processes of raciation themselves; the adaptations which may be of taxonomic relevance can only be understood in terms of the forces which have exerted selective pressures through time; this requires a knowledge of evolutionary history. However, taxonomy, *per se* is a synchronous approach to variability.

In short, we may say that certain definable geographic areas have existed throughout the world for the total range of human evolution. However, in many cases, sub-areas have also arisen within these broader ones, resulting in the formation of additional geographic races which have since disappeared due to the disappearance of the environments responsible for them. Although it is possible that species-level differences exist between modern man and lower Pleistocene forms, it is impossible to establish any kind of threshold and, hence, is immaterial to argue over the persistence of a geographic group from one species to its successor. The continuous process of evolution, and especially anagenesis, plus the successive adaptations to ever-changing environments, make it impossible to present a racial classification which reaches into geologic time and, at the same time, separates existing variation.

References

CLARK, W. E. LE GROS. 1960. The antecedents of man. Chicago, Quadrangle Books.

COON, CARLETON S. 1962. The origin of races. New York, Alfred A. Knopf.

COON, CARLETON S., STANLEY M. GARN, and JOSEPH B. BIRDSELL. 1950. Races . . . a study of the problems of race formation in man. Springfield, Illinois, C. C. Thomas.

GARN, STANLEY M. 1959. Readings on race, (ed.). Springfield, Illinois, C. C. Thomas.

―――. 1961. Human races. Springfield, Illinois, C. C. Thomas.

GARN, STANLEY M. and CARLETON S. COON. 1955. On the number of races of mankind. American Anthropologist 57:996–1001.

HOWELL, F. CLARK. 1952. Pleistocene glacial ecology and the evolution of "classic Neanderthal" man. Southwestern Journal of Anthropology, 8:377–410.

HULSE, FREDRICK S. 1960. Adaptation, selection, and plasticity. In The processes of ongoing human evolution. G. W. Lasker, ed., Detroit, Wayne State University Press.

―――. 1962. Race as an evolutionary episode. American Anthropologist 64:929–945.

KAPLAN, BERNICE A. 1954. Environment and human plasticity. American Anthropologist 56:780–800.

LIVINGSTONE, FRANK B. 1962. On the non-existence of human races. Current Anthropology 3:279.

MAYR, ERNST. 1963. Animal species and evolution. Cambridge, Massachusetts, The Belknap Press.

MONOD, THEODORE. 1963. The late Tertiary and Pleistocene in the Sahara and adjacent southerly regions. *In* African ecology and evolution, F. C. Howell and F. Bourliere, eds. Chicago, Aldine Publishing Company.

MONTAGU, ASHLEY. 1962. The concept of race. American Anthropologist 64:919–928.

NEWMAN, MARSHALL T. 1961. Biological adaptation of man to his environment: heat, cold, altitude, and nutrition. *In* Genetic perspectives in disease resistance and susceptibility, R. H. Osborne, ed., Annals of New York Academy of Sciences 91:617–633.

RENSCH, BERNARD. 1960. Evolution above the species level. New York, Columbia University Press.

SYLVESTER-BRADLEY, P. C. (ed.) 1956. The species concept in paleontology. London, The Systematics Association.

THIEME, FREDRICK, P. 1952. The population as a unit of study. American Anthropologist 54:504–509.

THOMAS, GWYN. 1956. The species conflict. *In* Sylvester-Bradley, *ed.*, The species concept in paleontology. London, the Systematics Association.

WASHBURN, SHERWOOD L. 1963. The study of race. American Anthropologist 65:521–531.

Geographical, Local and Micro-Races:
Race, 'Race' and *Race**

STANLEY M. GARN

(*Editor's Note*) There is disagreement concerning the scientific validity of the term "race." Garn suggests that the word can at least be used in a precise way by (1) having it refer to a population in the genetic sense and (2) indicating how inclusive a population is being referred to. Arranging populations in terms of a hierarchy which goes from the minimum, the Mendelian breeding population, to the maximum, the species, is a heuristic device useful in scientific communication. This use of "race" has no relation to the earlier type concept; it does not require that sharp boundaries exist between populations, and it is totally compatible with "population" as used by the geneticist and taxonomist. Nevertheless, it is important to note that to be meaningful in terms of evolution a taxonomy must have phylogenetic significance, and here we are completely in the dark when it comes to population differences which may be recognized as racial. When did these differences arise? Can any of them be identified in fossil forms? What information do they provide about the relationship of the world's populations? These questions remain unanswered, although Carleton Coon has certainly introduced some provocative hypotheses for their solution. So while we can talk about population differences and recognize that "population" can refer to a hierarchy of phenomena, each level of which can be referred to as a kind of "race," there is no way to use such a scheme as a classificatory device that has any phylogenetic significance.

*From Stanley M. Garn, *Human Races*, Revised Second Printing, pages 12–22. Copyright © 1961 by Charles C. Thomas, Publisher. By permission of the author and the publisher.

THE original edition of *Races* published in 1950, contained a listing of thirty living race-populations in man. In the very same year, in his *Genetics and the Races of Man*, William C. Boyd described a total of six races: however, one of them was both hypothetical and extinct. Though Boyd (1958) has more recently augmented his list of races, raising the number to thirteen, we are obviously dealing with different orders of magnitude.

Other listings of human races have run the numerical gamut. A century ago some workers divided mankind into but two races, a straight-haired race and a woolly-haired race. Most physical anthropologists have described from twenty to fifty distinct races, though some of these races refer to individual "types" and not to breeding populations. Specialists, working with particular areas of the world have been even more generous in their race-assignments, granting fifty or more for Europe alone (cf. Coon, 1950).

Faced with such a perplexing situation, such a range of numbers of races, it is customary to refer to "lumpers" and "splitters." Lumpers, among taxonomists, are those who group a number of distinct varieties into one broader, larger category, explaining that the differences are too trivial to warrant so complex a taxonomy. Splitters, on the other hand, take the microscopic rather than the macroscopic view holding that any distinct variety merits attention.

But the situation in regard to man is not simply a matter of lumping or splitting: rather it is due to an overly elastic use of the term *race*. For some workers, such as Boyd (1950) *races* are identical to geographically-delimited collections of races. Practically, Boyd's "races" are identical with the "stocks," "divisions," "primary races" or "major races" as defined by previous workers. To other human taxonomists, however, particularly those influenced by population genetics, a *race* is a *population*. Inevitably, therefore, equating "race" with population-collections results in a smaller number of races, while restricting the term race to actual populations results in a far larger number of races. It is as if the term regiment were variously employed to refer to platoons, squadrons, brigades and armies.

One expedient would be to coin a new set of words for taxonomic units smaller than the species. One might have the *species*, then the *stock*, then the *breed*, then the *variety*, etc. But there are dangers in setting up a completely new terminology, as mentioned in the last chapter. The most practical suggestion is one made by Bernhold Rensch, the German systematist, in 1929. He uses the term *geographical race*, to describe the broad, geographically-delimited population collections, and the term *local race* to refer to race-populations themselves. As Ernst Mayr (1950) puts it "this system facilitates communication without encumbering nomenclature."

While *geographical races* and *local races* adequately distinguish Bushmen, for example, from Africans in general, or Navahos or Hopi Indians from the broad category of Amerindians, these two terms are not quite enough to fit all of the data. The population of Oslo is genetically distinct from the population of Helsinki, yet neither is a true breeding population, a genetic isolate. Salerno and Padua are distinct in many respects, yet there is no fence about Salerno, and no moat surrounding Padua. Here Dobzhansky's term *microgeographical race* comes to our assistance in delineating statistically-distinct populations which cannot be delimited as circumscribed breeding-populations. However, and with apologies to Professor Dobzhansky, the term *micro-race* will be used throughout this book (instead of micro-geographical race) simply because it is less confusing, less likely to be confounded with *geographical race*.

Geographical races, local races and micro-races, these do not encumber nomenclature. Whosoever uses them is immediately aware of the fact that he is dealing with race, the taxonomic unit immediately below the species. These terms facilitate communication, in that they explicitly state which taxonomic unit is involved. With respect to geographical races, there is no plethora of them. As race-collections they certainly do not exceed ten. Of local races there is obviously a multitude numbering surely into the hundreds. The Navaho, Hopi, Zuni, Pima, Papago, Cocopa, Haida, Salish . . . these are a few of the local races among the American Indians. And micro-races, in densely populated areas of Europe and Asia—these run into the thousands, each hamlet being genetically somewhat distinct from the others.

Clearly, the one term race is not enough for us to use. By being more explicit we gain clarity and lose confusion.

Geographical Races

The *geographical race* is the largest of the three categories of races and encompasses (in each geographical region) the other two. For a geographical race is by definition, a geographically-delimited collection of similar races (Fig. 1). To a large extent the geographical races of mankind coincide with the major continents, and are therefore identical with *continental* races, as the term is used by Boyd and others. However, geographical races may also be spread over major island chains, as is evident in the Pacific today.

The existence of geographical races is due, of course, to the great geographical barriers, chief among them oceans, that formerly limited the expansion and migration of local races and protected them from the introduction of different genes. Thus, in pre-Colonial South America, there was little or no gene-introduction from either Africa or the Pacific. Gene flow in and out of South America was funneled through the narrow isthmus of Central America. The great sub-continent of Australia also represents a situation where geographical race and geography coincide, due to water barriers all around, and no major tradition of navigation and sea travel.

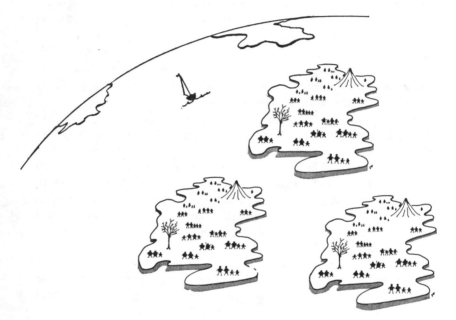

FIGURE 1. *A geographical race—a collection of race populations, sep-arated from other such collections by major geographical barriers.*

However, the continents [marked out in different colors] on the map do not perfectly delimit geographical races, whereas the geographical barriers to human migration do. Africa is separated from Europe, and its own northern region, by great ranges of desert, scarcely inhabited by a few wandering tribes, and by the Atlas mountains. South of the Sahara and through Africa to its southernmost tip there is one geographical race, comprising a very large number of local races, whereas North Africa is racially confluent with the Near East and Europe.

Similarly, the eastern limit to the geographical race inhabiting

Europe is in Western Asia, in the scarcely inhabited uplands, and not coincident with conventional continental divisions. However, the high and uninviting mountains that mark the Tibeto-Indian border on the maps have long restricted population interchange to a thin trickle. The facts of geography, the mountain ranges, the deserts and the oceans have made geographical races by fencing them in.

Within each geographical race the individual populations resemble each other more or less. In the aggregate, resemblances within geographical races are far greater than those between them. However, intra-population differences are still great, especially taken trait by trait or gene by gene. In each geographical race there are tall populations and short populations, heavy-set groups and linear groups. Certain human differences transcend geographical race, and are more meaningfully distributed with respect to climate or disease.

A geographical race is a collection of populations whose similarities are due to long-continued confinement within set geographical limits.

Local Races

In contrast to geographical races which are geographically delimited population collections, *local races* correspond more nearly to the breeding populations themselves. Whether isolated by distance, by geographical barriers or by social prohibitions, local races are totally or largely endogamous, and the very small amount of gene-flow ordinarily comes from contiguous and related local races (Fig. 2).

The Bushmen of South Africa are one example of a local race where the territorial limits are defined, and where breeding has been confined almost exclusively to the local race itself. The several native local races of Australia also typify the situation, as do the Ituri-forest Pygmies. Though the latter have contributed wives to the taller Negroes around them, gene-flow appears to be largely one-way, and the Ituri-forest Pygmies constitute a true breeding population to the present day.

Clear-cut local races such as these are largely independent evolutionary units, and as such are of particular interest. Other examples of local races include the Yemenite Jews, isolated reproductively from their Arab neighbors, and from other Jewish populations for millennia. Whereas the Yemenite Jews, now being absorbed into the Europeanized population of Israel, have religious affinities with the European, North African, Kurdistani and Oriental Jews, their status as a separate local race held for thousands of years.

FIGURE 2. *A local race—a breeding population adapted to local selection pressures and maintained by either natural or social barriers to gene interchange.*

As a further example of local races, one may consider the various Eskimo populations widely spread from Greenland across the Arctic to Alaska, the Aleutians and Siberia. Each has been separated from the other for millennia. It is questionable whether one Greenland Eskimo got to Alaska in the last five-hundred years. As to the Aleut, despite their proximity to Alaska, well under 1% of Alaskan genes have found their recent way into Umnak, Atka, or the Pribilofs.

Local races are most easily identified where populations are relatively small, and there is little doubt as to their limits as indicated by geographical separation or by cultural prohibitions on marriage outside of the group, as with the several Gypsy populations of Europe. Local races can also be delineated, though less neatly in the populous areas of the world. By way of example, the demographic populations of Northwestern Europe and Southern Europe share markedly different histories and are, on the whole, quite distinct. The former population, relatively late to expand, has done so following the discovery of the New World and the subcontinents of the Pacific and has poured into these territories. Thus it is that North America, New Zealand and Australia constitute territorial extensions of Northwestern Europe from a racial point of view, while Central and South America is more of an extension of the breeding population of Southern Europe.

The Northwest Europeans, though constituting a smaller taxonomic unit than the European Geographical race, are not as neat a population as those mentioned earlier in this section. Numerous special problems interpose themselves, the problem of differential migration (who migrated?) and differential selection in the new and at least temporarily hostile environments. Moreover, even among the stay-at-homes, there are local differences, as shall be mentioned shortly under micro-races.

Nevertheless, it is the local race that we view and measure somewhat more easily when the numbers are small, whereas the geographical race represents more of an abstraction. The population as a unit-of-study is identical with the local race, and becomes increasingly more difficult to investigate as it becomes less easy to delineate.

Micro-Races

For much of the world today, as in Europe and Eastern Asia, neat local races are hard to come by. Except for a few populations in Europe such as the Basques, or the Lapps, one cannot define a local race by an ethnographic survey. A man from Berlin marries a woman from Stuttgart, her brother lives in Hamburg and has married a Dane from Copenhagen, whose sister now resides in the Finnish University city of Turku (but is on leave in Cleveland).

Nevertheless, there are very real differences in the genetic makeup of cities, and continual changes in the frequencies of various genes in either the north-south, or the east-west direction. Some of the differences are so apparent that we can divide Europe into a series of local races, Northwest European, East Baltic, Alpine, Mediterranean, etc. Other differences are more subtle, visible to the trained observer, or detectable by the serologist or biochemist from his data.

Regional differences in Europe are in part due to ancient settlement patterns, and to the local perseverance of local races. Even though the genetic insularity of the old city-states has long been breached, propinquity is still a very real determinant of mating. "International" marriages, especially in the academic and professional classes, should not blind us to the fact that marriage, or mating, is a mathematical function of distance. With millions of potential mates, the male ordinarily chooses one near at hand. In fact, there is a third kind of genetic isolation. In addition to geographical isolation, as between continents, and cultural isolation, as between local races, there is isolation by numbers. The denser the population, the more nearly the boy marries the girl next door (Fig. 3).

FIGURE 3. *Micro-races. In a densely populated area local races may not be demonstrable, yet biological distance may maintain regional differences as in the centers* A, B *and* C *shown here.*

This latter phenomenon, which somewhat deflates the picture of the romantic human male, and allies him more nearly with the field mouse or mosquito (which have similar mating ranges) has the effect of maintaining micro-races. It will be eons, at the present rate, before Copenhagen is no longer different, genetically, from Oslo or Stockholm, or Venice from Naples or Rome. Furthermore, local selective factors will continue to be at work. Thus, one genotype will be favored in this city and another in that, maintaining and even exaggerating the genetical differences that now exist between micro-races.

Taxonomy and Research on Race

Given geographical races, local races and micro-races, there may appear to be some question as to their relative importance. From one point of view, geographical races may seem to be of greatest interest. Geographical races are large, and there are so few of them. From another point of view local races may be favored. After all, local races are natural populations (not collections of convenience); they are the basic evolutionary units and they can be studied in divers ways.

Actually, the importance of these successive taxonomic categories depends very much on the problem at hand. By way of example, the ancestry of the American Indians, and their relationship to Asiatics focuses attention on two geographical races. Differences between Europeans and Asiatics with respect to blood group B, the Diego factor, or the Rhesus-negative gene, again involve geographical races. The Polynesians, and possible explanations for their polymorphism, necessitate attention to contiguous geographical races, in Asia, in Melanesia and Papua, and in Australia.

At the same time, the diversity of populations within each geographical race introduces problems of its own. If we are to compare Amerindians to Asiatics, with an interest in common origins, which Amerindians and what Asiatics shall we compare? Shall we use weighted average values, which may be biased by particular populations, or try to select prototypical Amerindians and Asiatics in which case our comparisons obviously reflect the populations selected for use?

In contrast to geographical races, local races are both easier to define and simpler to investigate. Within the course of a year it is possible to measure and blood-type all living Aleut. It is possible to obtain a fair sample of all known Bushman bands. Moreover, with local races, we are interested in local selective factors; diet, disease and environmental stresses. Local races, therefore, commend themselves to the investigation of evolutionary forces. The degree of out-marriage can be determined in assaying the role of "drift." Survivors can be studied to determine possible directions of selection. With local races inhabiting a fixed territory, and where their neighbors can be examined as well, the role of admixture may be quantified. Local races, therefore, offer the maximum opportunity for evolutionary studies.

With micro-races, our human material approaches more nearly the demographic population rather than the natural or race-population. Micro-races are not delimited by geographical or even tribal barriers to gene flow. Nevertheless micro-races offer numerous opportunities to investigate the mechanisms of differentiation. In Saudi-Arabia, as in the more populous parts of Africa, the incidence of malarial infestation may be related to local differences in the frequency of the sickle-cell gene. In European cities it is possible to investigate differential survival in the face of smog, a problem we have begun to consider in Donora, Pennsylvania, Los Angeles and other American communities. Differential mortality and morbidity brings about genetic changes within populations, and micro-races offer the best opportunities at present for such comparative studies.

With respect to geographical races, local races and micro-races the question is not which is more important, but rather what questions we are trying to answer.

Summary

The number of races of mankind which varies from no more than two to several hundred according to the taxonomy consulted, ceases to pose a major problem if the taxonomic category used is precisely defined.

Immediately below the species is the *geographical race*, a geographically-delimited collection of local races which may differ markedly, one from the other. *Local races*, in turn, correspond to natural or breeding populations, and are at once the units of evolutionary change and the common subjects for investigation. *Micro-races*, though not isolated geographically or by extensive cultural prohibitions, still differ from each other in numerous ways.

Geographical races, local races and micro-races offer opportunities for very different investigations in relation to race. One is not more real or more fundamental than the other, but each provides the answer to different questions and the solution to different problems of ongoing evolution in man.

Suggested Readings

BOYD, W. C.: *Genetics and the Races of Man*, Boston, Little, Brown and Company, 1950.

BOYD, W. C.: *Genetics and the Races of Man*, Boston University Lecture, Boston, Boston University Press, 1958.

COON, C. S.: *Races of Europe*, New York, Macmillan, 1939.

COON, C. S., GARN, S. M. and BIRDSELL, J. B.: *Races. A Study of the Problems of Race Formation in Man*, Springfield, Thomas, 1950.

DOBZHANSKY, TH.: *Genetics and the Origin of Species*, Chapter VI, New York, Columbia University Press, 1954.

GARN, S. M. and COON, C. S.: On the number of races of mankind, *Am. Anthropol.*, *57*:996–1001, 1955.

MAYR, E.: Taxonomic categories in fossil hominids, *Cold Spring Harbor Symposia on Quantitative Biology*, *15*:109–118, Cold Spring Harbor, The Biological Laboratory, 1950.

RENSCH, B.: *Das Prinzip geographischer Rassenkreise und das Problem der Artbildung*, Berlin, Boentraeger, 1929.

SIMPSON, G. G.: *Principles of Taxonomy*, New York, Columbia University Press, 1961.

5

Intrapopulation Variation

Typology and Biometrics*

EUGENE SCHREIDER

(*Editor's Note*) In addition to classifying populations in terms of racial types, there has been an equally long tradition in physical anthropology to classify individuals within a race into types on the basis of their gross morphology. The assumption was that different kinds of characteristics of an individual are correlated and that the identification of such trait clusters would contribute greatly to our understanding of man. Thus from an analysis of an individual's physique certain statements and predictions could be made about his behavior, his susceptibility to common diseases, his potential performance for a given task, etc. This approach was nothing new to animal breeders, and it held such an intrinsic fascination for some students of man that until quite recently it was recognized as a major area of concern for physical anthropology. What led to its demise and what grew out of it are the subjects of Schreider's article. Not only has the type concept come under modern statistical fire, but it has also become evident that there is very low or no correlation among biochemical, physiological and anthropometric characteristics of an individual. While populations can be identified in terms of frequencies of traits, individuals obviously cannot be so characterized. Attempts have been made to classify individuals in terms of the degrees to which they manifest given traits but methodologically this has been difficult to objectify and, again, intercorrelations have been disappointingly low. The fundamental criticism of attempts at the typology of individuals is that any classification carried out solely as an end in itself has no validity. The study of intrapopulational variations while of vital concern to the

*From *Annals of the New York Academy of Sciences*, vol. 134, February 1966, pages 789–803. By permission of the author and the publisher. Translated from the French by Josef Brozek.

student of evolution will not produce a typology of individuals. The same is true for the study of individual variation as carried out by investigators interested in the functional aspect of the variables. Thus the quest for a typology of individuals, per se, has largely been abandoned, although the understanding of how and why individuals vary has become increasingly important for quite different reasons.

> Many laws regulate variation, some few of which can be dimly seen . . .
>
> —DARWIN, 1859

THE age-old search for human "types" has been motivated by the need to bring order into the chaos of the multitude of differences between individuals. If feasible, the classification of men into a small number of comprehensive categories would have appeal. Modern biometrics, concerned with the facts of variation and covariation, offers little support to the global categories of the classical typological systems.

Human Types

Some ten years ago, one could count over 60 typological systems for the characterization of body build, and there have been some additions since then.[1] Most of these systems share the fatal weakness of being based on an intuitive definition of types, not on a systematic analysis of human variability. Thus, classical typology is more akin to art than to science. Its impressionistic approach accounts for the differences between the typological systems. While some of the differences are primarily terminological in nature, others are fundamental. Types of body build recognized by some systems are totally disregarded by other systems.[2]

---

[1] The "classical" typologies were reviewed, in detail, by Schreider (1937). More recently, the concept of "constitutional types" was considered by Tanner (1953). The traditional typologies and the classificatory schemes based on factorial analysis were compared by Guilford (1957).

[2] E.g., the Lyons school (Sigaud, 1894; Sigaud & Vincent, 1912; Mac Auliffe, 1923 & 1926) distinguished four constitutional types: Digestive, muscular, respiratory, and cerebral. The German school (Kretschmer, 1930) operated with three types. The Italian school (Viola, 1933a, b, and c) recognized two body forms, roughly corresponding to the digestive and respiratory types.

The "types" proposed by the impressionistic typological systems are likely to represent extremes. Thus Kretschmer (1930) emphasized that his descriptions of types were based on "the most beautiful" specimens, "the rare and happy finds." Other typologists are not as explicit as Kretschmer but they too seek physiques that stand out in the crowd.

The identification of types by reference to the rare cases, representing extreme variants, explains the discontinuity of the proposed types. Most typologists seem not to be visibly distressed by the large number of individuals who do not fit their categories. One might think that this failure of the classificatory systems would have led to a revision of the principles on which the systems are based. However, abandoning the principle of "extreme cases" as a basis of typological classification would destroy the very essence of the systems.

This state of affairs elicited severe criticism. Thus Piéron (1949) wrote that, outside of pathology, the concept of type "is of limited interest since it applies only to a small fraction of individuals in a population." Extreme cases define the limits but not the distribution of continuous variables (Thorndike, 1938). While two individuals are at the opposite ends of the distribution of one variable (say, height), they may occupy an "average" position in regard to another variable (such as weight or intelligence).

Important methodological advances were made by the Italian school of Viola according to which an individual was classified on the basis of a complex of well selected measurements. Other investigators have pursued the same goal but less effectively (Manouvrier, 1902; Brugsch, 1918).

One of the crucial features of Viola's approach was that he chose the "average man" (the "normotype"), not the extremes of body build, as his point of reference. The deviations from the average were recognized as continuous. But Viola's students (Benedetti, 1933) realized that intercorrelations between the anthropometric characteristics used for typological appraisal are weak.

Pearl (1936) considered separately the morphology of the trunk and of the extremities. Here we have a realistic recognition of the fact that individuals, as a rule, do not fit a global type. The concept led logically, to the more modern notion of "components" (Sheldon et al., 1940) viewed as diverse morphological tendencies combined in a given individual. Viola was close to this idea but did not go far enough.

In recent years, a number of investigators rejected the impressionistic, intuitive approach and sought to arrive at general morphological dimensions by means of factor analysis (Burt, 1944 & 1946; Burt & Banks, 1947; Cohen, 1938 & 1941; Eysenck, 1947; Guilford, 1957; Hammond, 1942; Heath, 1950; Howells, 1951; McCloy, 1940; Moore & Hsü, 1946; Mullen, 1940; Rees and Eysenck, 1945; Schreider, 1951b & 1963a; Thurstone, 1946 & 1947).[3] These studies are not strictly comparable since different authors studied subjects of different ages and did not use the same assortment of body measurements.

When one considers only the studies of adults, the results, on the whole, are consistent. They confirm Viola's model, not derived by the statistical technique of factor analysis, which recognizes two morphological tendencies: linearity (leptomorphy) and laterality (brachymorphy) as departures from the balanced physique of the "average man."

A study of 11 different populations, for which a common set of anthropometric data could be obtained, confirmed the universal presence of such a bipolarity (Schreider, 1963a).[4] With size represented by the first centroid factor, the linearity-laterality emerges as the second factor. Morphological bipolarity is, then, a secondary feature of man's physique, not a dominant factor. This "constitutional dimension" accounts for a small fraction (7 per cent, on the average) of the total variance. To a biometrician, familiar with the fact that the correlations between somatic variables tend to be low, this does not come as a surprise.

The typology with which we were concerned so far dealt with external body form. This is a legitimate beginning, but not the end: the anatomy of the body surface, if its importance is exaggerated, ends up by being a superficial anatomy.

Some typologists endeavored to go beyond the surface to consider the variation of the internal organs. Their work retains a certain amount of interest since investigations of this problem are conspicuous by their rarity (Beneke, 1878, 1881; De Giovanni, 1904–1908).

[3] The method proposed by Delaporte (1946) was designed to handle situations in which a large number of measurements is made on each of a large number of individuals. This condition is much easier to satisfy when we deal with anthropometric data than when we are concerned with physiological and biochemical characteristics.

[4] While the bipolarity of the second centroid factor is a mathematical necessity, the distribution of positive and negative saturations of different body dimensions is not a mathematical artifact. The fact that factor loadings of a given body dimension have an identical sign in samples of populations as different from each other as the Frenchmen, Otomi Indians, and the African pygmies, attests the presence of common features in the human morphology. While the means and the relative frequencies bring out the group differences, correlations and the "factors" based on the analysis of the intercorrelations underline the unity of the human species.

Some authors considered differences in the inner organs in reference to body build (Mills, 1917; Uotila *et al.*, 1955) while others were concerned with "constitutional" characteristics of the cranium (Barbàra, 1933), of long bones and muscles (Brandt, 1931), or of the heart (Benedetti, 1937).

The true and lasting merit of these studies is difficult to assess. First, there are grave uncertainties about the morphological "types" which provided the initial frames of reference. Secondly, one can not be sure of what represents accidental, local variations and what documents significant data of constitutional anatomy (Baumann, 1955).

In regard to bodily functions, the situation is still less satisfactory. About ten years ago, in an excellent general review, Tanner (1953) wrote: "Very little has yet appeared on the relation between body build and physiological function." This comment is still largely true today.

The early endeavor of Pende (1928) to relate body form to an imbalance in endocrine secretion was premature. Even today the problem appears to be too complex.

Biological Variations and Correlations

The study of biological variations and correlations is the subject matter of biometrics (Schreider, 1952 & 1960; cf. Fisher, 1948; Mather, 1953; Teissier, 1945). Available biometric data are incompatible with the concept of a small number of all-encompassing typological categories.

There are several kinds of variations. First, the interindividual differences (the "intervariations," i.e., the differences *between individuals*) that are frequently impressive in their magnitude. While there is overlap and while the trend is not fully consistent for all the measurements, relative variability increases as we go on from anthropometry to physiology, and from physiology to biochemistry (Schreider, 1952 & 1958). This "hierarchy" seems to be present fairly widely in the animal kingdom; it has been observed even among the arthropods (Prat, 1956). In turn, within anatomy, physiology and biochemistry one may rank the variables in reference to the magnitude of interindividual differences that are present in a given population (Sargent & Weinman, 1962a, 1962b, 1963 & 1964).

The idea that interindividual differences may be substantial is a commonplace in anatomy, even though their characterization is apt to be descriptive rather than quantitative. The idea that individual differences in biochemical characteristics and physiological functions tend to equal or exceed the differences in structure is more difficult to "sell" because the classic concept of a "fixed" internal environment is still generally accepted. Let us consider some data. In 82 per cent of a population of 536 samples studied, the coefficient of variation for stature was between 3.0 and 3.9, and the total range was not much larger (Schreider, unpublished results). The coefficient of variation for the concentration of hydrogen ions in the blood, a characteristic of low relative variability, is of the same magnitude, namely 3.4 (Schreider, 1958). But can we conclude that either the hydrogen ion concentration or stature are "fixed"? Obviously, not.

The second category of individual differences comprises the *intraindividual* changes ("intravariations") taking place within the same individual over time. While our knowledge of intraindividual variations is less extensive, the magnitude of changes in physiological and biochemical characteristics is anything but negligible (Pucher *et al.*, 1934; Renbourn, 1947 & 1948; Renbourn & Draper, 1960; Sargent, 1951; Sargent & Weinman, 1962*a*, 1962*b*, 1963 & 1964; Schreider, 1952, 1956*a*, 1958*b*, 1958*c*, 1960 & 1962; Williams, 1956). This idea is apt to encounter violent opposition since it goes against the dogma of the fixity of the internal environment (Bernard, 1859 & 1878) and the doctrine of homeostasis (Cannon, 1929 & 1932). In their traditional formulations, these viewpoints recognize the existence of only "infinitesimal" fluctuations, "rapidly corrected" by the regulatory mechanisms of the organism. Thus the concern with "types" leads to considerations of some basic biological issues.

The idea that the range of intraindividual variation is very, very narrow has its roots in the paucity of adequate information and in the misinterpretation of such data as were available. Cannon illustrates the precision of homeostatic mechanism by the following example: When the concentration of sodium in the plasma rises from 3 to 6 per mill, osmotic disorder develops which leads to hyperthermia (Cannon, 1929). At first sight, since we are dealing with thousandths, the change appears altogether infinitesimal. But when we realize that the upper value is double the lower value, the change is very large. In fact, in biology we rarely find intraindividual variations of this magnitude.[5]

There are other misunderstandings as well. Let us consider *p*H of the blood, considered by most biologists as a remarkably stable characteristic. It is easy to forget that we are dealing with the *logarithm*

[5]In this presentation I do not consider, as a rule, the extreme values which may be accidental and which would unduly extend the range of "normal variation."

of the reciprocal of the hydrogen ion concentration and that this step, introduced simply to reduce the values to a convenient number, drastically reduces the variability of the concentration of H ions.[6]

While, as a rule, the intraindividual variations are less marked than the interindividual differences in a population (FIGURE 1), it is possible to identify individuals who for some variables exhibit almost the same range of variation as the population (FIGURE 2). In addition to circadian and seasonal fluctuations (Renbourn, 1947; Sargent, 1951; Sargent & Weinman, 1962a & 1963), there are the more rapid oscillations, the cause of which frequently escapes us. Different individuals vary around their modal value within a range which is also an individual characteristic (FIGURE 3). Thus, the probability of obtaining, in a single measurement, a value that is "typical" for a given person varies in different individuals and for different variables.

For blood sugar, in one individual the coefficient of variation (of intravariation, to be specific) will be 6.9, in another individual, 13.2; for serum cholesterol the values will vary from 6.1 to 13.4; for neutral fats, from 17.8 to 33.1. For arterial blood pressure, measured for an hour at 10-minute intervals, the intraindividual variation in some individuals may be absent while in other subjects it may be sizeable (FIGURE 4). We may speak of "interindividual differences in intraindividual variability" (*intervariation de l' intravariation*; cf. Schreider 1956a, 1958c, 1960 & 1962).

This complicates matters of individual variation. To make things worse, a given individual may be very stable in regard to some measurements and exhibit marked fluctuations in other variables.

Information on the reliability of repeated physiological and biochemical measurements is only indirectly relevant to the central topic of this presentation. The coefficient of reliability indicates the relative stability of a given physiological or biochemical variable over the specified period of time in the population under study. The homogeneity-heterogeneity of the population sample and the interval of time between repeated measurements will importantly affect the outcome.

With determinations repeated at the interval of one to two days, we obtained coefficients of reliability for plasma Ca^{++}, K^+, and Na^+ of 0.44, 0.33, and 0.29. Low as these values are, with repeated determinations made at an interval of one to two weeks they become lower still: 0.38, 0.12, and −0.10, respectively (Schreider, 1958a).

---

[6]The late professor J. B. S. Haldane pointed out to me that already his father, J. S. Haldane, considered a perfect stability of *pH* as a vitalist conception, incompatible with the physico-chemical facts (cf. Haldane & Priestley, 1935).

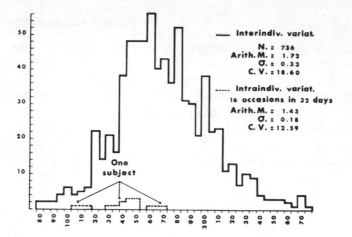

FIGURE 1. *Blood cholesterol level in young adult men.*

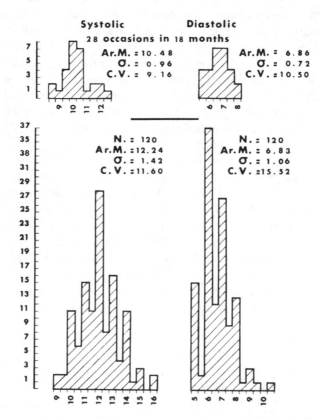

FIGURE 2. *Intraindividual (top) and interindividual (bottom) variation in blood pressure in adult males. Systolic (left) and diastolic (right).*

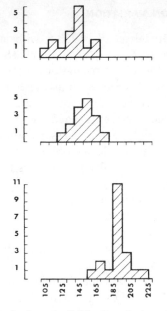

FIGURE 3. *Intraindividual variations in blood cholesterol in three adult men.*

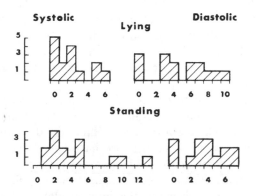

FIGURE 4. *Coefficient of relative intraindividual variation of blood pressure in 15 adult women.*

For blood sugar, measured twice at an interval of one hour, the coefficient of reliability is moderately high, 0.78; for measurements repeated at an interval of two weeks, the value dropped to 0.32, and for measurements separated by three months, to 0.04 (Schreider, 1963c, 1964d). Measurements of systolic and diastolic blood pressure, made a week apart, yielded coefficients of correlation of 0.45 and

0.43, respectively (Brozek *et al.*, 1953); with an elapsed time from 10 to 15 years, we found *r*'s of 0.24 and 0.29 (Schreider, 1962). But low reliability—and low intercorrelations—are not necessarily due to errors of measurement, as the previously cited examples have shown.

In anthropometry, where the error of measurement is typically small, especially for measurements that have skeletal reference points, one finds sometimes a high degree of association between some of the linear dimensions. But as a rule we obtain *r*'s not higher than 0.40. This finding was confirmed in all racial groups that have been studied in this regard (Schreider, 1963*a*).

The circumferential measurements are likely to exhibit a high degree of correlation but their biological meaning is different from that of the stable skeletal dimensions: The circumferences are subject to marked intraindividual changes, reflecting the status of nutrition and health of the organism. In starvation and during refeeding, all circumferences change in the same direction, even though not to the same extent, either absolutely or relatively (Keys *et al.*, 1950).

Thus, in the specified sense, the circumferential measurements portray the same general changes in the organism but measured in different parts of the body. This is principally due to the fact that the measurements are influenced by the size of the layer of the subcutaneous adipose tissue. The measurements made by skinfold calipers at different points of the body surface tend to be highly correlated.[7] When the thickness of the skinfolds is held constant, the coefficients of correlation between the circumferences tend to decrease (Schreider, unpublished data).

Several authors studied the correlations between skinfolds and the radiographic measurements of subcutaneous fat (Hammond, 1942; Garn, 1956; Brozek & Mori, 1958) and found them to be high. This is not remarkable, since here we have two different approaches to essentially the same aspect of human morphology.

While the correlations between the roentgenographic measurements of body fat are also sizeable, the intercorrelations between radiographic data on the size of bones or the size of muscles tend to be lower. More importantly, perhaps, the correlations between the three categories of tissue measurements—fat, muscle, and bone—are close to zero (Tanner *et al.*, 1959). Thus the new techniques confirm, on this point at least, the evidence provided by the traditional anthropometry: While some correlations are high, there are many

---

[7]Nevertheless, among intercorrelations between skinfolds (as among intercorrelations between circumferences) one finds some low values (Oppenheim, 1939).

that are weak or nonexistent. This does not provide aid or comfort to the proponents of global morphological types.

It would be only natural to think that the high correlations are the ones that are, biologically, the most important ones. This is not necessarily the case. Let us illustrate the point. There is a high correlation between the length of the foot and the stature. This correlation reflects the "specifically human" fact of erect posture. The close association between the two variables makes good sense, biologically. But there is a similarly high correlation between the length of the upper and lower limbs. Such a correlation, in a biped, is not essential. Apparently, it should be interpreted as a "vestigial" correlation. Such a relationship is essential in quadrupeds and perhaps also in the teleosts (Schreider, 1964c); in the teleosts the correlation between their pectoral and pelvic fins is even higher.

In physiology, the intercorrelations between different functions are, for the most part, very weak.[8] This is so much the case that only rarely is it possible and meaningful to factor-analyze physiological and biochemical data: The coefficients of correlation, which serve as the point of departure of factor analysis, are close to zero. Occasionally, the application of factor analysis helps to bring order into a complex set of interrelations. Thus, in the rat, Schreider (1956b) established the presence of a common regulation of the level of ketone bodies in a number of organs, contrasted with the absence of correlation between the level in the organs and in the blood.

It is strange that blood is viewed, without reservations, as the body's "internal environment" (milieu intérieur), even though it is, with few exceptions not in direct contact with the cells. In reality, we must think of a number of internal environments. Their mutual relations are inadequately known from the biometric point of view. In a special case, in man, the values of three important chemical constituents (sugar, calcium, and potassium) of two internal environments, the blood and the cerebrospinal fluid, yield coefficients of correlation in the neighborhood of 0.50 (Schreider, 1952). This is not exactly a negligible degree of association but, at the same time, the data indicate a surprisingly large degree of independence of the two internal environments.

Some of the low correlations are due, as noted earlier, to a large error of measurement. But this explanation has only limited validity. In physiology, we may attempt to account for the low intercorrelations in terms of the effects of intraindividual variation. When substantial

[8]The use of the correlation ratio, etc., on the assumption of nonlinearity of regression, generally does not change the situation.

fluctuations are present, a single measurement may not be truly representative of the individual. This would reduce the degree of association with other variables, should such an association be de facto present. It would be interesting and instructive to calculate the intercorrelations between the *modal* values established for each individual. This problem, not free of technical difficulties, calls for investigation.

Our information on the covariation of functions, determined in the same individuals over a period of time, is very limited. These intraindividual correlations, obtained for individuals studied during the same period of observation, may differ in magnitude and, at times, even in the direction (Schreider, 1958*b* & 1958*c*; Linder & Carmichael, 1935).

The low value of the majority of correlations obtained in human biology led some authors to the conclusion that the traditional statistical methods are not appropriate for biological research and that other approaches, especially those derived from the theory of information, would change the picture. Nevertheless, a weak correlation may be viewed as indicating that the amount of information that is being transmitted is limited, especially if considered in reference to the maximum of information that could be transmitted (Schreider, 1958*c*). The theory of information can not save the reputation of the concept of the "unity of the organism" (*l'unité de l'être vivant*) tarnished by biometric research.

These "facts of life" should neither surprise nor depress us. There is no necessity to have all biological variables exhibit a high degree of covariation. In fact, some high positive correlations would be incompatible with life. We have seen that, in two internal environments (the blood and the cerebrospinal fluid) the three constituents (sugar, calcium and potassium) varied largely independently. We may regard such an independence as an indication of the essential role of the "barriers" present in the organism. High correlations would indicate that these barriers are ineffective.

Comparative anatomy leads us to believe that, in the course of the evolution of the vertebrates, the number of intraorganic barriers has increased. The formation of autonomic "compartments," reflected in the low correlations between their biochemical characteristics, may be interpreted sometimes as being "defensive" in nature. By contrast, if its integration were perfect, the organism would not survive: In the presence of very high correlations between all the bodily structures and functions, even a minor, local derangement would result in the disruption of the total system. In reality, the remarkable autonomy of the "sub-systems," attested by some of the low or zero coefficients of correlation, accounts for the fact that the majority of the disturbances remain highly localized.

Whatever may be the validity of such an interpretation, the data clearly show that different aspects of the bodily economy are independent from each other. Even in the presence of correlations between x and y that are regarded in biology as "high," the amount of variance of y that remains "unexplained" by the variation of x is, typically, large. For this reason some authors (Brozek, personal communication) have suggested that we would do better using the coefficient of determination (r^2) rather than the coefficient of correlation (r) in describing the degree of association between biological variables.

The remarkable autonomy of the body's subsystems is incompatible with the close integration of many (or all) of the bodily characteristics implied in the classical concept of "types." In the light of present knowledge, it appears hopeless to search for global types in terms of which one could consistently classify individuals in regard to their morphological, physiological and psychological characteristics. The fact that authors of the typological schemes have not gone, for the most part, beyond the body form is not accidental. It may be worthwhile to reemphasize that when we calculate the coefficients of correlation between measurements of physiological functions and of body dimensions which, at least grossly, define body build, the correlations are weak or not significantly different from zero (Schreider, 1956c; Soula & Schreider, 1951). Higher (and biologically interpretable) correlations are obtained between measures of heat production and heat dissipation on the one hand and the measures of body mass and body surface (Schreider, 1950, 1951a, 1957, 1963d & 1964a). But even here the coefficients of correlation are far from 1.00, indicating that we are dealing with "stochastic" (probabilistic) and not with simple (causal) relationships.

We should not be amazed that in biology the coefficients of correlation, though significantly different from zero, are frequently low. Laugier (1955) noted that in man, factors—biological as well as social—interact. This complexity explains both the impressive extent of human variability and the difficulties encountered in our attempts at its systematic description and analysis.

Man is "heterogeneous" (Piéron, 1940–41) in regard to the direction and magnitude of the deviations from a standard of reference. Awareness of this fact is reflected, in typology, by the theory of "components." This theory is, in a very real sense, a negation of the classic concept of a small number of global "types" and leads to a veritable proliferation of "somatotypes" (Sheldon et al., 1954). While this is closer to the biological reality, the proliferation of typological categories drastically decreases the value of types as parsimonious ways of thinking about human variability (Piéron, 1946).

If someone comes up with a classificatory system that "works," we should not conclude, without adequate empirical evidence, that it works all the way, including the personality characteristics. It is amusing to speculate as to what would have been the history of typology had it begun with physiological measurements rather than with external body morphology. We may go one step further in our musings: Would it ever have gotten off the ground?

Types as Biostatistical Categories

Viewed as statistical tendencies, "types" represent a useful concept. They provide points of reference for the study of pathology (Lister & Tanner, 1955; cf. also Viola, 1933). Also, certain occupational groups appear to present, on the average, certain distinctive morphological characteristics (Maggi, 1962; Schreider, 1964b; Tanner, 1952). This does not imply that all individuals in a given group conform to the "type" (Schreider, 1954). Among the athletes who participate in the Olympic games and represent highly selected samples, certain disciplines are characterized by a distinctive average body build. Nevertheless, even here one observes variations within the specialties that may be sizeable (Tanner, 1964).

It should be noted that "occupational types" do not necessarily correspond to morphological categories defined by factor analysis. Some social groupings seem to exhibit such a correspondence. Compared to other manual occupations, the French peasants are "brachymorph." They are shorter, heavier, their circumferential measurements are larger, their vertical dimensions are smaller. In terms of function, their vital capacity and strength are lower, their blood pressure somewhat higher. Their performance in tests of intelligence is substantially poorer. Industrial and clerical workers show opposite trends. One finds a similar contrast if one compares "sessile" individuals (who have not changed residence) with the "migrators" (those who live in a different county than the one in which they were born; Schreider, 1964c).

We pointed out the existence of group differences in morphological, physiological and psychological characteristics. However, in regard to four biochemical characteristics (plasma proteins, hemoglobin, blood sugar, and serum cholesterol) there were no statistically significant differences.

The concept of types as biostatistical categories is not new, even if the terms are novel. Broca, who taught mathematics during one phase of his career and was "statistically minded," noted that a cranium, "typical" in all respects, simply does not exist. Consequently, when we speak of "racial types" we are concerned with groups, not with individuals (Broca, 1884). And Topinard, in the distant year of 1885 wrote: "The type is an abstract concept, an image that one creates." In Deniker's formulation (1926) somatic categories represent "theoretical constructs" resembling the concept of species in zoology. Deniker adds that we rarely encounter an individual who is truly "typical."

A "type," then, is no more real than the "average man." In actual practice we measure the *deviations* of a complex of characteristics from the "reference man." The deviations will not be of the same magnitude (or the same direction) throughout. Even in regard to body build, we can not characterize an individual globally. This does not mean that a characterization, limited in its generality, may not be useful.

The choice of the "basic" characteristics is still somewhat arbitrary and we should not become wedded to a particular descriptive system. Our exploration should be broad in scope and its point of departure should be the "systematic doubt," not an a priori classificatory system (Weinberg, 1938). We are concerned with "constellations of characteristics," defined statistically, not with "types" in the classical sense. Some of the "constellations" may be independent from each other (Schreider, 1954; Vandervael, 1964). "Global types," in which the organism is considered "as a whole," "in its unity," lack reality. What we can do in viewing "types" as biometric constructs, is to describe the differences between individuals and between groups, with reference to *selected aspects*. The knowledge of the partial constellations enables us to introduce some order into the essentially limitless complex of "dimensions" along which man can be measured.

In the search for the partial constellations of characteristics, we should not lose sight of the social variables, "exterior" though they are to the organism.

There are two other points that deserve emphasis. First, we must devote more attention to the study of intraindividual variation and of the covariation of the changes in biochemical and physiological variables that take place within individuals.

Secondly, we must explore more fully the functioning of the organism under conditions other than those regarded as "basal." It is a grave error to think that the role of regulatory mechanisms consists in reestablishing the "basal" values every time a "disturbance" occurs. A biologist who looks at the problem from the evolutionary standpoint cannot accept the view of the activity of an organism as a "disturbance." The regulatory mechanisms are old features of mammalian physiology. It is inconceivable that the regulatory mechanisms developed over thousands of years in order to assure the "stability" of the values which we determine at rest and in the postabsorptive state in the laboratory.

In fact, we know that at least some regulatory mechanisms operate more precisely at work than at rest. Thus, the reliability of repeated measurements of oxygen consumption is higher at standard work than at "rest" (Brozek *et al.*, 1953). Similarly, in a hot environment the cardiac rhythm fluctuates less than under conditions of normal temperature (Schreider, 1963*b*; Vogt, 1964). It is a pity that we know so little about how man's functions vary in the course of the ordinary life. The "postabsorptive" man has absorbed too much of human physiology. He represents neither a real man, nor a "norm."

The study of fluctuations of functions, present in daily life, will open important perspectives for research. One point of interest is the study of individual differences in magnitude, time, and degree of covariation of the intraindividual changes (*"intervariation de l'intravariation"*).

In reality, there is no "fixed" internal milieu. If we come to realize this clearly, we shall be able to see realistically the variability of bodily functions in and between individuals. The study of the covariation of intraindividual fluctuations will provide factual information in regard to the extent to which our organism operates as an integral unit (or as an assembly of integrated subunits).

In summary, it seems that before we can make any substantial progress in the study of "types," we must carry on fundamental biometric investigations directed to the study of interindividual and intraindividual variation and, to speak with Darwin (1859), of the *"correlated* variation, the importance of which should never be overlooked."

References

BARBÀRA, M. 1933. I fondamenti della Craniologia Costituzionalistica. Rome, Italy.

BAUMANN, J. A. 1955. Anatomie constitutionnelle. *In* Traité de Médecine Biotypologique. N. Pende, Ed. :68–85. Paris, France.

BENEDETTI, P. 1933. Sul valore di alcuni rapporti antropometrici come indici della costituzione nelle indagini collettive. Endocr. Patol. Costituz. *8:* fasc. 2–3.

BENEDETTI, P. 1937. L'évaluation morphologique du coeur sur le vivant en vue d'un classement biotypologique. Biotypologie *5:* 96–112.

BENEKE, F. 1878. Die anatomischen Grundlagen der Konstitutionanomalien. Marburg, Germany.

BENEKE, F. 1881. Konstitution und konstitutionnelles Kranksein des Mensches. Marburg, Germany.

BERNARD, CL. 1859. Leçons sur les propriétés physiologiques et les altérations pathologiques des liquides de l'organisme. I. Paris, France.

BERNARD, CL. 1878. Leçons sur les phénomènes de la vie communs aux animaux et aux végétaux. Paris, France.

BRANDT, W. 1931. Grundzüge einer Konstitutionsanatomie. Berlin, Germany.

BROCA, P. 1884. Mémoires d'Anthropologie. IV. Paris, France.

BROZEK, J., H. L. TAYLOR & A. KEYS. 1953. Variabilité et fidélité des mesures biologiques chez les geunes gens. Travail Humain *16:* 71–80.

BROZEK, J. & H. MORI. 1958. Some interrelations between somatic, roentgenographic and densitometric criteria of fatness. Human Biol. *30:* 322–336.

BRUGSCH, TH. 1927. Morphologie der Person. *In* Biologie der Person. Th. Brugsch & F. H. Levy, Eds. Fasc. 6.

BURT, C. 1944. The factorial study of physical types. Man *44:* 82–86.

BURT, C. 1946. L'étude factorielle des types physiques. Biotypologie *8:* 42–55.

BURT, C. & CH. BANKS. 1947. A factor analysis of body measurements for British adult males. Ann. Eugen. *13:* 238–256.

CANNON, W. 1929. Organisation of physiological homeostasis. Physiol. Rev. *9:* 399–431.

CANNON, W. 1932. The Wisdom of the Body. London, England.

COHEN, J. I. 1938. Determinants of physique. J. Ment. Sci. *84:* 495–512.

COHEN, J. I. 1941. Physique, size and proportion. Brit. J. Med. Psych. *18:* 323–337.

DARWIN, C. 1859. The Origin of Species. London, England.

DE GIOVANNI, A. 1904, 1907, 1908. Morfologia del Corpo Umano. 3 Vols. Milan, Italy.

DELAPORTE, P. 1946. Essai d'une méthode statistique de recherche des types. Biotypologie *8:* 14–23.

DENIKER, J. 1926. Les Races et les Peuples de la Terre. Paris, France.

EYSENCK, H. J. 1947. Dimensions of Personality. London, England.

FISHER, R. A. 1948. Biometry. Biometrics *4:* 217–219.

GARN, S. M. 1956 Comparison of pinch-caliper and X-rays measurements of skin plus subcutaneous fat. Science *124:* 178–179.

GUILFORD, J. P. 1957. Description de la morphologie humaine: Type, composantes, facteurs. Biotypologie *18:* 88–105.

HAMMET, F. S. 1920. Studies of variation in the chemical composition of human blood. J. Biol. Chem. *4:* 599–615.

HALDANE, J. S. & J. G. PRIESTLEY. 1935. Respiration. Oxford, England.

HAMMOND, W. H. 1942. An application of Burt's multiple general factor analysis to the delineation of physical types. Man *42:* 4–11.

HEATH, H. A. 1950. A factor analysis of women's measurements taken for garment and pattern construction. Chicago, Ill. (quoted by Howells, 1951).

HOWELLS, W. W. 1951. Factors in human physique. Am. J. Phys. Anthropol. *9:* 159–191.

KEYS, A., J. BROZEK, A. HENSCHEL, O. MICKELSEN & H. L. TAYLOR. 1950. The Biology of Human Starvation. :144. Univ. of Wisconsin Press. Madison, Wis.

KRETSCHMER, E. 1930. La Structure du Corps et le Caractère. Paris, France.

LAUGIER, H. 1955. *In* L'analyse factorielle et ses applications. Coll. CNRS. Paris, France.

LAUGIER, H., D. WEINBERG & L. CASSIN. 1940. Niveau de Vie et Caractères biologiques des Enfants. Paris, France.

LINDER, F. E. & H. T. CARMICHAEL. 1935. A biometrical study of the relation between oral and rectal temperature in normal and schizophrenic subjects. Human Biol. *7:* 24–46.

LISTER, J. & J. M. TANNER. 1955. The physique of diabetics. Lancet *2:* 1002–1004.

MAC AULIFFE, L. 1923. La Vie Humaine. Paris, France.

MAC AULIFFE, L. 1926. Les Tempéraments. Paris, France.

McCLOY, C. H. 1940. An analysis for multiple factors of physical growth at different age levels. Child Devel. *11:* 249–277.

MAGGI, R. 1962. I biotipi dello schermo americano. Statistica *22:* 291–327; 427–463.

MANOUVRIER, L. 1902. Sur les rapports anthropométriques. Bull. Soc. Anthrop. Paris *2*(3): 3.

MATHER, K. 1953. Biometry and the inductive method. Endeavour *13:* 140–143.

MILLS, W. 1917. The relation of bodily habitus to visceral form, position, tonus and mobility. Am. J. Roentgenol. *4:* 155–169.

MOORE, T. V. & E. H. HSÜ. 1946. Factorial analysis of anthropological measurements in psychotic patients. Human Biol. *18:* 133–137.

MULLEN, F. A. 1940. Factors in the growth of girls. Child Devel. *11:* 27–42.

OPPENHEIM, M. 1937. Evaluation des proportions des parties molles et du squelette chez les différents types morphologiques. Biotypologie 5: 93–95.

OPPENHEIM, M. 1939. Distribution de la graisse sous-cutanée et constitution morphologique. Biotypologie 7: 192–215.

PEARL, R. 1936. Constitution et santé. Biotypologie 4: 101–152.

PENDE, N. 1928. Le debolezze di costituzione. 2nd edit. Rome, Italy.

PIÉRON, H. 1936. Le problème des types d'intelligence. Biotypologie 4: 1–6.

PIÉRON, H. 1940–41. L'hétérogénéité normale des aptitudes. Année Psychol. 41–42: 1–43.

PIÉRON, H. 1946. La question des types psychophysiologiques. Biotypologie 8: 1–13.

PIÉRON, H. 1949. La Psychologie Différentielle. Paris, France.

PINEAU, H. & P. VASSAL. 1957. Etude des relations entre les circonférences des différents segments du corps et certains caractères somatiques uni ou tridimensionnels. C. R. Acad. Sci. 245: 1343–1345.

PUCHER, G. W., F. R. GRIFFITH, JR., K. A. BROWNELL, J. D. KLEIN & M. E. CARMER. 1934. Studies in human physiology. VI. Variations in blood chemistry over long periods of time, including those characteristic of menstruation. J. Nutrition 7: 169–193.

PRAT, H. 1956. Régimes de la thermogénèse chez la blatte américaine. Rev. Canad. Biol. 14: 360–398.

REES, W. L. L. & H. J. EYSENCK. 1945. A factorial study of some morphological and psychological aspects of human constitution. J. Ment. Sci. 91: 8–21.

RENBOURN, E. T. 1947. Variation, diurnal and over longer periods of time, in blood haemoglobin, haematocrit, plasma protein, erythrocyte sedimentation rate and blood chloride. J. Hyg. 45: 455.

RENBOURN, E. T. 1948. Normality in relation to human reactions. 9th Int. Conference Indust. Med. London, England.

RENBOURN, E. T. & J. DRAPER. 1960. La classification de la personnalité et la variabilité de quelques constituants du sang. Biotypologie 21: 37–49.

SARGENT, II, F. 1951. A critique of homeostasis: Season and metabolism. Arch. Meteorol. Geophys. Bioklimatol. B 3: 389.

SARGENT, II, F. & K. P. WEINMAN. 1962a. Variabilité physiologique chez l'homme jeune. Biotypologie 23: 137–171.

SARGENT, II, F. & K. P. WEINMAN. 1962b. Effectiveness of physiological regulation. In Climate, Health and Disease. VII. Physical Medicine Library. New Haven, Conn.

SARGENT, II, F. & K. P. WEINMAN. 1963. Physiological variability in young men. *In* Physiological Measurements of Metabolic Function. C. F. Consolazio, R. E. Johnson & C. J. Pecora, Eds. :453-480. New York, N.Y.

SARGENT, II, F. & K. P. WEINMAN. 1964. L'efficacité de la régulation physiologique. Biotypologie *25:* 18–48.

SCHREIDER, E. 1937. Les Types Humains. Paris, France.

SCHREIDER, E. 1950. Geographical distribution of body-weight/body-surface ratio. Nature *165:* 286.

SCHREIDER, E. 1951*a*. Anatomical factors of body-heat regulation. Nature *167:* 823–825.

SCHREIDER, E. 1951*b*. Analyse factorielle de quelques caractères susceptibles de définir la structure du corps. Biotypologie *12:* 26–32.

SCHREIDER, E. 1952. Quelques problèmes préalables à toute recherche de biométrie physiologique. Variations intraindividuelles, instabilité des milieux intérieurs, corrélations faibles et nulles. Biotypologie *13:* 20–58.

SCHREIDER, E. 1954. Les types humains: Methodes, resultats, concepts. Evol. Psychiat. *3:* 539–556.

SCHREIDER, E. 1956*a*. Quelques données sur la variabilité intraindividuelle et ses altérations pathologiques. Biotypologie *17:* 138–144.

SCHREIDER, E. 1956*b*. Relations entre les taux cétoniques du plasma et des organes. Experientia *12:* 315–316.

SCHREIDER, E. 1956*c*. Morphologie et physiologie. Bull. Inst. Nat. Orient. Prof. *12:* 1–12.

SCHREIDER, E. 1957. Gradients écologiques, régulation thermique et différenciation humaine. Biotypologie *18:* 168–183.

SCHREIDER, E. 1958*a*. Variations de Na^+, Ca^{++}, K^+, et $[H^+]$ du sang chez l'homme. Experientia *14:* 74–76.

SCHREIDER, E. 1958*b*. Variations et corrélations intraindividuelles de quelques caractères physiologiques et biochimiques chez l'homme. Biotypologie *19:* 99–107.

SCHREIDER, E. 1958*c*. Les Régulations Physiologiques. Essai de Révision Biométrique du Problème de l'Homéostasie. Paris, France.

SCHREIDER, E. 1960. La Biométrie. Paris, France.

SCHREIDER, E. 1962. Note documentaire sur les variations "spontanées" et posturales de la tension artérielle. Biotypologie *23:* 119–124.

SCHREIDER, E. 1963*a*. Les liaisons anthropométriques dans l'espèce humaine. Etude comparée de onze populations. Corrélations et analyses factorielles. l'Anthropologie *67:* 49–84.

SCHREIDER, E. 1963*b*. Le "phénomène de Barcroft" et la régulation du rythme cardiaque. Biotypologie *24:* 63–75.

SCHREIDER, E. 1963*c*. Some statistical aspects of blood sugar regulation. Nature *199:* 388.

SCHREIDER, E. 1963*d*. Physiological anthropology and climatic variations. *In* Environmental Physiology and Psychology in Arid Conditions. Proc. Lucknow Symp. (Unesco) :37–73. Paris, France.

SCHREIDER, E. 1964*a*. Ecological rules, body-heat regulation and human evolution. Evolution *18:* 1–9.

SCHREIDER, E. 1964*b*. Recherche sur la stratification sociale des caractères biologiques. Biotypologie *25:* 105–135.

SCHREIDER, E. 1964*c*. La Biologie Humaine. Paris, France.

SCHREIDER, E. 1964*d*. Correlations between blood sugar levels after insulin injection and ordinary meals. Nature *201:* 195–196.

SHELDON, W. H., S. S. STEVENS & W. B. TUCKER. 1940. The Varieties of Human Physique. New York, N.Y.

SHELDON, W. H., C. W. DUPERTUIS & E. McDERMOTT. 1954. Atlas of Men. New York, N.Y.

SIGAUD, C. 1894. Traité des Troubles Fonctionnels de l'Appareil Digestif. Lyons, France.

SIGAUD, C. 1914. La Forme Humaine. Paris, France.

SIGAUD, C. & L. VINCENT. 1912. Les Origines de la Maladie: Essai sur l'Evolution de la Forme du Corps Humain. 2nd edit. Paris, France.

SOULA, L. C. & E. SCHREIDER. 1951. Etude de l'interdépendance de quelques caractères anatomiques, physiologiques et biochimiques. Biotypologie *12:* 19.

TANNER, J. M. (no date). The present status of constitutional studies in relation to anthropometry, with special reference to Sheldonian somatotypes. *In* Bericht über die *6*. Tagung der Deutschen Gesellschaft für Anthropologie.

TANNER, J. M. 1952. The physique of students. Lancet *1:* 405.

TANNER, J. M. 1953. Growth and constitution. *In* Anthropology Today. A. L. Kroeber, Ed. Chicago, Ill.

TANNER, J. M. 1964. The Physique of Olympic Athletes. London, England.

TANNER, J. M., J. R. HEALY & R. M. WHITEHOUSE. 1959. Fat, muscle and bone in the limbs of young men and women: Their quantitative interrelationships studied radiologically. J. Anat. *93:* 563.

TEISSIER, G. 1945. Mathématique et Biologie. Paris, France.

THORNDIKE, E. L. 1938. L'organisation d'un individu. Biotypologie *6:* 252–258.

THURSTONE, L. L. 1946. Factor analysis of body-types. Psychometrika *11:* 15–21.

THURSTONE, L. L. 1947. Factorial analysis of body measurements. Am. J. Phys. Anthrop. *5:* 15–28.

TOPINARD, P. 1885. Eléments d'Anthropologie Générale. Paris, France.

UOTILA, U., P. FORTELIUS & A. TELKKA. 1955. Organ weights in Kretschmerian constitution types. Ann. Med. Exper. Biol. Fenniae *33:* Suppl. *14.*

VANDERVAEL, F. 1964. Biométrie Humaine. Liège, Belgium & Paris, France.

VIOLA, G. 1933*a*. Semeiotica della Costituzione. Milan, Italy.

VIOLA, G. 1933*b*. La Costituzione Individuale. Bologna, Italy.

VIOLA, G. 1933*c*. Critères d'appréciation de la valeur physique, morphologique et fonctionnelle des individus. Biotypologie *3:* 93–105.

VIOLA, G. 1937. Evaluation de la constitution humaine individuelle. Biotypologie *5:* 85–92.

VOGT, J. J. 1964. Répérage de la Contrainte Thermique au Moyen de Critères Physiologiques. Strasbourg, France.

WEINBERG, D. 1938. La biométrie différentielle et la biotypologie comme méthode pour la classification des individus et des groupes. *In* Comptes-Rendus du Congrès Intern. de la Population. *VIII.* Paris, France.

WILLIAMS, R. J. 1956. Biochemical Individuality. New York, N.Y.

WILLIAMS, R. J. 1960*a*. The biological approach to the study of personality. The Berkeley Conf. on Personality Development in Childhood. Univ. of California. Berkeley, Calif.

WILLIAMS, R. J. 1960*b*. Etiological research in the light of the facts of individuality. Texas Rep. Biol. Med. *18:* 168–185.

ZANNINI, D., S. COLLI & L. FONTANA. 1964. Constitution individuelle et adaptation au travail dans les conditions de surcharge thermique. Biotypologie *25:* 53–69.

Growth and Physique
in Different Populations of Mankind*

J. M. TANNER

(*Editor's Note*) During the period from birth to maturity the organism is perhaps more susceptible to environmental influences than at any other time in its life. Its survival depends upon the adequacy of its response during this crucial period. The suggestion has even been made that the adult is simply what's left over after the growth period, that is, the only evolutionary significance of adult traits is the role they played during infancy and childhood. It is therefore particularly important that the student of evolution recognize the nature and degree of individual and populational variations of the growth process. Tanner, in this article, first states some things that are known about human growth in general and how it is possible to distinguish environmental from genetic effects through population comparisons. He then goes on to discuss how differences in populations of adults must take into account population differences in the growth process, particularly differential growth rates. In a survey of growth studies carried out in different populations particular emphasis is put on determining how early in childhood the given populational differences occur. Intra-population variation is also noted, especially when socio-economic differences are indicative of genetic strata within the population.

Anthropologists have traditionally been interested in growth studies because they offer one of the best approaches to understanding the interaction of heredity and environment. Today we see such studies as a principal way of measuring population differences for features of particular evolutionary significance.

THE physique of a population—whether its members are tall or short, long- or short-limbed, broad or slender, muscular or slight, fat or lean, round-headed or long-nosed—depends on the distribution in it of numerous genes, on the mutual interaction of the products of these genes during development, and on the further interaction of these products with a wide variety of continuously changing environmental stimuli during the whole process of growth.

Such a system can respond very flexibly to alterations in the environment. Short-term alterations, such as a transient period of starvation, are met by homeorrhetic responses on the part of individuals; long-term alterations, such as an increase in solar radiation, by selective or evolutionary responses on the part of the population as a whole. These two types of response are not entirely separable, for they interact on each other. During a period of starvation a child may slow down in growth, and promptly catch up onto his previous growth curve when food again becomes freely available. This represents the individual homeorrhetic response. However, children whose growth regulation in the face of transient starvation is poor will be selected against. Such selection may occur either by a higher mortality at the time or by more subtle mechanisms such as reaching breeding age later, having narrower pelves (females, at risk in childbirth), or being smaller and less powerful (males, at disadvantage in competitive mating). The general ability to regulate growth in the face of a variety of environmental difficulties will be selected for in all populations. All children everywhere must be able to depart from and return to the lines of growth that characterize them.

The lines of growth themselves differ, however, from one population to another. We must suppose that in each of the major populations of the world the growth of its members was gradually adjusted, by means of selection, to the environmental conditions in which they evolved. The remnants of this process we should be able to see in modern populations—the remnants only, because relatively recent migrations have much altered the distributions of peoples, so that many no longer live in the areas in which they evolved.

These two aspects, the response of the individual and the response of the population, each have their separate counterpart in the study of growth. The first takes us into medical, social, and economic studies; the second into ecological physiology, human evolution, and history. Both have their place in the International Biological Programme, and both need continuing study and coordination, as I shall argue later, in some permanent International Bureau for Growth Studies.

In regard to the first aspect, growth is one of the best indices of child health that we have, and a continuous monitoring of the growth and development of children in under- and over-nourished populations is, or should be, a major concern of all public health authorities and governments. If we compare the growth of members of a single population under differing social, nutritional, and medical conditions we can see to what extent their present environment falls short of supplying those stimuli and substrates which are necessary if all members of the population are to fulfil the potentialities of their gene complex. If we continue to study different social groups in the population as social and economic development or regression occurs we can see clearly whether or not we have really advanced and whether we have favoured one social group at the expense of others.

As for the second aspect; if we study healthy, fully developed children and adults, or as near to them as we can find, in a variety of populations, we can arrive at some notion as to the elements in physique which have been adaptive and we can obtain a more informed view of the great biological variability of our species. In other words, we can advance the scientific study of man and the understanding of his evolution. It is true that only family studies will throw light on the genetic mechanisms concerned in the control of growth, but the physiological mechanisms can be investigated in populations, and so too can the effects of selection. In all that follows population, rather than family, studies are considered. Wherever possible, however, family studies should be made concurrently.

The Effect of Starvation and Disease on Growth and Physique

To begin with, we must get as clear a notion as we can of the effects of starvation and disease upon growth and physique. These are the environmental stimuli we hope to reduce or eliminate, in contrast to other more permanent aspects of the environment, such as climate and altitude.

It is convenient to distinguish clearly between effects on (1) rate of growth, (2) growth in size, (3) growth in skeletal shape, and (4) growth in tissue composition. These four effects may all occur together, or they may occur separately. If a child suffers an overall reduction in rate of growth at age 5, then clearly his size at age 5.5 must be affected, but not necessarily his size at 20 or adulthood. His shape and tissue composition may or may not be affected at 5.5

depending on whether the rate change is an overall one or peculiar to certain areas. It is perfectly possible for growth in size to be affected at all ages without the rate of maturation being slowed down; puberty and cessation of growth would occur at the usual age but at a smaller size than usual. Growth in skeletal shape could be affected without growth in size being changed, provided we took care that our definitions of skeletal size and shape were made so that the two were independently measured; and growth in tissue composition could, of course, be affected without growth in size or skeletal shape being necessarily involved.

In fact starvation seems usually to cause effects in a certain order, so that shape changes seldom, if ever, occur before size and rate changes are far advanced. Differences in gene complex on the other hand seem most frequently to affect shape and tissue composition. Thus we have already some guide as to the likelihood of a given population difference being due mostly to gene differences or to starvation and disease.

Besides distinguishing possible effects in this way, we must also clearly distinguish different causes. The effects of acute temporary, and chronic persistent, starvation may be very different. We must also remember that all the effects depend upon the age of the child, and all or many depend also upon sex, boys in general being more easily affected than girls.

Acute temporary starvation occurs from time to time in many populations. It may be associated with war, or temporary economic collapse, or physical disaster. In some populations it may occur fairly regularly at a certain time of year, so that the condition is a sort of half-way house between acute temporary and chronic persistent starvation. We can observe individual children from time to time with acute starvation due to psychological or medical causes. Unless the starvation is severe, all that happens is that the child's growth and development slow down, and when food is again available speed up to a rate above normal until the child has quite caught up again to its previous growth curve. Mild temporary starvation has clearly no lasting effect. But we do not know exactly how severe and how long-lasting starvation has to be before it produces a permanent effect, that is, a reduction in size of the adult. Probably this depends on the age at which it occurs, permanent effects being more rapidly produced in young children and possibly adolescents than in children in the mid-growth years. Possibly for a given degree of malnutrition, the critical time is proportional to the natural velocity of growth. One can imagine a sort of metabolic debt signifying 'unsatisfied growth potential' being built up as time passes and no growth occurs; I have elaborated elsewhere a hypothesis of how such a mechanism might operate (Tanner, 1963).

If rats are partially starved from birth to 21 days and then allowed to eat as much as they like, they at once have a catch-up spurt of growth, but it is insufficient to restore them to the normal curve of their litter-mates and they remain small all their lives (Widdowson and McCance, 1960; McCance, 1962). If rats are partially starved from 14 to 21 days they catch up better but still not entirely; if they are partially starved from 21 days to 40 days they are capable then of catching up completely. The rat is born at a much earlier stage of development than man, so that the birth-to-21 day period corresponds to the latter part of the foetal period in man. Malnutrition of the foetus is probably quite rare in man, but the rat experiments do show that, if we are seeking to explain some of the differences in size between populations as due to malnutrition, we should scrutinize most carefully the first two or three years, for it is influences at that time which are mostly likely to produce manifest and persistent effects.

Both temporary and permanent effects of periods of malnutrition are much less upon skeletal shape than on size. The answer to the question 'Are Nilotics linear because they eat too little at some particular time or throughout growth?' is clearly in the negative. At one time it was thought that acute or chronic malnutrition could change body proportions, and by analogy with some early results in cattle, it was suggested that short legs relative to the trunk length was a sign of malnutrition at an early age, as it may be in calves. Later work on rats and pigs has shown that the cattle results are not of general application and indeed the early results have not been uniformly repeated even in cattle. Widdowson's starved small rats had the same proportions of tail to body length, and of femur length to femur breadth, as the well-nourished larger rats, and also the same bone composition at each age. Apart from fat (and hence body weight) the only difference in shape seems to have been in the relation of head size to body length. As the head was much nearer adult size than the body at birth to 21 days, when starvation occurred, it remained relatively large in the starved small animals.

One good piece of evidence on this point in man comes from Greulich's (1957) study of Japanese children reared in California compared with those reared in the worse environment of Japan. The California-reared children were bigger at all ages, but the relationship of sitting height to leg length was practically the same throughout growth under both conditions (as shown by plotting Greulich's data on standard sitting height/stature charts). In general the proportion of limb to trunk, which varies so much from one population to another, is strongly regulated by genetic programming, in a way that overall body size is certainly not. This regulation can be seen very clearly in children who are severely dwarfed due to lack of growth hormone. They maintain normal proportions of limbs to trunk not only while they are dwarfed but even while they are catching up at four times the normal rate of growth when given human growth hormone (Tanner, unpublished). Similarly, there are recorded a number of cases of identical twins, one of whom has been malnourished or has had a chronic disease. This one has always been smaller than the healthy twin, but of the same skeletal proportions.

An exception to this rule may occur in hypothyroidism. Hypothyroid children are said to have legs which are relatively shorter than their trunks, even for their small overall size. This does not seem to be true of juvenile hypothyroids, whose disease starts after age 3 or 4. But in children who are hypothyroid at birth this disproportion may well exist, and may even be persistent, especially if therapy is not begun immediately after birth. Here again we see that it is disturbances in the early stages of growth which are least readily put right. A recent paper (Stock and Smythe, 1963) has in fact suggested that undernutrition during infancy may cause decreased brain growth and subsequent intellectual damage. Twenty-one very undernourished children in South Africa were followed, from 1 year of age to about 5 years, and the growth of their head circumference was compared with that of a control group whose parents had the same head circumference as the parents of malnourished children, but who lived in good circumstances. It appears that the head circumference of the malnourished was indeed less than that of the controls even at the time when the growth in both groups was nearing completion. The malnourished children also scored less in tests of mental ability, but this means very little since their homes were appalling and their parents non-existent or hopelessly improvident: in these circumstances the stimuli necessary for the development of mental ability are well known to be lacking. However, it is clear that research should be concentrated upon the early growth of the brain, particularly in areas where undernutrition is rife.

Whether growth of tissues, such as muscle, may be differentially affected by starvation or disease is not known. Here again we need data, and particularly data in the early years, and at adolescence when a new spurt of muscular growth occurs. The technical means of measuring widths of fat and muscle and bone in the limbs is at hand in simple X-rays (see Tanner, 1962) which can be used even in remote field conditions. Until this is done we cannot really be sure how much of the characteristically slender muscles of some East African Negroes are due to inheritance or to starvation. We do know, however, that the amount of muscle in Europeans is largely governed by inheritance, just as is bone (Hewitt, 1958; and see Osborne and De George, 1959). It seems likely that the shape of the muscle covering the bones and also the shape of the fat covering the muscle are both chiefly gene-determined. However, the amount of the muscle is governed, to some extent, by exercise, and the amount of fat is governed, to a far greater extent, by diet and sloth.

As for chronic malnutrition, there is little in practice that we can say to distinguish its effects from those of acute food shortage, although the distinction is of much theoretical importance, and will certainly be of practical importance when our data are better. In this respect it is important, for the IBP and later, to collect data on the best nourished and most healthy children in the population in under-developed countries so as to determine their growth potential. Knott (1963) has recently given figures for well-off Puerto Rican children which show them to be as large as Middle-West Americans from 7 years onwards and larger than the Spaniards from whom they are chiefly descended. Burgess and Burgess (1964) have likewise given 'healthy' figures for East Africans, and Tanner and O'Keefe (1962) for Nigerian girls from 12 years onwards.

Acheson and others have maintained that the trend towards greater height that has occurred in the adult, as well as the child, population of Europe, America, and Japan during the last 80 to 100 years reflects better nutrition and less disease. He asserts that even relatively mild disease or subnutrition will cause chondrogenesis to stop while permitting osteogenesis—the turning of cartilage to bone—to continue. If this did occur it would certainly cause ultimate stunting. However, the evidence for such dissociation is very poor, since in most illnesses it seems that the two processes are retarded or advanced together. A degree of special pleading has tended to enter this discussion. Recently Acheson and Fowler (1964) have estimated that the sons of well-off men in London would, when fully grown, exceed their father's height by 1.9 inches; the sons of miners in the Rhondda Valley whose fathers grew up in conditions of unemployment and often misery were estimated to exceed their fathers by 2.3 inches. The hypothesis to be tested is that the differences between the circumstances of fathers and sons during the growing period—small for the London group, large for the Rhondda—have brought about a differential effect on growth. This the authors declare to be shown, despite themselves saying that the difference of 0.4 inch between the means is far from significant. But the facts are in themselves very interesting and remind us that we have at present no sure explanation of the secular trend. Probably in certain areas it is chiefly due to better nutrition and less disease; probably in others chiefly to heterosis and the breaking of isolates. We lack data on this from tropical and underdeveloped countries and it is much to be hoped that the IBP will lay the foundation on which continuing studies of the trend may be built (see Tanner, 1962, p. 143; Milicer, 1962; Craig, 1963).

There is also a well-defined social class difference in European countries, the children of well-off parents being larger at all ages, and as adults, than children of poorly-off ones. The better-off also appear to have a lower weight for the same height. They seem to be a little more linear, less squat, and less muscular. This may be due to their being better nourished, but it could also be due to some inherent relation between size and/or shape and ability to rise in a European-type society, combined with assortative mating. Children with many siblings are significantly less in height and weight at each age and have a later puberty than children with few, presumably for similar nutritional-care reasons (see Tanner, 1962, p. 142; Valsik et al., 1963). These social class differences are a good example on a micro-scale of the differences between populations that we are trying to explain. They may be due to environment, and chiefly nutrition; but there may be also a genetic differential involved. The two interact inextricably.

DISEASE AND GROWTH. All that has been said about malnutrition applies equally to the effects of disease. A short and mild disease in a well-nourished child produces such a transient effect that if it exists it cannot be detected (see Tanner, 1962, pp. 130–134; Meredith and Knott, 1962). More severe diseases cause slowing of growth followed by a catch-up if the disease is cured. Probably critical periods for the effects of disease on growth exist, as they do for malnutrition, and certainly disease and undernutrition interact, not necessarily in an additive fashion.

Chronic disease, however, is our chief concern, and we are just beginning to have reports on the effects on growth due to eradicating malaria or hookworm or other similar diseases in areas in Africa and South America. In general the effects seem to be not spectacular. Thus reduction of the incidence of malaria in a heavily parasitized population in Tanganyika did not result in any significant increase in the weights of children during the first 18 months after birth (Draper and Draper, 1960); and children with repeated heavy malarial infections in the Gambia were no smaller by age 3½ than those protected by chloroquine (McGregor et al., 1956). Similarly being heterozygous for sickling haemoglobin S, even in malarious areas where its possession is supposed to confer an advantage in mortality, does not affect growth in height or weight (Garlick and Barnicot, 1957; Roberts, 1960). Diseases which cause a large reduction in regular haemoglobin content of the blood have a larger effect.

Neither disease nor malnutrition should be accepted uncritically as the cause of differences in growth between, for example, African and European populations. McGregor, Billewicz, and Thomson (1961) studied the growth of 187 children in rural Gambia from 9 months onwards. Though 43 per cent died before age 7, the heights and weights of these in the year previous to death were no different from the heights and weights of survivors. Growth was similar to that of Europeans in the first 6 months, then slowed until 2 years, when it resumed at the European rate. The authors say this slowing is not nutritional in origin in this area of rural Africa and think that undernutrition in certain children more likely follows disease than is the cause of it. They lay the chief blame on the inefficient development of active immunity.

Differences Between Populations in Growth and Physique

Anthropologists have documented some of the physical differences between populations with a zeal that approaches the excessive; but other aspects of physique such as muscle width have been less well studied, and the all-important question of how members of each population grew during childhood so as to attain their characteristic size and shape has been studied least of all. This is the field in which studies, internationally planned but nationally conducted, could contribute immensely to an understanding of the genesis of human variation.

What follows is not an exhaustive catalogue of studies of growth and physique in non-European populations—useful though that would be at the present time—but a selection and discussion of a number of the chief attempts to explain adult differences in physique by reference to differential growth rates.

One of the best of such studies is that of Hiernaux (1964) on the growth of the Tutsi and Hutu peoples of Rwanda. The Tutsi are tall, linear people, with an average adult male height and weight of 176 cm and 57 kg. The Hutu are shorter and stockier, with averages of 167 cm and 58 kg. There are two ways by which the Tutsi could grow to be taller. Either they may be longer at birth or shortly after and grow slightly more in length throughout their childhood; or they could grow at the same rate, but for a longer period, adding their extra 9 cm after the Hutu had stopped growing. The former is in fact the case. Both Tutsi and Hutu grow slowly compared with European children, probably because their nutrition is suboptimal, but both cease growth at about the same age (being 93–94 per cent of mature height at age 17), have menarche at the same age (about 16.5 years) and show the reversal of boys-taller to girls-taller at the same age (14 years). Hiernaux's data start at age 6 only, so we cannot tell exactly when the characteristic height-weight differences first were obvious. They are clear enough at age 6, however, Tutsi averaging 4 cm taller than Hutu, with almost identical weights. They probably start immediately after birth and reflect genetic differences of the same sort as those which cause boys' forearms to grow, from birth onwards, relatively a little faster than girls' (see Tanner, 1962). Tutsi and Hutu were growing up in a similar environment (the survey was made in 1957–8) but the Tutsi were better nourished, being the ruling caste. Despite this the Tutsi weight for given height was considerably lower than that of the Hutu. In the same paper Hiernaux gives figures for a group of Hutu reared from birth in Congo mining camps, where they were somewhat better nourished than in Rwanda. Only boys aged 6 to 9 are adequately represented and these are taller, by 2 to 2½ cm, than the Rwanda Hutu. They are also about 4 kg heavier.

This study raises virtually all the problems that we need to discuss in planning the IBP studies. They are as follows.

1. CHRONOLOGICAL AGE. In this study age was known. When age is unknown, differentiation between the growing-faster and the growing-for-longer hypotheses is impossible. Except in special circumstances, there seems to be virtually no way out of this impasse. Certain pairs of measurements change their relationship during growth; for example the head circumference, which is relatively advanced at birth and grows little later, and the leg length, which is relatively retarded at birth and grows much later. Hence the ratio, leg length/head circumference, increases as the child gets older; or, better, the figure for leg length adjusted to head circumference by a regression increases as the child grows. This ratio, or the position in the regression chart, could therefore be used to estimate the child's age, but only within a given population under given conditions. If we have to compare two

populations we would have first to be sure that in whatever other aspects of physique they differed, in the relation of leg length and head circumference they were the same at all ages. This seems virtually impossible even if both populations are equally well nourished. If one population's growth is retarded in all respects, perhaps by malnutrition, then the argument breaks down completely. A more accurate estimate of age can be made from combining a whole series of measurements—this is called 'shape age' and is currently under statistical investigation in my laboratory and others—but again this only works within, not between, populations.

Given a single population under stable environmental circumstances, the chronological age of the children could be 'reconstructed' at the end of a 5-year longitudinal study perhaps, starting with groups at birth, 5, 10, and 15 years. Either through measurement ratios or perhaps better by taking hand and wrist X-rays for skeletal age the appearance of known 1-, 2-, 3-, 4-, and 5-year-olds is secured and then those children who were, on this criterion, 4, 5, &c., five years ago located. The skeletal ages of the whole child population could be reconstructed in this way, but no allowance could be made for the variation between skeletal and chronological age in individual children older than 5 years. Reconstruction by reference to tooth eruption has the same difficulties but perhaps to a lesser degree.

We need to find something which is entirely unaffected by malnutrition and disease, and absolutely the same for all populations. Only age satisfies this criterion. Perhaps amongst physical measurements the one which most nearly approaches the criterion is the number of erupted teeth. The eruption of teeth seems to be less affected by malnutrition than maturation of the skeleton or physical growth. This is particularly the case for the primary dentition (Voors, 1957; Voors and Metselaar, 1958) which also seems, in our relatively scanty data, to vary less from one population to another than does the secondary. In eruption of secondary dentition East African and South African Bantu and Dutch New Guinea children are ahead of Europeans; in primary dentition this is not the case, but American Negroes are somewhat ahead of American Whites (see Tanner, 1962, p. 71).

We may say, then, that in IBP surveys so far as possible only children of known age should be included and much ingenuity and time may have to be expended getting parents to date their children's birth accurately by reference to remembered local events. Secondly, so that we may investigate further the possibilities for the future, tooth eruption should be recorded on all children, particularly those in the stage of primary dentition. If X-rays are available more sophisticated methods for dental maturity should also be used. Radiographs of the mandibular teeth will give a dental maturity rating at all ages.

2. CROSS-SECTIONAL AND LONGITUDINAL STUDIES. Hiernaux's study is cross-sectional and this has not been detrimental for the purposes for which the study was designed. We have to keep in mind, however, exactly what cross-sectional studies will and will not do. They tell us the attained heights, weights, &c., at each age. They tell us, up to but not during adolescence, the mean velocity of growth from year to year in each measurement. They enable us to compare two populations for size and shape at a given age. They enable us to say something about differences in rate of change of size and shape before adolescence, though we cannot make a significant test of population differences since we do not know the standard errors of the mean velocities. However, we can approximate them by a general knowledge of the results of longitudinal studies. Cross-sectional studies do not tell us how much a population varies in growth rate. They give us an idea of the average age at which the adolescent acceleration reaches its peak (though a slightly biased one) but little idea of the magnitude of the average peak velocity. They do not give a true figure for the average age at which growth ceases, since the latest-finishing subjects affect the height-achieved averages. We may wish to know whether two populations which differ in some measurement as adults were the same before adolescence, one having a greater adolescent spurt in the measurement; or if the differences arose before adolescence, the quantities added in the spurt being the same. A general notion of which has occurred may be obtained from cross-sectional studies, but not a precise answer. If menarcheal age is available as a guide to when adolescence occurs, this improves the tentative answer; the same is true of skeletal age.

Thus in the IBP cross-sectional studies are useful, but should be supplemented where possible by longitudinal studies particularly of infancy and adolescence. These longitudinal studies should extend over a minimum of 5 years.

3. AGES REPRESENTED. In Hiernaux's study the first age represented is 6 years. For this reason we cannot say whether the increased rate of growth in height of the Hutu begins at birth or later. In the IBP all ages from birth to maturity, i.e. at least 25, should be represented. For the first year 3-monthly groups should be used and from 1 to 2

years 6-monthly groups. This implies that there should be three or four times as many 0- to 1-year-olds and twice as many 1- to 2-year-olds measured as 3- to 4-, 4- to 5-year-olds, &c.

4. BOYS AND GIRLS. In Hiernaux's study both boys and girls are represented. Hence we can see at what age girls' height begins to exceed boys', which is a valuable guide to the age of beginning of the girls' adolescent spurt. The same is true of the age at which this trend reverses. Secondly we can see whether there is any significant sex-population interaction. This may be important. The response of girls to a variety of environmental disturbances is less than that of boys; girls seem to be better canalized (see Tanner, 1962, p. 127). Hence a lesser growth of boys in one population compared with another, in the presence of equal growth of girls in both, points to an environmental difference between the populations (as for example in Graffer, Asiel, and Emery-Hanzer, 1961). This is not an absolute criterion since sex-limited genes may differ between the two populations, but less usually.

For the IBP then, girls and boys should be studied simultaneously.

5. MEASUREMENTS OF DEVELOPMENTAL AGE. Without some measure of developmental age we cannot answer accurately the basic question as to whether the Tutsi grow for longer—whether they are the same height as the Hutu at each skeletal age, for example, but have a lower skeletal age for each chronological age—or grow more. Hiernaux answered this in his paper by reference to menarcheal age, which was known, and by reference to the percentage of adult height reached by his oldest age groups, that is 17-year-olds. Both methods are useful; obtaining figures for menarche may be easier than obtaining a sample of healthy 25- to 30-year-olds for the adult mature measurement. Neither technique tells us whether the situation in height relative to stage of development changed between 6 and 17. It might be that at 6 the Tutsi had a more advanced skeletal age than the Hutu and that their superiority of height at that age corresponded simply to faster growth and development; the height of the two groups for skeletal age might be the same. This might have gone on till adolescence was approached. Then the Hutu might have had a more rapid advance during adolescence, catching up to the Tutsi in skeletal age by the time of menarche, without having a correspondingly greater increase in their adolescent height spurt. Such would be the picture of population-age interaction for rate of growth. Admittedly such a thing is less likely than the more simple situation,

and it probably does not occur in the Tutsi-Hutu comparison. But as between Chinese and Europeans (see below) it seems to be present, just as the analogous interaction takes place between different individuals in the same population.

Thus in IBP studies some measure of developmental age should be included. Menarche is by far the easiest. All that is necessary is to ask a large sample of girls of known age from about 9 to 17 whether or not they have yet begun to menstruate and fit the resulting percentage incidence curve by logits or probits (see Burrell, Healy, and Tanner, 1961). The presence of secondary sex characters such as pubic hair, breasts, and male external genitalia can be dealt with in the same way, though less accurately. (Good examples are the papers of Lee, Chang, and Chan (1963) on the maturation of Chinese girls in Hong Kong as related to social class and of Bottyán and associates (1963) in Hungary.) Pictorial standards for judging development are given in Tanner (1962). Skeletal ages should be done where possible also, using the left hand and wrist and either the Greulich-Pyle or the Tanner-Whitehouse assessments.

In the IBP therefore menarcheal age should always be investigated, and secondary sex character age and skeletal age where possible.

In passing it may be noted that menarche may not occur at the same place on the height curve in all populations. Its position is rather constant in European groups, but in Nigerians it may perhaps occur later, that is nearer the point of cessation of height growth (see Tanner and O'Keefe, 1962). Hong Kong girls mature early, but have the same relation of menarche and mature height as Europeans. However, in Hong Kong girls the relative timing of appearance of breasts and pubic hair differs from that observed in Europeans and white Americans; pubic hair appears relatively later in the Chinese (Lee, Chang, and Chan, 1963).

CHINESE-EUROPEAN DIFFERENCES. Another interesting difference of rate occurs in Hong Kong children. From 6 to 15 years in boys and 6 to 12 years in girls, the skeletal maturity of Hong Kong children is retarded relative to the American Greulich-Pyle standards. However, at adolescence a change occurs and the Chinese pass more rapidly through the standards than the Americans, so that they are advanced after 12 in girls and 15 in boys (Low, Chan, Chang, and Lee, 1963). Here then is our example of the population-age interaction in rate of growth (or non-parallelism, to use another biometrical analogy) discussed above. It is not possible to tell from the cross-sectional studies whether this rapid adolescent skeletal development is accompanied by a stature spurt with a higher peak velocity than in Europeans; the figures suggest it may be so in boys. When plotted on the 1954 standard British charts the Hong Kong girls' average height lies at the 25th percentile from 9 to 11, reaches the 30th at 13 and 14, and drops to the 10th at 15, 16, and 17. It seems here that the adolescent spurt was of average European intensity, occurred early, and finished more rapidly than in Europeans. The best-off members of the Hong Kong population showed similar timings, though a different size level. The girls were at the British 50th percentile for height at 9 to 11, rose to the 65th at 12, had menarche at 12.5 compared with the British 13.1, and fell to the British 15th percentile by age 15. Well-off boys were at the 40th percentile at 9-11, 50th at 12 rising to 60th at 14, and dropping back to the 20th at 17. Clearly there are many interesting timing differences, but their full extent can only be elucidated by longitudinal study.

NEGRO-WHITE DIFFERENCES. There are, of course, many differences in build between Negroes and Whites. The Negro has long legs and arms relative to the trunk length, narrow hips, less muscular calves, and heavier bones. Not only is this true of the average American Negro student compared with Whites, but it even holds in Olympic athletes, amongst competitors at each type of sport (Tanner, 1964). Hurdlers, for example, have long legs, but Negro hurdlers have longer legs than White hurdlers. Weight-lifters, both White and Negro, have short legs, but the White lifters are shorter than the Negro.

We know very little of how these differences come about. One very well attested difference, however, is in the rate of maturing. Negroes, whether in America, West or East Africa, are ahead of Whites at birth in skeletal ossification, even compared with Whites living in better economic circumstances. This probably reflects an inherited difference in hormone secretion during the late foetal period, for their permanent teeth also erupt earlier, and the basis of these teeth is laid down in the uterus, though later than the laying down of the primary teeth, whose eruption date differs less between the races (see Tanner, 1962, pp. 66 and 77; Massé and Hunt, 1963). The Negro child maintains his advancement for about 2 to 3 years if living in good economic circumstances; it is reflected in a greater rate of growth in length and weight and a greater maturity of motor development and behavioural milestones. But after this age even in good circumstances the African child appears to decelerate in growth curve of the two races having a different shape, just as do the velocity and development. This may well be a natural occurrence, the velocity curves of males and females, in both races. The same thing is seen between members of the same population. Hewitt (1958) has shown that sibs resemble each other in having either a rapid growth of calf muscle from 6 months to 3 years followed by a relatively slower growth from 3 to 5 years, or the reverse pattern. This is a fairly complicated problem in growth velocities, and can only be satisfactorily solved by longitudinal studies on various populations living under good nutritional circumstances.

INDIAN-ASIAN DIFFERENCES. Berry and Deshmukh (1964) have recently shown that the somatotype distribution of Indian students differs greatly from that of European ones and probably even more from Asians (Heath, Hopkins, and Miller, 1961). Indians are less mesomorphic and more ectomorphic. This difference has also a genetic component, and starts early in childhood. In Singapore, Indian children had a lower weight for height than Chinese and Malayan children living in similar circumstances at all ages from 3 months to 5 years (the oldest studied), though by 5 years they were actually taller (Millis, 1957, 1958). More studies of children of different ethnic groups living in a similar environment are very desirable.

PRIMITIVE POPULATIONS. None of what has been said so far refers to primitive populations, and one of the avowed tasks of the IBP is to study these so as to have records of them before they disappear or are assimilated. Few primitive populations have been adequately studied from the point of view of either physique or growth. There is little on the Eskimo or the Andean, little on the Pygmy or the Australian Aboriginal. We have heights and weights, but no chronological ages, on Shilluk and Dinka in the Sudan (Roberts, 1961), but this has actually led to a probably incorrect interpretation of the genesis of their linearity (see Hiernaux, 1964). A few studies on American Indians have been done (see Kraus, 1954), but nothing on Tibetans or dwellers in Himalaya. Yet we know there are vast differences between these populations, not only in adult physique but in childhood. Margaret Mead, Tony Schwartz, and I studied somatotype pictures of all members, adults and children, in a Sepik River village community in New Guinea. Both men and women were strikingly mesomorphic compared with Europeans, and the children seemed to show the same type of build. Certainly between many primitive communities there is no overlap at all in physique. It takes no great anthropologist to distinguish any one Dinka from any one

Manus even if the facial features, skull contour, and skin colour are all obliterated. The techniques developed in the study of more advanced cultures are mostly quite easily applicable to these groups, and we must hope that in the IBP their children's growth will be studied now before it is too late.

CLIMATE AND ALTITUDE. We do not at present know to what extent the differences between populations are due to climate and altitude. We must presume that these geographical features originally governed the selection of growth-controlling genes and hence led to the emergence of the differences we see now. The adaptive significance of the various features can only be assessed by physiological studies, and at least some of these should if possible be carried out on children as well as adults, for the adaptation may be relevant to the growing period rather than adult life. Most selection takes place before the reproductive age is reached. It seems less likely that many of the differences in growth pattern are directly due to the action of climate and altitude on the growing child, except in such instances as emphysematous chests in very high altitude dwellers. A test of this is provided by people of one race who grow up in the area mostly inhabited by another. Europeans reared in the Sudan do not grow up with the Dinka physique, nor do Africans reared in Liverpool grow thick European-type calves. Englishmen who pass their youth in Japan are not, so far as we know, characteristically short-legged. Nevertheless a study of persons reared in a *milieu* very different from that of their parents would be a very desirable addition to the IBP programme. Italian migrants to Boston are being studied intensively by Boutourline Young. Few results have yet been published. Greulich's (1957) excellent study of Japanese migrants to California has already been mentioned. Two great difficulties are presented by all migrant studies, however: first migrant parents seem never to be a random sample of the nation they leave, being usually larger and more intelligent than the stay-at-homes (even if they only migrate from one English county to another); and secondly food habits and opportunities are very seldom the same for migrants as for sedentes. Thus the effects of climate and altitude are hard to assess by this means. A similar difficulty beset Wurst's (1961) study of the growth of Austrian children in relation to altitude. The higher the villages, the poorer were the people, the worse was the food and the greater the calories expended on walking to school. Thus though the high-altitude children were smaller at all ages, the reasons for this cannot be disentangled.

Summary

1. A summary is given of present knowledge of the effects of malnutrition and disease on growth and physique. Disturbances of the environment affect first rate of growth, then, if prolonged, final size. Only very severe disturbances affect shape. It is likely that malnutrition in the early years has a more lasting effect than malnutrition later.

2. Differences in patterns of growth between different populations are then considered, an attempt being made to distinguish those which are inherited from those which occur as a result of malnutrition or disease. A comparison of two African populations is cited and used as an example for the development of a list of guiding principles to be observed when making growth studies in the IBP. The limitations of cross-sectional and longitudinal studies are discussed and the usefulness of such landmarks as menarche, whose mean and variability can be assessed even on cross-sectional data.

3. It is proposed that a small International Bureau for Growth Studies be set up, to co-ordinate present and future knowledge, which at the moment is widely scattered and collected with little reference to existing work. The function of such a Bureau would be somewhat similar to those of the International Blood Group Centre.

References

ACHESON, R. M. and FOWLER, G. B., 1964. 'Sex, socio-economic status and secular increase in stature', *Br. J. prev. soc. Med.* 18, 25–34.

BERRY, J. N. and DESHMUKH, P. Y., 1964. 'Somatotypes of male college students in Nagpur, India', *Hum. Biol.* 36, 157–176.

BOTTYAN, O., DEZSO, GY, EIBEN, O., FARKAS, GY, RAJKAI, T., THOMA, A., and VELI, GY, 1963. 'Age at menarche in Hungarian girls', *Annls hist. nat. Mus. natn. hung.* 55, 561–571.

BURGESS, A. P. and BURGESS, H. K. L., 1964. 'The growth patterns of East African schoolgirls', *Hum. Biol.* 36, 177–193.

BURRELL, R. J. W., HEALY, M. J. R., and TANNER, J. M., 1961. 'Age at menarche in South African Bantu girls living in the Transkei reserve', *Hum. Biol.* 33, 250–261.

CHANG, K. S. F., LEE, M. M. C., LOW, W. D., and KVAN, E., 1963. 'Height and weight of southern Chinese children', *Am. J. phys. Anthrop. 21*, 497–509.

CRAIG, J. O., 1963. 'The heights of Glasgow boys: secular and social influences', *Hum. Biol. 35*, 524–539.

DRAPER, K. C. and DRAPER, C. C., 1960. 'Observations on the growth of African infants with special reference to the effects of malaria control', *J. trop. med. Hyg. 63*, 167–171.

GARLICK, J. P. and BARNICOT, N. A., 1957. 'Blood groups and haemoglobin variants in Nigerian (Yoruba) schoolchildren', *Ann. hum. Genet. 21*, 420–425.

GRAFFAR, M., ASIEL, M., and EMERY-HAUZEUR, C., 1961. 'La taille et le périmetre cephalique pendant la première année de la vie', *Acta paediat. belg. 15*, 61–74.

GREULICH, W. W., 1957. 'A comparison of the physical growth and development of American-born and native Japanese children', *Am. J. phys. Anthrop. 15*, 489–515.

HEATH, B. H., HOPKINS, C. E., and MILLER, C. D., 1961. 'Physique of Hawai-born young men and women of Japanese ancestry, compared with college men and women of the United States and England', *Am. J. phys. Anthrop. 19*, 173–184.

HEWITT, D., 1958. 'Sib resemblance in bone, muscle and fat measurements of the human calf', *Ann. hum. Genet. 22*, 26–35.

HIERNAUX, J., 1964. 'Weight/height relationship during growth in Africans and Europeans', *Hum. Biol. 36*, 273–293.

KNOTT, V. B., 1963. 'Stature, leg girth and body weight of Puerto Rican private school children measured in 1962', *Growth 27*, 157–174.

KRAUS, B. S., 1954. *Indian Health in Arizona.* University of Arizona Press, Tucson.

LEE, M. M. C., CHANG, K. S. F., and CHAN, M. M. C., 1963. 'Sexual maturation of Chinese girls in Hong Kong', *Pediatrics 32*, 389–398.

LOW, W. D., CHAN, S. T., CHANG, K. S. F., and LEE, M. M. C., 1964. 'Skeletal maturation of southern Chinese children in Hong Kong', *Child Develpm. 35*, 1313–1336.

MCCANCE, R. A., 1962. 'Food, growth and time', *Lancet 2*, 621–626.

MCGREGOR, I. A. and BILLEWICZ, W. Z., 1961. 'Growth and mortality in children in an African village', *Br. med. J. 2*, 1661–1666.

—— GILLES, H. M., WALTERS, J. H., DAVIES, A. H., and PEARSON, F. A., 1956. 'Effects of heavy and repeated malarial infections on Gambian infants and children', *Trans. R. Soc. trop. Med. Hyg. 2*, 686–692.

MASSÉ, G. and HUNT, E. E., 1963. 'Skeletal maturation of the hand and wrist in West African children', *Hum. Biol. 35*, 3–25.

MEREDITH, H. V. and KNOTT, V. B., 1962. 'Illness history and physical growth III. Comparative anatomic status and rate of change for schoolchildren in different long-term health categories', *Am. J. Dis. Child. 103*, 146–151.

MILICER, H., 1962. 'Investigations on the physical development of youth', *Physical Education in School* (Eds. W. MISSIURO and J. SADOWSKA). Institute of Physical Culture, Warsaw.

MILLIS, J., 1957. 'Growth of pre-school Malay infants in Singapore', *Med. J. Malaya 12*, 416–422.

—— 1958. 'Growth of pre-school Chinese and Southern Indian children in Singapore', *Med. J. Malaya 12*, 531–539.

ROBERTS, D. F., 1961. 'Körperhöhe und Gewicht nilotiden Kinder', *Homo 12*, 33–41.

STOCK, M. B. and SMYTH, P. M., 1963. 'Does undernutrition during infancy inhibit brain growth and subsequent intellectual development'? *Archs Dis. Childh. 38*, 546–552.

TANNER, J. M., 1962. *Growth at Adolescence*, 2nd ed. Blackwell, Oxford.

—— 1963. 'Regulation of growth in size in mammals', *Nature, Lond. 199*, 845–850.

—— 1964. *Physique of the Olympic Athlete*. Allen and Unwin, London.

—— and O'KEEFE, B., 1962. 'Age at menarche in Nigerian schoolgirls, with a note on their height and weights from age 12 to 19', *Hum. Biol. 34*, 187–196.

VALSIK, J. A., ŠTUKOVSKY, R., and BERNATOVA, L., 1963. 'Quelques facteurs geographiques et sociaux ayant une influence sur l'âge de la puberté', *Biotypologie 24*, 109–123.

VOORS, A. W., 1957. 'The use of dental age in studies of nutrition in children', *Documenta Med. geogr. trop. 9*, 137–148.

—— and METSELAAR, D., 1958. 'The reliability of dental age as a yardstick to assess the unknown calendar age', *Trop. geogr. Med. 10*, 175–180.

WIDDOWSON, E. M. and McCANCE, R. A., 1964. 'Some effects of accelerating growth, I. General somatic development', *Proc. roy. Soc. B 152*, 188–206.

WURST, F., WASSERTHEURER, H., and KINNESWENGER, K., 1961. *Entwicklung und Umwelt des Landkindes*. Osterreichicher Bundesverlag, Vienna.

Some Problems in the Study of Quantitative Inheritance in Man*

J. N. SPUHLER

(*Editor's Note*) In addition to professional training in some area of human biology, the physical anthropologist usually has a specialist's knowledge of the socio-cultural environment in which man lives. This dual perspective is particularly important if his research deals with quantitative inheritance, because it is here that the interaction between heredity and environment most greatly affects the phenotype. In the following article Spuhler discusses some aspects of this interaction and the difficulties involved in studying it. He develops the point that an understanding of quantitative inheritance depends largely on better ways of analyzing the non-genetic component of human variation. For example, the distribution of genes within a population is determined by mating patterns. Thus social patterns (rules) can influence geneotype frequencies which in turn are responsible for the nature of at least some of the phenotypic variation found in the population. Some mating patterns are non-random relative to a given social variable, as, for example, when there is assortative mating with respect to genealogical position of the mates, as in preferred first cousin marriage. Under certain conditions this may result in inbreeding with possible measurable phenotypic consequences. Spuhler cites such a case.

THE hypothesis that the genetic part of quantitative variability depends in general on multiple gene loci distributed over the chromosomes is the most reliable explanation of the observed characteristics of continuous variation in man and other organisms. The hypothesis is not entirely satisfactory because it cannot adequately be tested (Haldane, 1946, Hogben, 1951, Wright, 1952).

*From *American Journal of Human Genetics*, vol. 6, March 1954, pages 130–139. By permission of the author and the publisher.

In the formal genetics of discontinuous variations, hypotheses on mode of inheritance can be formulated and tested with accuracy. Discrete characters are associated with a specified number of genes according to rules reflecting the patterned and random regularities of chromosomal behavior in gamete and zygote formation.

We assume that continuous variation represents the combined effect of multiple gene and environmental determiners. Compared to the case for discontinuous variations, this assumption is vague. Because of the vagueness it is extremely difficult to formulate testable hypotheses regarding the detailed mode of inheritance for continuous variations. The chief difficulty is the large number of contributing variables. Since we cannot formulate a precise hypothesis, it follows we cannot predict test results within close limits. Further, the lack of a precise and appropriately detailed model means that any estimate based on the imprecise model will not be efficient (Nedler, 1953).

Thus, for the present, if we are to investigate continuous variation in man, we must use inefficient methods of analysis. The prospect is not good that we will soon know enough to have a predictive understanding of continuous variation in human individuals. However, the methods we have are superior to the published materials for the study of quantitative genetics of man. These methods will be considered by the discussants: Drs. Lush, Comstock, and Dempster. My assignment from Dr. Green is: "First, to present some actual data on quantitative traits in the Navaho Indians, and Second, to confine the presentation to thirty minutes." I am instructed: ". . . merely to allude to methods of analysis while pointing out questions of genetic interest. Thereby it will be possible to depend upon the discussants to present methods and evaluation of the methods."

The complexity of the genetics of quantitative variation is illustrated by Fig. 1 (adopted with major modifications from Lerner, 1950). What we observe is phenotypic variation. After analysis, phenotypic variations may be divided into two sorts: (1) characters, and (2) traits. Here "characters" mean phenotypic attributes or attribute sets whose variation (for a defined environment) has been demonstrably associated with a defined set of genes. The definition of "character" presupposes certain specific genetic information. Since there are a limited number of genes in man, there are a limited number of characters. Generalizing from known cases the variation of characters is usually (but, theoretically, not necessarily) discontinuous. "Trait", as used here, means all phenotypic attributes or attribute sets that are not "characters." No specific genetic information (or, negative information alone) is presupposed in the definition of traits. The variation of traits is often (but not necessarily) continuous. Traits may be associated with "factors", that is, with unidentified genes. Statements about factors (as in the sentence "stature is controlled by multiple factors") presuppose different prior information than statements about genes. By genetic analysis with positive results traits may become characters. Some such distinction between characters and traits, between genes and factors, helps to keep exposed our ignorance of the genetics of many human variations. The Navaho variations to be discussed in this paper are traits. Before considering these traits, however, we need to take a quick view of some background information on the genetics of human populations.

In theory, the variation of characters may be proportioned into two sources: (1) Genetic variation, and (2) Non-genetic variation. The genetic variation of a population is a function of the frequency and distribution of genes. The major modes of change of gene frequencies are mutation, selection, mixture between breeding populations, and genetic drift. The conditions of gene distribution within a breeding population are set by the system of mating. It is not necessary, before this audience, to characterize the modes of change nor the requirements for a steady state of population gene frequencies and distributions. Later, examples will be given to show how knowledge about inbreeding and assortative mating may aid the study of quantitative inheritance.

The modes of change and the conditions of steadiness for the non-genetic fraction of human variations are the subject matter of a wide variety of physical, life and behavior sciences. The scheme for the

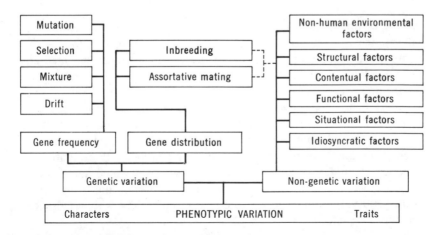

FIGURE 1. *A scheme showing some determinants of phenotypic variation.*

non-genetic part of Fig. 1 is an adaptation of one suggested by Kluckhohn and Mowrer (1944). If we start with a given item of individual behavior in a societal context we may analyse the background of the behavior by abstracting out those factors which are resident in persons or groups of persons (structural, contentual, functional, idiosyncratic and situational factors) as opposed to those that are not resident in persons (non-human environmental factors—geographical, non-human organismal factors, etc.). Structural factors refer to the ways individuals get status positions in society. Sample names of status positions are "father," "mother," "citizen," "geneticist." Contentual factors refer to the ways individuals get roles for acting in a given status. The behavior in two societies with the same structure may differ because of variation in the roles assigned to individuals in similar status positions. Individuals occupy a variety of statuses and roles simultaneously. The behavior in one status-role often is not independent of behavior in another status-role. Functional factors refer to the interconnectedness of these in ongoing behavior. Those aspects of individual behavior not referable to structural, contentual, functional or situational factors are called idiosyncratic factors. Finally, the behavior of two individuals within the same structural, contentual, and functional framework may differ, to an extent greater than can be assigned to idiosyncratic factors, because of variation in the situational factors—the precipitate of past experiences, and all other things which define the situation in which particular behavior occurs.

This is not the place to discuss in detail methods of analysis of the non-genetic component of human quantitative variability. The difficulties of a satisfactory analysis here are probably greater than for the genetic component. Satisfactory resolution of problems of quantitative inheritance will require better methods of analysis of the non-genetic component. Geneticists could make much fuller use of the methods developed by the behavior and life sciences for analysis of human environments.

There is no single scheme for the interpretation of human behavior which is both (a) widely accepted among behavior and social scientists, and (b) adequately verified by empirical testing. Although some such scheme is known to be necessary for studies of the quantitative genetics of human behavior, most of the ways in which such studies may be valuable in the study of morphological and other non-behavioral variations have yet to be explored. There is time to sketch a single example.

Consider the system of mating. The distribution of genotypes in a population is a function both of the kinds and frequencies of genes present and of the system of mating. No human society is known where mating is random for all possible criteria (excluding sex). But the cultural criteria for mate selection vary greatly between societies. For instance, with regard to inbreeding, in some societies brother-sister mating is socially sanctioned (Ptolemaic Egypt), or at least acceptable (the Caiçara of Brazil, see below), while in others it is taboo. With regard to assortative mating, in some societies (to pick a social criterion) a progeny-tested unmarried female may have high, and in others, distinctively low marriageability. Structural factors determine what kinds of relatives—biological and social—are recognized. Contentual factors and functional factors set the rules for behavioral interaction of these relatives. Within the area of behavior which is permissive rather than required, observed instances of behavior can be explained further by idiosyncratic and situational factors. In many societies a male's mother's brother's daughter is an ideal mate. But whether two particular cross-cousins do in fact marry (and thus conform to approved but not required behavior) is a consequence of the idiosyncrasies and the past experiences of the two individuals. Within the limits set by demographic factors—themselves determined by an interplay of biological, social and cultural factors— the system of mating in human populations has socio-cultural determinants; and, in turn, the system of mating is a codeterminant of the distribution of genotypes and thereby of quantitative morphological variations in the population.

Before I talk about the Navaho, I want to make, but not to elaborate here, one more methodological observation. It is simply this. Not only do we need to have bigger and better methods of analysis from the statistical side, but also we need to find and to use more suitable material for our investigations. I do not mean organisms other than man. To do this we will have to study subjects other than school children and other individuals who can be comparatively easily ascertained because they can be controlled through an institutional setup. Two items tell the sort of thing I have in mind: (1) Human inbred material does occur in highly useful amounts and places. Yet inbred human material has not been used in recent studies on quantitative genetics. (2) Fertile multiple mating occurs in almost all human societies (cf. our own serial polygyny). Yet nothing comparable to the between-sire and between-dam methods of animal genetics has been used in human studies.

Navaho Data[1]

Two traits will be used to illustrate some problems met in the study of quantitative variation in human populations. The data are from the Ramah Navaho, a local group of Indians living in west central New Mexico who numbered 614 individuals in September, 1950. The present population was founded in 1868 by individuals born about 1820–1840 and is now in its eighth generation. The genealogy of about 1,200 members, living and dead, is known.

The two traits are stature and head height. Stature was selected for discussion, first, because it is the most extensively reported quantitative human trait, and, second, because, from the time of Galton, it has been the most popular quantitative trait for human genetical analysis. The second trait, head height, was selected because it has diagnostic value in distinguishing regional American Indian morphological varieties, for example, the eight varieties defined by Neumann (1942, 1952) for aboriginal North America, and because it illustrates certain difficulties of interpretation for quantitative traits.

The distribution of these two traits for five subgroups of the Ramah population will be given. The five subgroups are:

1. Total adult series
2. Adult offspring of related parents, that is, inbred adults
3. Adult offspring of unrelated parents
4. Unrelated parents
5. Related parents

Stature was measured with an anthropometer following standard technique. Measurements were read to the nearest millimeter. In the males the range of values is 150–183 cm., the mean is 167.32 ± 0.53, and the standard error is 5.31 ± 0.05. In the females the range is 145–165 cm., the mean is 156.42 ± 0.55, and the standard error is 6.03 ± 0.05. These values were obtained before rounding to centimeters. The values for the Total Adult Series are the values for the 221 individuals measured.

You will note immediately that the sample shown here (103 males and 118 females) is smaller than 614, the size given earlier for the Ramah population in 1950. This illustrates one serious problem of

---

[1]Ten tables of Navaho data, presented as slides at the conference, have been omitted from this paper.

genetic studies in human populations—the samples are never ideally large. Of course, usually this is a practical rather than a necessary difficulty. Adequate studies on human subjects are very expensive both in money and time, especially where the subjects represent a "natural" population as opposed to an institutionalized group.

Actually our total measured Ramah Navaho series is 482 individuals. It is a judgement sample selected to be representative of the group with regard to geographical location of family homes, sex, age, degree of acculturation, economic and social status. The sample constituted 78.5 per cent of the total population.

Here we have reduced our sample size by 45.8 per cent by excluding observed children, that is, persons under 17 years of age. We could include the children in a study of quantitative inheritance by employing one of a number of procedures for correcting measurements of children to predicted adult values. While such corrections are never fully satisfactory (different children move through a generalized growth space on different paths and at different rates), the careful use of age corrections permits fuller utilization of information for the parent-child relationship. If ample material is available the analysis can be kept more simple by excluding the children. However, the growth cycle difficulty is not entirely removed by limiting the analysis to adults—the ontogenetic cycle in man is such that parents are usually somewhat worn, shrunken, bent or broken by the time their children reach adulthood. Usually there is not sufficient material to restrict the data to a narrow age level.

Head height was measured in millimeters following the Harvard technique with the anthropometer. In the total series the males have a range of 114–139 mm., with a mean of 126.80 ± 0.56 and a standard error of 5.62 ± 0.06. The females have a range of 111–136 mm., with a mean of 124.33 ± 0.51 and a standard error of 5.53 ± 0.05.

Before looking at the correlation for stature and head height among the various subgroups, let us consider briefly an important point suggested by head height. The problem of what to measure and what is measured is a persistent difficulty in the study of quantitative genetics in man.[2] Often measurements can be made quite accurately between two or more anatomical points. But the biological stuff between the

[2]There is not time to discuss in any detail the problems of observational error and of scale. On the problem of scale see, for morphological traits, Mather (1949) and Wright (1952), and for behavioral traits, Stouffer, *et al.* (1950). On observational errors in physical anthropometry see Boyd (1929) and Davenport, Steggerda and Drager (1934).

points may be quite heterogeneous between individuals (Washburn, 1951).

On the living, head height is measured from porion to vertex. On the skull, or on a lateral x-ray plate, the height measurement is usually the basion-bregma diameter. The range of Navaho head height measurements is from 111 to 139 mm. Conventionally these measurements are classified into three categories: high, medium and low head height. Suppose we have a head height measurement that falls in the category "low head height." There are at least four possible interpretations of this datum:

1. The entire skull may be small, and thus the head height not relatively low at all,

2. The skull may in fact have a relatively high vault but the base may be flat—the declination of the pars basilaris on the Frankfort plane is such that the lower component of the height is short.

3. The skull may have a relatively low vault—one with the upper component of the height short, or

4. The skull may show a combination of low vault and flat base.

A number of workers, mainly anthropologists and osteologists, have suggested that if we subdivide the traditional measurements such as head height into their morphological components, we would find that the variation of the individual components would follow more simple modes of inheritance than that of the "total" measurement. I doubt very much that this will prove to be a general finding, but I do feel that redefinition of the "parts' of the human organism—as in morphological component analysis—will help us to arrive at more consistent results, especially for some kinds of anthropological problems.

We are now ready to look at the correlations for the distribution of these traits in pairs of relatives. For present purposes, the comparisons are restricted to same-sex pairs. As in all Primates phylogenetically later than the gibbons, there is considerable sex dimorphism in the Navaho. For instance the stature of Navaho females in this sample of adults ranges over 20 units on the centimeter scale, while the range for males is 33 units, the mean differences between the sexes being 10.9 units. In actual analysis traits with different distribution for the sexes, of course, should be handled separately unless the values for one or both sexes are transformed. The argument is more simple when we restrict analysis to the same sex but the restriction reduces the amount of information available on a natural population by at least one half. The alternatives to such a restriction include that of expressing the values of one sex in terms of the other, and of using the notions of mid-parent and mid-offspring.

Restrictions of comparisons to the same sex are accompanied by another difficulty. Given that genetic factors are involved in the variability of the trait under consideration, then to the extent that positive phenotypic assortative mating occurs, the child will resemble the like-sexed parent not only because of factors received from that parent, but also because of factors received from the unlike-sexed parent, the one not entered into the same-sex correlation. The correlation within 77 Navaho mated pairs is $r = -0.18$ for stature and $r = +0.08$ for head height. The 95 per cent fiducial limits are $-0.55 \leqslant r \leqslant +0.25$ for stature and $-0.42 \leqslant r \leqslant +0.48$ for head height. The data given here are not sufficient to tell us that assortative mating safely can be ignored in any analysis of the genetics of Navaho stature and head height.

It is of incidental interest to suggest that knowledge of the breeding structure of a population may be essential to a proper understanding even of traditional anthropological results where populations are described in terms of normal curve statistics. Gini (1950) has shown that the distribution of stature in some large and seemingly representative European population samples is leptokurtic. W. Lenz (1952) suggested that this finding would be expected under a system of positive phenotypic assortative mate selection for stature, and, further, that a number of European groups had been shown to practice this kind of mate selection. But some populations with platykurtic distributions are known. In general it would seem that a quantitative genetic trait would be expected to show a leptokurtic distribution under a system of positive phenotypic assortative mating and a platykurtic distribution under a system of negative phenotypic assortative mating.

Parents are classified as unrelated when they have no biological relationship in the eight generations known for the Ramah group. Related parents, of course, have one or more common biological ancestors within the known parental generations. The population mean coefficient of inbreeding over all eight generations (1,118 individuals) is 0.0066 (Spuhler and Kluckhohn, 1953). The mean coefficient for inbred sibships, over the last four generations, is 0.0175. The highest coefficient for an individual sibship is 0.0977 (where the parental, multiple relationship is full first cousins, full first cousins once removed, and full third cousins), and the lowest coefficient for an inbred sibship is .0005 (half fourth cousins).

The Navaho inbred material reported here is by no means the best that could be made available. Although the mean inbreeding coefficient is about four times the estimates reported for Europe and two times those reported for urban areas in Japan, it is lower than the estimate (.0254) for the Dunker isolate in this country (Glass, et al., 1952). In terms of population size the amount of inbreeding at Ramah is relatively small. The operation of cultural values keep the Ramah coefficient low. The point that needs to be made is that populations are available where considerable inbreeding is in practice. For instance, Willems (1952) has reported (from the standpoint of cultural anthropology) some Caiçara communities on the southern coast of Brazil where both father-daughter and brother-sister matings produce offspring with some frequency, and this with local social approval. Study of even a small number of such cases would be of great value. Further, Ellis (1936, p. 142), in a paper based on the genealogical studies by Silva Leme (*Genealogia Paulista*), found 42.8 per cent of marriages were consanguine among the upper classes of the Plateau of Sao Paulo during the 19th century, and the degree of inbreeding in this stratum of the Planalto Paulista population appears to be increasing rather than decreasing. Ethnological information on numerous other inbred populations can be found in the anthropological literature (Lévi-Strauss, 1949; Murdock, 1949). But as is shown by the work of Eaton, Glass, and Steinberg on isolates in this country, you need not leave home to find suitable material for study of the quantitative genetics of man.

Data will not be presented here on the few known sets of Navaho twins. Dr. Kallmann will discuss twin methods. The great advantage of twin methods for the study of quantitative genetics in man (assuming there are only two sorts of twins and the methods for diagnosis of the two sorts are trustworthy in practice) is that it should measure all of the epistatic and dominance variations as well as the additive ones. A disadvantage is that for most practical problems, we want to have information relevant to singletons rather than to twins who never constitute more than a small fraction of natural human populations. There have been less than a dozen pairs of twins in the history of the Ramah population. Also, there seem to be some primary difficulties in transferring statements about quantitative inheritance in twins into statements about singletons (for examples of such difficulties see Price, 1950).

Summary

Some problems in the study of the quantitative genetics of man are discussed using data from the Ramah Navaho Indians of New Mexico as illustrative material. Information is presented, but not analyzed, on the distribution of stature and head height in the adult Ramah Navaho sample for parent-child and sib-sib pairs, for related and not related parents, and for inbred and not inbred offspring.

References

BOYD, E. 1929. The experimental error inherent in measuring the growing body. *Am. J. Phys. Anthrop. 13:* 389–432.

DAVENPORT, C. B., M. STEGGERDA AND W. DRAGER. 1934. Critical examination of physical anthropometry on the living. *Proc. Am. Acad. Arts Sci. 69:* 265–284.

ELLIS, A. 1936. *Os primeiros troncos paulistas e o cruzamento euroamericano.* Sao Paulo.

GINI, C. 1950. The distribution of stature is hypernormal. *Acta Genet. Statist. Med. 1:* 361–376.

GLASS, B., ET AL. 1952. Genetic drift in a religious isolate: An analysis of the causes of variation in blood group and other gene frequencies in a small population. *Am. Nat. 86:* 145–159.

HALDANE, J. B. S. 1946. The interaction of nature and nurture. *Ann. Eugen. 13:* 197–205.

HOGBEN, L. 1951. The formal logic of the nature nurture issue. *Acta Genet. Statist. Med. 2:* 101–140.

KLUCKHOHN, C. AND C. GRIFFITH. 1951. Population genetics and social anthropology, *Symp. Quant. Biol. 15:* 401–408.

KLUCKHOHN, C. AND O. H. MOWRER. 1944. "Culture and personality": A conceptual scheme. *Am. Anthrop. 46:* 1–29.

LENZ, W. 1952. Über den Einfluss der Homogamie auf die Verteilungskurven der menschlichen Körperhöhe. *Acta Genet. Statist. Med. 3:* 97–100.

LERNER, I. M. 1950. *Population genetics and animal improvement.* Cambridge University Press.

LÉVI-STRAUSS, C. 1949. *Les structures élémentaires de la parenté.* Paris: Presses Universitaires de France.

MATHER, K. 1949. *Biometrical genetics. The study of continuous variation.* New York: Dover Publications.

MURDOCK, G. P. 1949. *Social structure.* New York: The Macmillan Co.

NEDLER, J. A. 1953. Statistical models in biometrical genetics. *Heredity 7:* 111–119.

NEUMANN, G. 1942. American Indian crania with low vaults. *Hum. Biol. 14:* 178–191.

———— 1952. Archeology and race in the American Indian. In: J. B. Griffin, ed., *Archeology of eastern United States,* University of Chicago Press, pp. 13–34.

PRICE, B. 1950. Primary biases in twin studies; A review of prenatal and natal difference-producing factors in monozygotic pairs. *Am. J. Hum. Genet.* 2: 293–352.

SPUHLER, J. N. AND C. KLUCKHOHN. 1953. Inbreeding coefficients of the Ramah Navaho population. *Hum. Biol.* 25: —. (In press).

STOUFFER, S. A. ET AL. 1950. *Measurement and prediction.* (Studies in social psychology in World War II, Vol. 4), Princeton University Press.

WASHBURN, S. L. 1951. The new physical anthropology. *Trans. New York Acad. Sci.*, Ser. II, 13: 298–304.

WILLEMS, E. 1952. *Buzios Island. A Caiçara community in southern Brazil. Monographs Am. Ethnol. Soc.* 20.

WRIGHT, S. 1952. The genetics of Quantitative Variability. In: Agricultural Research Council, *Quantitative Inheritance*, London: Her Majesty's Stationery Office, pp. 5–41.

6

Genes and Ancestry

Four Achievements of the Genetical Method
in Physical Anthropology*

WILLIAM C. BOYD

(*Editor's Note*) What's the best way of comparing populations? For a long time anthropometry provided a means of comparison. Many thousands of the world's people were measured, and a number of international meetings were held to standardize the measurements. With the advent of genetics and the decline of the type concept, anthropometry was pretty much relegated to the tailor shops. The next great hope for population comparison was blood grouping. This time the variables were known to be heritable, not to change during an individual's lifetime, and it was evident from the beginning that different populations had different frequencies of blood group alleles. But as time went on certain problems about the comparative use of blood groups were realized. Blood groups could not identify a population; they could only characterize it after its parameter had been defined by some other means. Often different blood groups gave conflicting indications when two or more populations were compared. But most serious of all, blood group frequencies were not stable population markers because at least some of them were selectively not neutral. The result of all this was a certain amount of disillusionment about using blood groups in all but rather closely controlled population comparisons. In the following article Boyd makes the point that all is not lost, in fact, in certain cases the blood groups have provided information about population origins and mixture that would have been unobtainable in any other way.

*From *American Anthropologist*, vol. 65, April, 1963, pages 243–252. By permission of the author and the publisher.

THE use of genetical methods in physical anthropology, which really began with the Hirszfeld's classical paper (1919:675) is no longer new and is now widely accepted. Genetical methods are referred to, in an approving tone, in many books and articles published during the last few years. The late Prof. Hooton (1946) devoted 18 pages out of 788 to genetical methods, and Montagu (1960:327) devotes 93 out of 771 to the subject, giving it a very up-to-date treatment, and stating, ". . . if we are to trace the relationships of the varieties of man to one another, it is necessary that we rely on criteria which possess a more permanent character than the shifting sands of head shape. . . . Such characters are available in the blood groups, in the M-N in the Rh-Hr blood types and in the hemoglobin and haptoglobin types of man."

In addition to the characteristics mentioned by Montagu, we now know of a number of other inherited traits of man that either are or will doubtless become useful. One might well ask, are there any longer any skeptics? The answer to this question seems to be: yes, there are skeptics, and some of them are rather vocal. Worse than this, examination of some of the books and papers written by authors who seem to welcome the genetical method suggests that they, in reaching their conclusions, actually make very little use of the data and modes of reasoning that such methods provide.

Layrisse and Wilbert (1960) state that in their experience about four out of ten physical anthropologists are still doubtful about the value of blood grouping in their science. Probably most of us have had one or more of the older physical anthropologists inquire, in conversation, "Now frankly, what have blood groups ever proved that we didn't know already?"

L. Oschinsky (1959:1) has not hesitated to carry the war into his enemy's country. He says, "Nowhere has Professor Boyd posed the question as to whether or not the characteristics he is choosing are taxonomically relevant. . . . Unfortunately for Professor Boyd, it is the polygenic features such as skin colour, hair texture, nose shape, lip thickness, which have the greatest taxonomic value. *And why is it necessary to understand the mechanism of inheritance* if one is concerned with the question of distinguishing between the various racial groups which, Professor Boyd states, is one of the chief aims of physical anthropology?" (my italics)

A few years ago, at a seminar at Columbia University, a distinguished American physical anthropologist delivered a detailed attack on the blood groups as anthropological criteria, partly on the grounds that they may respond too readily to selection pressures. More recently, two Polish anthropologists, Bielicki (1962:3) and Wiercinski (1962:2) have also attacked the use of genetical methods, and readvocated the use of conventional morphological criteria.

Perhaps it is true that I never posed or attempted to answer the question brought up by Oschinsky. Let me attempt to answer it now. Believing that races are the result of the adaptation of different populations to the environments in which they live, I believe that any feature in which two populations differ has taxonomic value. I am not convinced that the characters enumerated by Oschinsky have greater taxonomic value than have, for example, the blood groups, and I have pointed out elsewhere (Boyd 1956:993) certain advantages that genetically analyzed characters such as the blood groups possess.

Back of many of these recent attacks on genetical methods there is an argument that has come to find increasing favor with those of the old school who continue to doubt the usefulness of genetic methods. This argument seems to be based on Birdsell's demonstration (1951:259; 1952:355) that genetic drift would be more likely to bring about fixation or extinction of extreme types when these types are determined by genes acting at one or a few loci than it would when a considerable number of loci are involved. Some writers seem to have concluded from this that the same is necessarily true of the action of natural selection. Statements implying this are even found in certain textbooks.

Actually, whether selection will act more slowly on multifactorial characters than on those controlled by a single locus is a difficult and comprehensive question that has not been sufficiently investigated, even from the theoretical angle. A preliminary mathematical study of the problem shows that the answer depends on the particular genetic model we choose.

For the sake of simplicity, let us restrict our multifactorial case to the situation where two loci are involved. If the two genotypes are determined by two complementary factors, the rate of elimination of the unfavorable genotype *would* be slower than in the unifactorial case (C.C. Li, unpublished calculations).

On the other hand, if we assume that to get the unfavorable trait the cooperation of two loci is required, and that the trait does not appear in an individual unless some particular one of the alleles at that locus is represented in double dose, then the rate of removal of this undesirable trait from the population is *exactly the same* as the rate of removal in the unifactorial case.

But . . . Dr. Li has also shown (unpublished calculations) that if the gene effects are not all additive and three phenotypes result, then if the selective coefficients against two of the phenotypes are the same as in the unifactorial case, the unfavorable multifactorial trait is removed *faster* than the unfavorable unifactorial trait.

Since we do not know which of these models (if any) corresponds to the actual situation with respect to any actual human multifactorial trait, it would seem premature to base a decision on a hasty and probably emotion-packed extrapolation from Birdsell's demonstration in relation to genetic drift.

If we look for experimental evidence, it is mostly conspicuous by its absence, but Hiernaux (1962:29) does state that he has observed a shift in the morphology of the Bantu towards that of the Pygmies, in the tribes who have recently migrated into the equatorial forest of the Eastern Congo, without any similar shift in blood group frequencies.

In the light of all this, there does not seem to be at the present time any good reason to reject genetically analyzed traits and rely solely on morphological and other multifactorial characters. In fact, as we shall see below, there is other evidence that suggests that in some places at least selection has altered the incidence of frizzy hair, dark skin, etc. much faster than it has altered the blood group frequencies.

It is to be feared that our comparatively recent discovery that the blood groups are not selectively neutral (although the selective forces demonstrated thus far are mostly very weak) has reawakened the hope formerly held that the physical characteristics previously used for racial classification will turn out to be less rapidly altered by selection and therefore of more value in reconstructing the past. But if it was naive of us to reason that since we could not think of any way in which selection could attack the blood group frequencies it did *not* affect them, it would be doubly naive of us to argue now that since we have not found the nature of the selective pressures that affect the frequency of the genes controlling hair form, skin color, lip thickness, etc., there are no such pressures. Fleure (1945:580) showed fifteen years ago that this puzzle is not "beyond all conjecture", and suggested that pigmentation, at least, is connected with the intensity of ultraviolet radiation from the sun and sky.

In so far as genetic drift (the Sewall Wright effect) is concerned, I believe Birdsell's demonstration is valid. But how big a role has drift played in the formation of our present human races? Admittedly, many authors have made extensive use of the concept of drift in their speculations on the past history of man, and I have been one of the worst offenders. It is now my conviction that I and others employed this notion too freely; drift may actually have operated only in certain special cases. All authorities now agree that the most important agency of race formation is natural selection acting in isolation on random mutations. R. A. Fisher, who usually had his feet on the ground, was never convinced that drift was an important agency.

However this may be, it is now clear that the advocates of the use of genetical methods did not win the victory they thought they had, but got instead an uneasy truce that is now being disturbed by occasional pot-shots from certain unsubdued *franc-tireurs*. This being so, we ought perhaps to ask ourselves if the question, quoted above as coming up frequently in conversation, has a good answer, or indeed any answer at all. *Have* genetic methods made any new contributions to physical anthropology?

I believe we can answer this question in the affirmative, and in support of this would like to cite four examples. These concern the Gypsies, the American Negro, the Lapps and the Papuan pygmies.

A. The Gypsies

Confirmation of the Indian origin of the Gypsies was the earliest achievement of the genetical method, but it did not lead to any radical reversal of opinion, for it merely served to strengthen an opinion that was already generally accepted. The method was used, even by its originators, mainly as a test of the possibility of using serological data when reasoning about the past history of a human group.

The Gypsies were known to claim an Indian origin for themselves, and linguistic studies by George Borrow and others had established the fact that their language was a debased and diluted form of one of the modern derivatives of Sanscrit. But though the Gypsies, like the Basques and Jews, maintain that they never mix with the surrounding peoples (or maintain that if they do, any resulting progeny are not considered Gypsies), some Gypsy groups, particularly in Britain, are so like the people they live among that some authorities doubt their Indian origin. I once took blood from several Gypsies in a Welsh hospital, supposing them to be Welsh, without noticing anything different about them. R. B. Dixon, in his controversial *Racial History of Man*, said of the Gypsies, "It seems probable that *if of northwest Indian origin*, they may, before leaving there, have had some Alpine mixture . . ." (my italics).

In 1921 Verzár and Weszeczky (1921:33) removed whatever doubt remained by determining the blood groups of some Hungarian Gypsies. The results showed that the blood groups of the Gypsies still

TABLE 1. *Blood Group Frequencies of Gypsies, Indians and Hungarians.*

POPULATION	NUMBER TESTED	PER CENT IN GROUP			
		O	A	B	AB
Gypsies (Hungary)	385	34.3±2.4	21.0±2.1	39.0±2.5	5.7±1.4
Indians*	1000	31.3±1.5	19.0±1.2	41.2±1.6	8.5±0.9
Difference		3.0±2.8	2.0±2.4	2.2±2.9	2.8±1.7
Hungarians	1500	31.1±1.2	38.0±1.3	18.7±1.0	12.2±0.9
Difference between Gypsies and Hungarians		3.2±2.7	17.0±2.4	20.3±2.7	6.5±1.6

(The numbers following the various percentages are standard deviations.)
*From Hirzfeld's original paper (1919:675)

agreed quite well with those of the Indian soldiers tested by the Hirszfelds at Salonika, and differed significantly from those of the Hungarians (Table 1). This result was obtained with the aid of the ABO blood groups alone, as the twenty or so additional systems now available to us had not yet been discovered.

Note that in Table 1 the blood group frequencies of the Hungarian Gypsies, though strongly supporting the idea of an Indian origin, differ from the Indian frequencies slightly, and in the direction to be expected (more A, less B) if the Gypsies had mixed somewhat with other stocks, such as the surrounding Hungarians. We could even calculate from these figures (see Section B), if we wished to assume that the ancestors of the Gypsies had the blood group frequencies of Hirszfeld's Indian soldiers, what proportion of Hungarian genes Verzár's Gypsies had acquired. Which brings me to the next achievement of the genetical method.

B. Quantitative Treatment of Race Mixture

When two populations having different frequencies of a gene mix, the frequencies of the gene in the resulting mixed population can be predicted if the proportions in which the two populations mix are known. It is simply a question of taking a weighted average of the sets of two gene frequencies. Bernstein (1931) showed thirty years ago how to make such calculations and mentioned that they could be reversed to estimate from the gene frequencies of a mixed population the proportions in which two ancestral populations must have mixed to produce it. This procedure is exactly like the well known procedure called "indirect analysis" in quantitative chemical analysis. Various authors have made use of the method (see Boyd 1950). Stevens (1952:12) has shown how to apply the method of maximum likelihood to the problem. His procedure is, however, too lengthy to summarize here.

An excellent example of the use of genetical methods to calculate the degree of mixture a given population represents is provided by the paper by Glass and Li (1953:1). In a careful study making use of the frequencies of seven genes (R_0, R_1, T, r, B, A, and R_2) Glass and Li reached the conclusion that the amount of White mixture in the North American Negro is 30.565 per cent. It is hardly necessary to remark that such a result could never have been obtained by a study of genetically unanalyzed traits such as skin color or morphology. In dealing with such problems genetical methods make a unique contribution to anthropology.

C. The Lapps

The exact position of the Lapps among the peoples of Europe has long been a controversial question. For a long time they were classified with the Mongoloids. Haddon (1925) included them in his "Urgian" (evidently a misprint for Ugrian) group with the Tungus, Cheremis, etc. Deniker (1900) classified the Lapps as "Hyperborean," apparently a branch of his Mongolian group. C. S. Coon states, ". . . the original ancestral Lapps represented a stage in the evolution of both the Upper Paleolithic Europeans and the mongoloids," (1939:305).

These and other authors recognized that the Lapps were a highly specialized human group, and genetical methods certainly confirm them in this. Examination of nearly any of the isogene maps in Mourant's book (Mourant 1954) shows that the Lapps have characteristically different frequencies of nearly all of the blood group genes (see Fig. 1). On nearly all of the maps a little area, like a "high" or "low" on a weather map, can be recognized, of which one can say, "There are the Lapps." And also, just as is the case with another isolate, the Basques, the gradual gradation of the Lapp gene frequencies into those of the populations around them shows that isolation has been imperfect, either during the formation of the Lapp race, or afterwards, or both.

But the earlier writers were wrong in thinking there was anything mongoloid about the Lapps. The Lapps have very low frequencies of the blood group B gene, whereas mongoloids have high B. The Lapps have a high frequency of the A_2 gene (the highest in the world) (Allison et al. 1956:87); this variant of A is absent in the mongoloids. The M frequencies of the Lapps are low, whereas those of the mongoloids are "normal" or high.

All the genetic evidence agrees in indicating that the Lapps evolved into their very distinctive race *in situ*, and none of the evidence suggests that they are even partly of mongoloid origin. The Lapps are Europeans. Actually, some physical anthropologists were coming to this conclusion on the basis of morphology, but it seems likely that without genetical evidence to reinforce these conclusions there would have remained many a doubt.

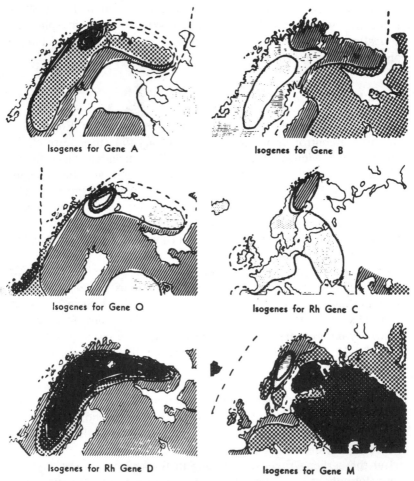

Isogenes for Gene A

Isogenes for Gene B

Isogenes for Gene O

Isogenes for Rh Gene C

Isogenes for Rh Gene D

Isogenes for Gene M

FIGURE 1. *Blood group gene frequencies among the Lapps.*

D. The Oceanic Pygmies

In several inaccessible areas of the islands that extend from the south-west of Asia there are found groups of natives characterized by their short stature, close-curled or frizzy hair, highly pigmented skin, and other "negroid" features. Such individuals, who are generally referred to as Negritos (Spanish, "little Negroes"), have been found in the Philippines, the Andaman Islands, the Malay peninsula, southern Siam and New Guinea. There has always been a strong temptation for anthropologists to consider these Negritos as somehow derived from Africa. When some were found to be pygmies, the temptation became irresistible. Stirling (1943) stated that they all belonged to the same basic stock. Montagu (1960:439) hedges a little, "Africa and south-eastern Asia and Oceania are quite a long way from each other. The Negroids of today are, generally, poor seafarers; were their ancestors so, too? It is difficult to say; Melanesians often make voyages by sea in small outrigger craft of 50 miles or more. There is no reason to suppose that their ancestors could not do likewise." Howells (1959:329) is more emphatic, ". . . it is as plain as the nose on your face that the Negritos are intimately related to fully developed Negroes—a specialized kind of man—in skin, hair form, nose shape, and so on. The Negritos are really all similar and must have a common origin. And Negritos and Negroes cannot have appeared on separate continents; they too must have had a common origin. How do we get the Negritos into the Pacific from Africa?"

At least one writer has gone to the trouble of describing a hypothetical migration route of the Negritos from Africa to the Pacific, with way-station stops in Arabia and India.

It is apparent that such writers are making certain assumptions, though they may not state them explicitly: (a) They assume that the local environment has virtually no influence in determining the physical type of the human race that evolves in it. (b) They assume that if two human stocks look alike superficially, they must be related by common descent, at least partially. (c) They assume that similar adaptations to similar environments never take place. One reason this third assumption is made may be because the phenomenon is known by the epithet "parallel evolution." Now if race formation is primarily due to the action of natural selection, neither of these assumptions is necessarily true, and it is more reasonable to assume that: (a) The local environment greatly influences the evolution of the racial type that eventually adapts itself to it. (b) Similar environments will often, or at least occasionally, bring about similar racial adaptations. It is mainly a question of how similar the environments really are and whether a supply of the right mutations is or becomes available.

In the case of the Negritos we can test these opposing points of view by genetical methods. If the Negritos came somehow from Africa, bringing with them their dark skins, frizzy hair, broad noses, and thick lips, they should have brought with them the African blood group frequencies, and no continent has a more characteristic blood group picture than Africa south of the Sahara. Did they?

The blood groups of the Papuan pygmies have been studied by Graydon, Semple, Simmons and Franken (1958:149) and those of the Andaman Negritos by Lehmann (1954). Their results, compared with results found in Africa by Hubinot and Snock (1949) and Jadin, Julien and Gusinde (see Boyd 1939:113), are shown in Table 2.

TABLE 2. *Blood Group Gene Frequencies in African and Pacific Negritos.*

POPULATION	NUMBER TESTED	FREQUENCY OF GENE								
		A	B	O	M	N	R_0	R_1	R_2	r
Pygmies, Belgian Congo	2557	0.198	0.249	0.553	0.468	0.523	0.630	0.074	0.194	0.101
Papuan Pygmies	139	0.075	0.139	0.786	0.102	0.898	0.030	0.850	0.119	0
Andaman Negritos	52	0.54	0.08	0.38	0.61	0.39	0	0.92	0	0

The ABO gene frequencies, it is true, do not sharply distinguish the three populations (though the Andaman Negritos certainly seem to have more A than the other two groups); the other two blood group systems show definite and distinctive differences. A characteristic feature of the African pygmies, as of Africans in general, is the high frequency of R_0; this is not reflected in the other two populations shown in Table 2, as it certainly should be if they were of African origin. In fact, the Andaman Negritos seem to have no R_0 at all. The African pygmies, like other Africans, have "normal" frequencies of M and N (M and N about equal); the Papuan pygmies, like other Papuans, have much more N than M. The Rh negative gene (r or cde) is present in the African pygmies (it is almost a monopoly of the Africans and the Europeans), but is absent from the other two populations. Both the Papuan and the Andaman

Negritos show the characteristic high Pacific value of R_1, over 10 times as high as that found in the African pygmies.

These numerous and marked genetic differences are not compatible with the supposition that the Pacific pygmies were somehow derived by migration from Africa, or even with the supposition that they are the product of a mixture of some older Pacific stock and some Africans who somehow managed to get to the Pacific and thus contributed their skin, hair, and lips to the hybrids. Any significant African contribution to the ancestry of the Pacific Negritos would have brought also some Rh negative genes, raised the R_0 frequency significantly above zero, lowered the R_1 frequency, and probably raised the M frequency. Graydon *et al.* are being very conservative when they say, "Despite the finding of a high R_0 frequency in Malayan Negritos the present authors believe that the weight of the blood grouping evidence makes it unlikely that the African and Asian pygmies are related. Previously expressed similar views regarding the lack of relationship between the African and Oceanic Negroes" (1958:169).

It would seem that genetical methods, though relatively new, have already made distinctive and worthwhile contributions to physical anthropology.

Summary

Certain recent arguments against the application of genetical methods in physical anthropology are examined, and four examples are offered of contributions made by such methods: (a) confirming the Indian origin of the Gypsies, (b) computing the percent of White mixture in American Negroes, (c) establishing that the Lapps are a highly distinctive separate race, but European, (d) showing that the ancestors of the Papuan pygmies did not come from Africa.

References

ALLISON, A. C., B. BROMAN, A. E. MOURANT and L. RYTTINGER, 1956. The bloodgroups of the Swedish Lapps. Journal of the Royal Anthropological Society *86:*87–94.

BERNSTEIN, F., 1931. Die geographisch Verteilung der Blutgruppen und ihre anthropologische Bedeutung. Comitato Italiano per lo Studio dei Problemi della Populazione. Rome.

BIELICKI, T., 1962. Some possibilities for estimating inter-population relationships on the basis of continuous traits. Current Anthropology *3:*3–8.

BIRDSELL, J. B., 1951. Some implications of the genetical concept of race in terms of spatial analysis. Cold Spring Harbor Symposia on Quantitative Biology 25:259–314.

——, 1952. On various levels of objectivity in genetical anthropology. American Journal of Physical Anthropology 10:355–362.

BOYD, W. C., 1939. Blood groups. Tabulae Biologicae 17:113–240.

——, 1950. Genetics and the races of man. Boston, Little, Brown.

——, 1956. Anthropologie und Blutgruppen. Klinische Wochenschrift 34:993–999.

COON, C. S., 1939. The races of Europe. New York, The Macmillan Co.

DENIKER, J., 1900. The races of man. New York, Charles Scribner's Sons.

DIXON, R. B., 1923. The racial history of man. New York, Charles Scribner's Sons.

FLEURE, H. J., 1945. The distribution of skin color. Geographical Review 35:580–595.

GLASS, B., and C. C. LI, 1953. The dynamics of racial intermixture— an analysis of the American Negro. American Journal of Human Genetics 5:1–20.

GRAYDON, J. J., N. M. SEMPLE, R. T. SIMMONS and S. FRANKEN, 1958. Blood groups in pygmies of the Wissellakes in Netherlands New Guinea. American Journal of Physical Anthropology 16:149–171.

HADDON, A. C., 1925. The races of man. New York, The Macmillan Co.

HIERNAUX, J., 1962. (Discussion of papers by A. Wiercinski and I. Bielicki in Current Anthrop.) Current Anthropology 3:29–30.

HIRSZFELD, L. and H. HIRSZFELD, 1919. Serological differences between the blood of different races. The Lancet ii, 197:675–679.

HOOTON, E. A., 1946. Up from the ape. 2nd edition. New York, The Macmillan Co.

HOWELLS, W., 1959. Mankind in the making. New York, Doubleday and Co.

HUBINOT, P. O. and J. SNOEK, 1949. Reparition des genes Rh (CDE cde) chez les pygmees Batswa des Ntomba, Comptes Rendus de la Societé de Biologie, Paris 143:579–581.

LAYRISSE, M. and J. WILBERT, 1960. El Antigeno del Sistema Sanguinea Diego. Editorial Sucre, Caracas.

LEHMANN, H. and E. W. IKIN, 1954. Study of Andamanese negritos. Transactions of the Royal Society of Tropical Medicine and Hygiene, 48:12–15.

MONTAGU, M. F. A., 1960. An introduction to physical anthropology. Springfield, C. C. Thomas.

MOURANT, A. E., 1954. The distribution of the human blood groups. Springfield, C. C. Thomas.

OSCHINSKY, L., 1959. A reappraisal of recent serological, genetic and morphological research on the taxonomy of the races of Africa and Asia. Anthropologica *1:*1–25.

STEVENS, W. L., 1952. Statistical analysis of the A-B-O system in mixed populations. Human Biology *24:*12–24.

STIRLING, M. W., 1943. The native peoples of New Guinea. Smithsonian Institution War Background Studies No. 9. Washington.

VERZÁR, F. and O. WESZECZKY, 1921. Rassenbiologische Untersuchungen mittels Isohämagglutininnen. Biochemisches Zeitschrift *126:* 33–39.

WIERCINSKI, A., 1962. The racial analysis of human populations in relation to their ethnogenesis. Current Anthropology *3:*9–10.

7

Selection: Mechanisms and Evidence

Mechanisms and Trends in Human Evolution*

JAMES F. CROW

(*Editor's Note*) To the beginning student, fossil evidence may seem intuitively more convincing of evolution than vital statistics from modern populations. At least the student might feel that way until he reads the evidence, presented here by Crow, on how the forces of evolution are operating right now on civilized man. In general, genetic change is a slow, conservative process, resulting in a gradual remodeling of some existing genetic state. This process operates as a consequence of genetically different individuals leaving disproportionate numbers of offspring in successive generations. Crow hypothesizes that the drop in the risk of death during the reproductive period is perhaps more than compensated for by an increasing trend to differential reproduction as an ever smaller percent of the current generation is responsible for an ever larger percent of the next.

Crow also discusses Darwinian fitness, heritability, and the factors involved in different contemporary societies that alter the operation of selection. The question is raised whether adaptation is possible when the modern environment is being so rapidly altered through technology. It is conceivable that the genetic consequences of today's demographic changes may run counter to existing social values. Yet man is probably exceedingly flexible due to his tremendous genetic variability. And this, coupled with a technology that can compensate for untoward genetic effects, are considerations which make the human situation quite different from that of other animals. Once again, it is evident that the understanding of human evolution, with reference to past or present

*From *Evolution and Man's Progress*, edited by Hudson Hoagland and Ralph W. Burhoe, pages 6–21. Copyright © 1961 by the American Academy of Arts and Sciences and Copyright © 1962 by Columbia University Press. By permission of the author and the publishers.

populations, requires the consideration of the effect of any number of non-biological variables which directly or indirectly may affect the composition and expression of the gene pool.

THE most important trend today in the mechanisms of human evolution is the radically changing pattern of birth and death rates. Until recently the death rate was high, particularly for children, while those who lived to maturity showed a high reproductive rate. Now, in most technologically advanced countries, there is a very low death rate and a voluntarily low birth rate. The most important consequence is the effect on world population. The birth rate has fallen rapidly, but in most areas not so rapidly as the death rate, so that population grows at a faster rate than ever. If we can avoid a thermonuclear war, then surely the most pressing problem for men in the next century will be one of sheer numbers.

The principal concern of this paper, however, is not the absolute numbers of the population, but the trends in the kinds of persons who compose it. The guiding force in biological evolution is selection. Selection implies that some types of individuals leave more descendants than others do, whether because of their greater ability to survive or their greater fertility. Mutation provides the variant forms that are the raw materials of evolution. The gene-shuffling process we call Mendelian inheritance is a mechanism for arranging these variants in endless combinations. The structure of the population may permit some isolation of subgroups with possible evolutionary consequences; but the general direction of the evolution of the population is determined mainly by selection. Those genes that on the average enhance the fitness of their carriers will increase in numbers in later generations. In this connection, "fitness" is used in a strictly Darwinian sense as a measure of actual survival and of reproduction, and not (as J. B. S. Haldane has cautioned) fitness for "football, industry, music, self-government, or any other activity."[1]

Differential Survival and Reproduction

First of all, we must realize that selection depends on differential mortality and fertility. No genetic change will ensue unless individuals having different genetic makeups contribute in different proportions to future generations. At the crudest level, we can measure the extent to which different individuals of one generation are differentially represented by children in the next generation, irrespective of the causes of the differences. As a measure of genetic selection, this is clearly unsatisfactory, for many such differences are purely accidents of time and space; automobile wrecks and thermonuclear bombs kill tall and short people, indiscriminately. To some extent, differential survival and reproduction depend on an individual's characteristics, such as his health; but health is partly determined by early environment.

The human birth rate is an example of the effect of early selection. A newborn child of intermediate weight has a greater chance of surviving for the next few months than a larger or smaller child has. To this extent there is selection for birth weight; but birth weight is certainly not determined by the gene makeup alone: the intrauterine environmental factors are also of great importance. Even if traits were entirely determined by heredity, this would not necessarily mean that the population is readily changed by selection. To continue with the same example of weight at birth: a gene that causes a slight increase in weight will be disadvantageous in an infant that is otherwise too large, but advantageous in a small child. A size-determining gene, therefore, is subject to contradictory pressures in selection, and its frequency in the general population accordingly does not change much, even though the population is subject to intense selection.

The conclusion is that selection alone is not always capable of effecting a genetic change in a population. Some traits are largely unresponsive to selection; if we select a group of seven-footers as parents, we will not necessarily have a population of giants in the next generation. Animal and plant breeders use a statistical concept called "heritability" to describe the effects of selection on a population. A trait that has a high heritability is readily changed by selection; a trait that remains only slightly changed, or not changed at all, has a low heritability.[2] There may be several reasons for a low heritability: (1) the trait may be determined environmentally, rather than genetically; (2) on the other hand, it may be largely or even completely determined by the genes, and it will still have a low heritability if the gene frequencies are in some sort of selectively balanced state, or if there are complex interdependencies between different genes or between genes and environment.

In discussing the trends in human evolution, let us consider the effect of existing patterns of births and deaths on the genetic makeup of the population, and what the effect of various possible eugenic proposals might be. The answers to such questions are unknown, except in broad outline. As a preliminary question, let us return to the amount of potential selection inherent in the pattern of births and deaths, whether or not it is genetically effective, so as to enable us to set some limits on the amount of selection that could occur.

Has Human Selection Nearly Stopped?

In 1850 about one-fourth of all the children born in the United States died before the age of five years. The 1959 death rates are such that 63 years would have passed before this proportion of the population would have died.[3] There has been a similar though less spectacular fall in the birth rates in the last century. Does this mean that natural selection has been virtually eliminated as an evolutionary agency in the human species?

If every individual had the same number of descendants, whatever that number, there would be no selection. As emphasized earlier, selection depends on the differential contribution of different individuals—that is, on *variability* in fitness. The appropriate measure of this variability is what I shall call the "Index of Opportunity for Selection." This index shows the rate at which the genetic composition of the population would change if all the survival and reproductive differences were directly reflected in changes in gene frequencies. For the statistically minded, this index is the square of the coefficient of variability in the number of progeny per parent.[4]

It is revealing to divide the index into two components, one related to deaths, the other to births. The index of opportunity for selection by death has greatly decreased in the last century, as would be expected from the falling death rate. If the mortality between birth and the average age of reproduction is 50 percent, then the index is 1.00, if the death rate is 10 percent, it is 0.11. These two death rates correspond roughly to those of the late nineteenth century and the recent past, so that in two generations the index of selection by death has dropped to about one-tenth of its former value.

Clearly, the low death rate has reduced the opportunity for selection by death. Whether the actual genetical selection has been as drastically reduced is another question. In earlier times, most deaths resulted from infectious diseases, and it is likely that not many deaths were appreciably influenced by the individual's genotype. Today, a much larger fraction of all pre-adult deaths occur from recognizably genetic causes. It is probably true, therefore, that the amount of genetically effective selection by death has not been as drastically reduced as the drop in the index would suggest. It is nevertheless true that the amount of opportunity for changes in genes because of differential mortality is greatly reduced.

During this same period, on the other hand, the index of selection because of differential fertility has actually risen in many technologically advanced countries. The data in Table 1 show the values for several selected populations. The pattern is consistent, striking, and perhaps surprising. With the fall in the birth rate, the index becomes greater rather than less. The highly fertile populations are uniformly fertile, whereas the changing pattern of birth rates has somehow produced more variability in the number of children. It may well be that very recent changes in the United States may have reversed this change somewhat, as contraceptive practices have spread more uniformly through the population; but the general trend is very clear. Just as the decrease in the index of selection by death does not mean a corresponding decrease in genetically selective deaths, an increase in the index of selection by birth does not imply a necessary increase in genetic change. Many factors that determine the size of families in a population in which this is largely a voluntary decision are not genetically determined.

The statement made in the above paragraph that recent trends in the United States are the reverse of the long-time trend can be documented. The reversal is more striking than I. had expected. Norman Ryder has kindly called my attention to some newer data (reported by him in *Demographic and Economic Change in Developed Countries*, Princeton University Press, 1960, page 125). In the cohort of women reaching age 45-49 in 1960 the mean has risen

TABLE 1.   *Index of Opportunity for Selection because of Differences in Fertility in Various Populations.*

POPULATION	MEAN NUMBER OF CHILDREN	INDEX
Rural Quebec	9.9	.20
Hutterite	9.0	.17
Gold Coast, 1945	6.5	.23
New South Wales, 1898–1902	6.2	.42
United States, born 1839	5.5	.23
United States, born 1866	3.0	.64
United States, aged 45–49 in 1910	3.9	.78
United States, aged 45–49 in 1950	2.3	1.14
Ramah Navaho Indians	2.1	1.57

*The figures are based on the total numbers of children born to women who had survived to the end of the reproductive period. For the sources of these data, see Crow, James F., "Population Genetics: Selection" in *Methodology in Human Genetics*, Walter J. Burdette (ed.) (Holden-Day, Inc., San Francisco, 1962) pp. 53–75.

to 2.6 and the index has dropped to .68; in the cohort one decade later, although the families are not all completed, the mean is over 3 and the index is less than .5. So it appears that recent trends toward uniformity of family size along with a slight increase in the average have reduced the index to the level of much earlier times.

The important conclusion is this: the amount of differential reproduction that now exists, a differential of which we are hardly conscious and which we do not ordinarily regard as a social burden, would, if applied to a highly heritable trait, be such as to make possible a rapid change in that trait. The loss of opportunity for selection because of a lower death rate is approximately compensated for by a greater opportunity, one that is inherent in the pattern of birth rates.

Prenatal Mortality

Although most prenatal mortality is very early and is therefore not a large cause of human misery, it is probably a major factor in selection for some human genes. In man, the total embryonic death rate is unknown, since there is no accurate measure of the number of conceptions; but in cattle, sheep, mice, swine, and rabbits, it averages some 30 to 40 percent. It now appears likely that two factors, not previously thought important, are substantial contributors to this death rate.

One factor is chromosome abnormalities. The disease of mongolism has been found to depend on the presence in triplicate (rather than duplicate) of one of the small chromosomes, so that there are 47 chromosomes instead of the regular 46. This irregularity occurs with a frequency of about one in 700 births. The corresponding deficiency type with only one chromosome is probably more common, if we can judge from data on Drosophila, and it probably leads to embryonic death. Aberrations because of similar errors on the part of three other chromosomes have recently been discovered. The remaining chromosomes presumably make mistakes, too, and probably most of these result in embryonic death, for the cases so far discovered, despite their being attributable to some of the smallest chromosomes, are grossly abnormal children. If we consider the large number of chromosomes and the various kinds of errors and rearrangements that are possible, it is likely that these chromosomal abnormalities are a substantial cause of embryonic mortality.

The other newly realized factor in embryonic death is maternal-foetal incompatibility. Apparently, an embryo of blood group A or

B with a group O mother has a risk of some 10 percent of dying as an embryo, presumably from antigen-antibody reactions between embryo and mother. On the other hand, in combinations in which no such incompatibilities exist, the group O embryos, and presumably the other homozygous types, are found in deficient numbers at birth and therefore must have died as embryos. Altogether, it has been estimated that about 6 percent of all fertilized eggs die before birth owing to the effects of this single gene locus. If this analysis is correct, the ABO blood-group genes are the largest known single cause of genetic mortality.

If the other blood group factors (MNS, Rh, Kell, Lewis, and several others) have effects of comparable magnitude, then these few genes must account for a substantial part, perhaps a majority, of all embryonic deaths. Nothing is known about most of the other genetic polymorphisms, such as different types of serum proteins. Perhaps they too are maintained by differential embryonic death.

We should not conclude that all embryonic mortality is owing to blood-group genes and to chromosome aberrations. In cattle, swine, and guinea pigs, there is a definite rise in embryonic mortality when the parents are consanguineous. Such an association of embryonic death with inbreeding shows that at least some such deaths must be attributable to recessive genes, and presumably the human organism is the same in this respect. Finally, it is clear that not all embryonic death is because of the embryo's genotype. There is a marked increase in embryonic death in swine and guinea pigs when the *mother* is inbred. Thus, embryonic survival depends to a large extent on the mother's health and vigor, which in turn depends on her genes and her environment. I know of no information that would indicate any striking change in the pattern of embryonic deaths in recent years. This would seem to be the one part of the picture of human natural selection that has not changed radically.

Postnatal Death

The spectacular drop in postnatal death rates has been in the main because of a greater control over infectious diseases. One after another of the epidemic diseases have been eliminated as major causes of death, either by prevention or cures. Haldane has argued that for the past several thousand years the major selective factor in human survival has been resistance to disease. As man changed from a nomadic hunting life to one of more densely populated agricultural and manufacturing communities, the danger of death from wild animals became less, while the danger from communicable disease must have increased.

Today these diseases have virtually disappeared from much of the world. Moreover, this change, when measured against the long years of man's history, has been virtually instantaneous. This means that whatever genetic mechanisms of resistance to disease were developed during our thousands of generations of contact with the diseases, these mechanisms are still with us. Resistance to disease in part depends on general health and vigor, and to this extent the genes selected for disease resistance in the past are still valuable. But Haldane has suggested that resistance to infectious diseases in many cases involves highly specific mechanisms that are of no use in other contexts and may in fact be harmful.

An example is the sickle-cell anemia gene (common in Africa), because in some manner it confers a measure of resistance to one type of malaria. Despite the fact that a double dose of the gene causes a severe anemia that would nearly always be fatal in a rigorous environment, the gene is retained because in a single dose it leads to increased malaria resistance. Today many populations, well on the way to freedom from malaria, thanks to modern sanitation and insecticides, still carry a gene which still exacts its price in anemia deaths with no longer any compensating benefit from malaria resistance. There is the possibility that several genes whose present function is obscure are relics of former disease resistance mechanisms in which they were some way involved, or were selected for other less obvious reasons that are no longer relevant.

The Effect of a Changed Environment

In the history of most evolving species a change in the environment is almost always bad. The reason is that, through natural selection in the past, the organism has acquired a set of genes that are well adapted to this particular environment. A change in the environment is almost certain to necessitate some gene replacements. Thus, much of evolution is spent keeping up with what, from the standpoint of any one organism, is a steadily deteriorating environment, the most serious and rapidly changing aspect of which is the improvement of competing species through their own evolution. Man, however, is unique in that most changes in the environment are of his own doing. Therefore, the environment instead of deteriorating is getting better, at least for most genotypes. Consider, for example, the precipitous drop in childhood death rate, with only a slight compensatory rise in adult death from such diseases as cancer.

I suspect that in the majority of cases a changed environment ameliorates rather than obliterates the harmful effect of a mutant gene. A gene that is harmful in one environment is usually so in others as well, though not necessarily to the same extent. For example, the science of blood transfusion has decreased the severity of hemophilia but has by no means rendered it innocuous. Insulin has greatly helped to control diabetes, but the insulin-treated diabetic would be still better off if he had not had the disease at all.

If the effect of an environmental improvement is to lessen rather than remove completely the harm caused by a gene, the effect is one of postponement rather than prevention of the harmful effect. Consider a lethal mutant gene that causes the death of its bearer. Suppose that a new drug reduces the probability of death to 10 percent. The gene will now persist in the population for an average of ten generations before it is eliminated from the population. By a system of mutation cost-accounting, in which ten persons exposed to a one-in-ten risk of death are equal to one person with a certainty of death, the drug has not helped except by postponement.

As human beings, we are primarily interested, not in the effect of a gene on fitness *per se*, but in its associated effects on health, happiness, intelligence, and other aspects of human well-being. From the standpoint of long-range human welfare, the most beneficial kind of environmental advance is one that reduces the amount of suffering and unhappiness caused by a mutant gene by a greater degree than the increase in fitness. On the other hand, an environmental change that, for example, increases the fertility of persons with a severe or painful disease without a corresponding decrease in the amount of suffering caused by the disease will in the long run cause an increase in human misery.

Another consideration that must inevitably enter into any such discussion as this is the cost of the environmental improvement. For it must be remembered that any such improvement must be a permanent one, continued from this time on. No one need regret the inability of the human body to manufacture some of our needed vitamins; they are cheap and easily available in the food supply. Nor is a genetically conditioned susceptibility to smallpox any great problem. There is no reason to think that this disease will not remain under effective and relatively cheap and simple environmental control.

On the other hand, a person who has a genetic defect that is corrected only by expensive surgery or by repeated blood transfusions throughout a lifetime might well consider having a smaller number of children than he otherwise would, so that this cost, measured either in economic hardship or human suffering and frustration, might be correspondingly less to the next generation. Furthermore, a genetic defect may be more costly to others than the affected person—his family, his community, society as a whole—if, for example, he requires institutional care.

Mutation

So much has been written recently on this subject that any interested person can find a number of articles that are authoritative or easy to read, and in some cases both. I shall be content with only a few remarks. Many abnormal genes owe their frequency in the population to the "pressure" of recurrent mutation. In each generation new mutants arise, to be eliminated later, often very inefficiently, by natural selection. Eventually, these processes will come to balance, though in man it is likely that the conditions determining the balance are changing so fast that the population never has time to reach an equilibrium.

It is clear that under this circumstance the harmful effect of mutation is proportional to the number of new mutants that arise. In fact, if the metric chosen is simply Darwinian fitness, the harm done to the population is exactly equal to the total mutation rate, as was first shown by Haldane and then independently by H. J. Muller.[5] A major problem for future research is how the effect can be measured in more tangible terms of human happiness or satisfaction. If the harmful genes are maintained by a balance between opposing selective forces, the effect of an increase in the mutation rate is no longer easily measured, even in units of Darwinian fitness; but the direction of the effect is the same, though less. Despite disagreement in details among geneticists, the conclusion that an increased mutation rate is harmful is universally accepted.

I would maintain that the ideal mutation rate for the human population, now and in the near future, is zero. It might be argued that mutation is needed for the maintenance of genetic variability for future evolution, and ultimately this is true; but for the time being and a very long time in the future, the reservoir of existing genes, which are to some extent pretested by the very fact of their continued existence, can supply any variability that man needs for his evolution. If mutation were to stop entirely, we should probably not know it for thousands of years, except by a reduced frequency of such diseases as hemophilia and muscular dystrophy. Meanwhile, it is clear that the present rate is too high for our immediate welfare, and anything that can be done to decrease it, or at least keep it from increasing, is to the good. This brings up the question of the radiation hazard. There is reason to believe that the present levels of radiation from natural sources, medical and dental uses, and from the military and industrial uses of nuclear energy are probably responsible for only a minority of human mutations—though we must agree that the evidence is largely circumstantial and from experimental animals. Certainly, the amounts of radiation should be reduced whenever possible. But I should like to urge that more attention be given to possible chemical mutagens. In our complex chemical society, it is quite possible that some widely used compounds are highly mutagenic. And of course, should a way be found to lower the "spontaneous" rate, so much the better.

In summary, there is enough genetic variability for man's evolution in the foreseeable future without the introduction of new mutations. Surely, a combination of genes and environment that admits of a range of physique from pigmies to giants, of mental abilities from an idiot to Shakespeare, Newton, and Mozart, and of ethical standards from Himmler to Schweitzer provides as wide a range of variability as we could need—although one recalls Haldane's remark that, if we want a race of angels, we would have to obtain new mutations, both for the wings and for the moral excellence.

I should point out that the existing range of variability in a population does not limit the future possibilities that might arise by a recombination and selection of existing genes. If, for example, Mozart's constitution had contained the maximum concentration of genes favoring musical genius of anyone yet known, this does not by any means imply that his was the best genotype that could have been constructed from the pool of genes available in a large population.

Population Structure

Another trend in recent human evolution has been the increasing amalgamation of previously isolated sub-populations. The increased interdependence of various geographical regions and increased ease of travel are rapidly destroying the earlier pattern of a world divided into relatively small isolates, each undergoing a separate biological and cultural evolution. In a small population, all the people are likely to be somewhat related. Therefore, this trend toward isolate-breaking has an immediately beneficial biological effect through a reduction in the amount of inbreeding. To this extent the benefits of hybrid vigor are added to whatever effects accrue from cultural amalgamation.

Whether the outbreeding effect is substantial or small is difficult to determine. Any attempt to study this is hampered by the confounding effects of environmental changes accompanying the presumed genetic effect. This is especially true for interracial marriages, for the hybrid population is likely to find itself in a social environment different from that of either parent group.

Sewall Wright has argued that for maximum evolutionary opportunity a subdivided population is best. When isolates disappear, some opportunity to test different gene combinations and (probably more important) to develop unique cultures is lost. Yet the steady breaking-down of isolates is going on, and the trend is likely to continue. I would suggest that some of the immediate genetic effects (for example, less inbreeding) are beneficial, and that the genetic variability will be conserved about as well either way. To me, the social consequences of the disappearance of some cultures is more serious. I believe that in the long run the best solution is not to oppose cultural and genetic fusions, but to work for a society which tolerates the greatest amount of individuality, whether this is genetic or acquired.

Birth Selection Instead of Death Selection

As mentioned earlier, the deleterious effects of many (I think most) mutant genes are diluted and postponed by an improved environment, rather than obliterated. Despite the fact that many of the deaths in the past were accidental or caused by diseases that are not now relevant, some of them were genetically selective in eliminating mutants that otherwise would now be causing harm. To the extent that these deaths no longer occur or are reduced in number, the genetic makeup of the population is deteriorating. We may not be conscious of this, for the environment is improving too rapidly, but the damage is still there to be reckoned with by any society that is conscious of its genetic future. The question is: can we use birth selection in an effective and socially acceptable way to compensate for decreased death selection?

To suggest to a person whose hereditary disease has been cured or repaired that he have no children at all may be (except for severe and highly heritable conditions) an undue imposition. But to reduce the number by half perhaps would make little difference to his happiness yet effect a substantial genetic change, if the practice were widespread. The reduction of future human misery by the detection of normal persons who carry hidden harmful genes is effective for some diseases and can become more so as knowledge increases. To prevent the reproduction of all persons with genetic feeble-mindedness (phenylketonuria) would change the incidence of disease less than 0.5 percent in the next generation. But if each heterozygous carrier had only half as many children as he would otherwise have, or if sperm from another person were used when the husband is a carrier, this would reduce the abnormal-gene frequency by 50 percent, and the disease incidence for the next generation would be greatly reduced.

There is a limit to this possibility, though. Probably we each carry some half-dozen detectably harmful genes. Eventually, a system would be required by which those persons who knew they had an exceptionally large number of disease-producing genes would voluntarily reduce the number of children they produced.

It is generally agreed that such diseases as muscular dystrophy, hemophilia, and phenylketonuria should be controlled. Most people would agree that parents who are likely to have children with such traits should be informed. Hereditary counseling is surely in order, and is already widely accepted. I hope that society will revise its notions about therapeutic abortion and artificial insemination, wherever genetic diseases are involved.

On the other hand, society is not agreed, nor is it likely to agree in the near future, about what if anything is to be done about such quantitative, usually multigenic traits as intelligence. A few words are in order about the extent to which such changes could be made, if there were a conscious selection of some sort. The history of animal breeding has shown that substantial changes can be made by selection for quantitative traits when these have not been strongly selected in the past. The ability of dog breeders to produce bizarre forms is apparent to everyone. It is also striking that the milk production of an average cow now is far better than the best some years ago. On the other hand, selection for increased viability and fertility in livestock has been considerably less successful.

This probably means that it would be easier, by selection, to change the intellectual or other aptitudes of the population than to change the incidence of disabling diseases or sterility. This is not to say that there has not been some selection for intelligence in the past, but it has surely been much less intense than that for fertility, for example.

Since society owes so much to a small minority of intellectual leaders, a change in the proportion of gifted children would probably confer a much larger benefit on society than would a corresponding increase in the population average. These potential leaders would probably produce enough change in cultural and other environmental influences to be worth considerably more than the contribution of their genotypes to the genetic average. It has frequently been suggested that when artificial insemination is used, because of sterility or genetic disease in the husband, the donors might be selected from men of outstanding intellectual or artistic achievement. Were this widely practiced, I believe that the occasionally highly gifted children, though probably a small proportion of all the children produced, might still be a most important addition to society.

It is important to realize that even a very intense selection may make only very slow changes in the gene makeup of the population, since many of the traits of greatest importance have a low heritability. Similarly, any dysgenic effects of an accumulation of mutations because of medical advances or an excessive reproductivity of the genetically less well endowed, also act very slowly. Therefore, while we need not rush into hasty or ill-considered solutions, it is time to start discussing the problem. We must remember that natural selection has been cruel, blundering, inefficient, and lacking in foresight. It has no criterion of excellence except the capacity to leave descendants. It is indifferent as to whether living is a rich and beautiful experience or one of total misery. Post reproductive ages are of no consequence, except in so far as older parents and grandparents aid in the survival of the young.

Selection under individual human control, on the other hand, could be greatly different. Its means are birth selection, not death selection. It can make use of scientific knowledge such as biochemical tests of carriers of harmful genes, or genetic knowledge of relatives. It can have foresight. It can have criteria of health, intelligence, or happiness—not just survival and fertility. And it can make use of the various scientific and technological advances (sperm storage, egg transplant, and other more distant prospects) as they are discovered.

We must remember also that the decision is not as to whether man should influence his own evolution. He is already doing this by his revolutionary changes in the environment, by medical advances, by the invention of contraceptives. The issue is not *whether* he is influencing his evolution, but in what direction.

References and Notes

[1] J B. S. HALDANE, "Parental and Fraternal Correlations in Fitness," *Annals of Eugenics*, 1949, *14:* 288.

[2] For discussions of this concept, see D. S. Falconer, *Introduction to Quantitative Genetics* (London: Oliver and Boyd, 1960); and I. M. Lerner, *The Genetic Basis of Selection* (New York: Wiley, 1958).

[3] *Statistical Bulletin* of the Metropolitan Life Insurance Company, March 1960.

[4] This was originally called the "Index of Total Selection," but I gladly accept G. G. Simpson's suggestion that it be called the "Index of Opportunity for Selection." The Index is defined as the variance of the number of offspring per individual divided by the square of the mean number. The children are counted at the same age as the parents, and those who die before the reproductive age are counted as leaving zero descendants. For example, if half the persons have 3 children and half have 1, the mean number is 2, the variance is 1, and the index is ¼. If half have 6 and half have 2, the mean is 4, and the index is the same, ¼, as it should be, for these two populations have the same evolutionary consequences except for total numbers. For a derivation, justification, and discussion of this index see J. F. Crow, "Some Possibilities for Measuring Selection Intensities in Man," *Human Biology*, 1958, *30:* 1–13.

[5] H. J. MULLER, "Our Load of Mutations," *American Journal of Human Genetics*, 1950, *2:* 111.

Cultural Determinants in Natural Selection*

FRANK B. LIVINGSTONE
JAMES N. SPUHLER

(*Editor's Note*) Man has an unusual capacity to cope with environmental changes without becoming highly specialized genetically. Evidently he is a creature who compensates for a lack of specialization with an ability to modify his behavior through learning. Very little is known about the limits of the genetic flexibility which underlie this capacity. Even if this flexibility turns out to be very extensive, it would not mean that man is therefore unaffected by natural selection. In fact, the learning capacity itself becomes a factor in the operation of selection through a complex feedback. Willful alterations in the environment create new selection pressures which may or may not run counter to the cultural value which prompted the original willful change. The physical anthropologist is particularly interested in the interaction that takes place between man's two kinds of heredity: genetic and cultural. This interest often leads the investigator into the often vacant middle ground between the biological and the social sciences. This article by Livingstone and Spuhler indicates some of the thinking and research that has been carried out from that middle vantage point.

THE basic fact of natural selection is that some individuals within a species leave more descendants than others. The basic fact of cultural behaviour is that learning is mediated by symbols. Although a distinction between natural and artificial selection is useful in some areas of applied population genetics, it is not particularly helpful in a discussion of the cultural determinants of selection in man. Culture

*From *International Social Science Journal*, vol. XVII, 1965, pages 118–120. By permission of the authors and the publisher.

is a natural phenomenon, a biological adaptation of the hominids with a non-genetic mode of inheritance depending on symbolic communication rather than fusion of gametes. It has greatly supplemented hominid genic evolution.

Selection within a breeding population is defined to include exhaustively all systematic modes of change in gene frequencies which do not involve mutation, gene flow, or genetic drift. Selection includes the effects of differential rates of mortality, mating, fecundity, fertility, and emigration. By definition it seems clear (though not yet adequately measured over a wide variety of cases) that cultural factors may influence selection pressures by contributing differentially to the passage of individuals through the life cycle, for example, by variable effects on nutrition, sanitation, preventive, palliative and curative medicine, age of sexual maturity, duration of the fertile period, marriage and divorce rates, spacing of births, and emigration.

The concept of fitness is used in population genetics to measure selection pressures. Fitness is the capacity to survive and to leave descendants and it is always measured retrospectively. The simplest measure of fitness of an individual is the mean number of children in a given category from parents in that category, both being counted, at the same point in the life cycle, usually at birth.

Other possible concepts of fitness, including representation by descendants in remote periods, individual adaptability versus population adaptedness, ideas on what 'ought to' rather than what in fact does survive and reproduce are not widely used in population genetics because they are not amenable to quantitative treatment and do not have predictive value.

Where strict monogamy is not the practice, it may be convenient to measure fitness by counting the number of daughters per mother. Separate measures of fitness are necessary where the effect of a gene on fitness differs by sex: for example, in populations where males are hunters and females gatherers, the selective disadvantage of genes for defective colour perception may be greater in males than in females. Since there is overlapping of generations and variable ages of reproduction in human populations often it is better to measure fitness by integral equations leading to instantaneous rates of increase.

The working of selection may be examined at the level of the individual, the phenotype, the genotype, and the gene. Using demographic data and an index devised by Crow, Spuhler showed the range of maximum potential rate of change by selection (where zero inicates no change) is greater in ten tribal populations (0.6-3.7) than in ten State populations (0.4-1.6), or in ten national populations

(0.8-1.7). In these thirty populations the mortality component goes down, and the fertility component up, with increasing complexity of culture as measured by economic criteria, the mortality being the smaller component in 5 of 10 tribal, 8 of 10 State, and 9 of 10 national populations. Although there may be some decline, almost as much selection may be occurring in industrial societies as in hunters and gatherers.

Brues speculated on the relations between body-build phenotypes and the efficiency of food-getting activities in different cultures. She suggests large body size and muscle mass would be favoured selectively in cultures using hand-held bludgeoning weapons for hunting, a more linear build in cultures using the spear, and wide shoulders, short limb segments with relatively short and thick muscles in those using the bow and arrow. The work of the early agriculturalists is assumed to favour a medium body build, heavily muscled and broad in hip and shoulder. It is highly desirable that these suggestions be tested empirically.

On the level of the genotype and gene, there is evidence that culturally determined differences may alter the selection coefficients associated with the ABO blood-group genes and mating types. The best evidence comes from family studies in three Japanese communities. In communities with relatively poor economy, segregation analysis shows there is selection against heterozygotes by foetal deaths in incompatible matings, and selection in favour of heterozygotes in compatible matings. In a community with better economic conditions, these selection differentials were not detected (Hiraizumi). Although critical tests have not been carried out, it seems likely that the well-known, small-scale, patchy distribution of the genes at the ABO locus may be the result of local variation in selection pressures, as well as other modes of change in gene frequency, e.g., genetic drift.

Perhaps the best-documented case of cultural determinants of selection at the gene and genotype levels concerns the distribution and frequency of the genes for haemoglobins A and S in the native populations of West Africa (Livingstone). Regarding the haemoglobin AS locus the fitness of individuals is a function of their genotype, the endemicity of *falciparum* malaria, and the state of medical care. With holoendemic malaria and poor medical care the fitness of the three genotypes is of the order: AA = 0.84, AS = 1, SS = 0. With better medical care the fitness of SS may become 0.30 or higher. In the absence of malaria, the fitness of AA and AS are both approximately unity. Livingstone has traced the genesis of this complex relationship between man, mosquito, and protozoan as a sequel to the introduction of iron tools for clearing the tropical forest, the cultivation of food plants giving high yields of calories on tropical soils, and the formation of settled agricultural communities which provide both an ecological setting favourable to *Anopheles gambiae* and a human population higher in density than that of the hunters and gatherers who were earlier occupants of the region.

Culture may be considered as a special kind of learned behaviour. Episodes of evolutionary change in all animal populations are often initiated by changes in learned behaviour (Waddington). With a change in some environmental factor, an animal population learns to behave differently: it changes its way of life or its ecological niche. Then this changed way of life may produce changes in mortality and fertility rates which in turn may lead to changes in the fitness of various genotypes. Changes in selection pressures thus may result in changes in gene frequencies. In such cases the change in learned behaviour is a principal reason for the animal population's survival of the environmental change. From this point of view, the Negro populations did not survive in West Africa because of the high frequency of the haemoglobin S gene; rather some Negro populations have high frequencies of the S gene because they learned to live and to survive in tropical West Africa. Culture, and learned behaviour in general, is a principal cause of hominid evolution.

Population Genetics
of the A-B-O Blood Groups*

ALICE M. BRUES

(*Editor's Note*) If the common blood groups turned out
to be less than what was hoped for as population
markers their value as evidence for the operation of
evolution is still only partially realized. For example,
there are good indications from family data that in the
A-B-O system, selection is operating against the A-O
heterozygotes under certain circumstances. Yet the gene
frequencies for A or O which would eventually result
as a consequence of this selection do not exist in the
world's populations that have been tested. This suggests
that a counter pressure is selecting for the heterozygote
although there is no evidence for this.

The point of such a· demonstration for the A-B-O
system is that the existence and maintenance of polymorphisms in human populations is a major unsolved
problem. While we can be theoretically confident that
the great variation in blood group allele frequencies
found in man has come about through the action of
evolutionary forces, particularly natural selection, the
actual identification of the specific responsible mechanisms has seldom been successful.

FOR a long time following the discovery of the A-B-O- blood group
system, it was believed that these genes were quite neutral in
respect to the survival of their bearers. The blood types, in fact, were
welcomed by anthropologists as representing traits which could be
considered immune to natural selection, so that gene frequencies once
established in a population would remain constant for the centuries,
and afford reliable means for assessing the relationships and ancient

*From *Journal of the Oklahoma State Medical Association*, vol. 56, 1963,
pages 225–230. By permission of the author and the publisher.

migrations of various peoples of the world. Several factors contributed to this belief, not the least being the facts that all three of the blood types are found in the great apes, no species having less than two of them, indicating that blood group diversity is an ancient heritage among the Hominoidea; and that although some racial and regional differences in gene frequencies are present in modern man, the divergence is limited. The evidence appeared to be that blood group frequencies changed only with monolithic slowness, if at all.

This comfortable hypothesis became untenable in 1947, when Waterhouse and Hogben clearly demonstrated that there were maternal-fetal incompatibility reactions involving the A-B-O blood group system. In their original paper they found a deficiency of about 25 percent in the number of A children born to O mothers, as compared with the number expected. Numerous later investigations have confirmed this finding. This discovery might at first glance appear to be only a minor exception to the theory that the blood groups were immune to natural selection. However, it immediately necessitated recasting our entire concept of the manner in which blood group gene frequencies are maintained at relatively stable levels. In order to understand this it is necessary to review certain basic theorems of population genetics as they apply to situations in which natural selection is taking place.

The simplest sort of natural selection is that in which some particular gene always confers some sort of biological advantage, by way either of enhanced survival, or of greater fertility on its possessor. The frequency of such a gene will tend to increase from generation to generation, depending on the magnitude of the advantage conferred and the mode of manifestation of the gene itself. (The term dominance is to be avoided in this connection since it pertains properly to our ability to distinguish homozygous from heterozygous genotypes by means readily available to us. As we shall see later, genotypes which are indistinguishable by ordinary tests need not be alike in selective advantage). This simple type of selection, in which a particular gene is always "good," leads with greater or less speed to a condition where this gene has replaced all its alleles except insofar as they are meagerly restored by mutation. Only rarely would we expect to encounter such a phenomenon in progess; for the most part we see only the end results—prevalence of genes which we now consider "normal" though at one time they were innovations.

More complex types of selection depend on gene interaction. The possibilities of interaction of non-allelic genes are of course nearly infinite: at present we will speak only of an interaction of allelic genes which transcends an additive effect; *i.e.* where the heterozygous individual who has one each of two allelic genes is either more or less fit than *either* homozygote. Let us first dispose of a possibility of which few cases are known: that in which the heterozygote is discriminated *against* by natural selection. In such cases there is a constant loss of heterozygous individuals from the population, either overtly, by premature death, or covertly, by reduction of fertility. Since loss of a heterozygote removes from the gene pool of the population one of each allele concerned, that allele which is originally the least common will be eventually eliminated. There will be a sort of equilibrium point at the 50-50 gene frequency, where in theory the loss of each heterozygote leaves the population still 50-50. However, this is a knife-edge equilibrium, for as soon as a chance deviation in one direction or the other occurs, the downhill course will be continued till one gene is eliminated. More importantly, it would be only under very extraordinary circumstances that such an equilibrium could arise in the first place. If either one of the genes appeared in a population in which the other was established, it would, since it was comparatively rare, nearly always be combined with the established gene in a heterozygous genotype. It would, in that combination, be deleterious and would tend to be eliminated. Thus the central equilibrium point would not be attainable by natural processes except a precisely balanced hybridization. The situation discovered by Waterhouse and Hogben is a case basically of this type, since it involves elimination of a heterozygote (OA) although it has certain special features which will be discussed later.

Much commoner, probably far commoner than we have specific knowledge of, is the sort of situation in which the heterozygote formed by the combination of two allelic genes is *superior* to the homozygotes in survival value. Such situations, undoubtedly including many cases in which we have no specific means of identifying either gene, appear to underlie the phenomenon known as heterosis or hybrid vigor, which was known and even investigated more or less systematically long before the inception of anything resembling modern genetics and which through its agricultural applications is familiar now to many persons whose knowledge of genetics is limited. Heterosis in population genetics leads to the situation known as balanced polymorphism, by which a population which contains more than one of the possible alleles at a given locus, tends to remain in this heterozygous state. Now the commoner a gene is within a population, the higher is the ratio of its homozygous appearances to that of its heterozygous appearances. Consequently, when the gene frequencies of the population start to diverge from the optimum percentage level, the gene which is becoming too common for best advantage finds itself discriminated against and the one which is becoming rare becomes more desirable than before. Thus the wandering population is gently pushed back to its balanced condition. If the selective values of two homozygous genotypes are the same, the system will balance with the genes 50-50; however, if they are different there will be a balance at some other level. Most workers now believe that some such mechanism underlies nearly all cases where populations remain for considerable lengths of time in a continuing heterozygous condition with respect to two or more allelic genes. This hypothesis seems particularly called for in instances where populations are of relatively small size, since random sampling from generation to generation eventually tends to eliminate heterozygosity in a purely statistical manner if some compensating mechanism is not present.

We may now examine in more detail the problems raised by Waterhouse and Hogben's discovery and see why it had such a disruptive effect on our concepts of the nonfunctional nature of the blood groups. As soon as the fact of incompatibility risk of the AO fetus in the OO mother was accepted, we were presented with a case of the rather rare type of selection against the heterozygote. However, this case presents some special features. Normally we assume that adverse selection acts by eliminating a certain percentage (over and above what we consider normal or average attrition from conception on) of a particular genotype within a certain population. In this case there is an added specification that this shall occur only if the mother has a particular genotype. Note that while we often speak of the "incompatibility of A fetus to O mother," it means specifically "of OA fetus . . ." since an O mother cannot have an AA child. So the extent of the risk to OA individuals depends actually on how many of them have mothers who lack the A gene. (For the moment, to avoid excessive complications, we are assuming that our population —let's say they are full-blood Indians—lacks the B gene altogether.) Now half of all mothers of OA children have the A gene since there is a 50 per cent chance that the child's A gene is his maternal gene. However, if this particular child received the A gene from his father and the O gene from his mother, the mother's other gene is an unknown quantity. If it happens to be A, no incompatibility exists. So the "safe" cases from the point of view of OA fetus are 0.5 plus a quantity representing 0.5 times the percentage of A genes in the population. If the A gene is very common, incompatibility almost never will occur. If the A gene is very rare, nearly all of the 50 percent cases in which the A gene came from the father rather than the mother, will present an incompatibility situation.

The result of all this is that incompatibility of OA fetus to O mother will strike the OA zygotes with a frequency varying from a maximum at very low population percentages of the A gene, to exceedingly low rates where the A gene is nearly universal. The basic premise of anti-heterozygote selection, however, still holds that it affects most seriously and tends to deplete whichever is the rarest of the two genes. The net effect of the incompatibility reaction, supposing that no other selective differentials exist between the various genotypes, is to produce a pattern in which a precarious equilibrium would exist at the gene frequency 0.5 A, 0.5 O. Any group which began to diverge from this point (and any group, no matter how large, would eventually jog loose) would, if it diverged in the direction of more O, skid downward at an accelerating rate towards 100 percent O. If it diverged in the direction of more A, it would move upwards at a decelerating rate and finally reach a point where the last remaining O genes, in a population in which incompatibility could almost never occur, would likely be lost at last by mere chance processes. In either case the process becomes asymptomatic as the rarer gene disappears. If this is the situation we would expect it to be most unusual for any population to be found at the 50 percent level or near it, for that matter anywhere between 50 percent and 100 percent O, unless it had recently been formed by the mixture of other groups and had not had time to "settle down." Most groups, after a number of generations of such selection, would either have lost A altogether or gravitated to a level of close to 100 percent A. Now this could hardly be more different from what we actually find when we examine data on various world populations, of which we will be principally interested right now in the aboriginal peoples of America and Australia who did not have the B gene. A considerable number of these groups have indeed stabilized at 100 percent O; however, the remainder are scattered out over a range extending up to 55 percent A, the highest recorded A in the world. None are in the nearly or entirely A range which would be one of the areas stable under the incompatibility effect. Many, however, are in the intermediate range of frequencies which the incompatibility effect would quickly disrupt.

We have the paradox then of known incompatibility reactions between the A and O genes, producing a form of antiheterozygote selection, while the world distribution of frequencies somewhat more resembles the pattern we would expect from pro-heterozygote selection. In order to bring sense into this picture, we begin to look for some selective advantage of the heterozygotes, in respect to fertility or youthful survival, which would be sufficient to counteract the adverse effects of incompatibility. It is important to note that what we need to find is something favoring the heterozygote; not, as has frequently been stated, something to "compensate for loss of A." It is true that if we think in terms of a population like our own, which has an A frequency between 20 and 30 percent, the problem in this particular range does appear to be "loss of A" through incompatibility, because A is the less common gene than O and therefore more readily hurt by antiheterozygote selection. However, in any population which once exceeded 50 percent A, as do some North American Indian ones at the present time, the incompatibility problem would be "loss of O." As we shall see later, thinking of blood group selection as a property of the gene rather than as a function of the heterozygous condition is a hazard to successful investigation.

The problem is of course not as simple as outlined above, since the presence of the third gene B in most large populations of the world complicates the relations considerably. If the only result of incompatibility were an internecine war between O and A, the B gene would finally take over, unless it were subject to some retarding effects also. This now appears to be the case for not only was OB soon found to be lost in matings involving O mothers, but extensive work by Matsunaga and his associates has shown that incompatibility reactions of about the same magnitude take place between AO fetus and B or AB mother and between BO fetus and A or AB mother.

Investigation of all possible forms of selection in the ABO system has been very active in the last decade and has resulted in what appears to be somewhat chaotic results. The basic values for the incompatibility reactions seems to be well established as a roughly 20 percent risk to all fetuses exposed to one of the incompatibility situations. The possible ways in which other selective effects may be manifested and the ways in which evidence of them has been sought are varied. Since rather large numbers of cases are necessary to establish statistical significance, it has been necessary in many cases to resort to data which were originally assembled for other purposes, and not in a way ideal for studying selection. The incompatibility situation is a special form of selection in that it is brought about in a way not depending on the genotype of the individual affected alone, but by reaction to a particular factor in the environment, namely the genotype of the mother. Selection favoring or disfavoring a particular genotype may of course be dependent on other environmental factors which may vary from time to time or from place to place. No relation involving strictly geographical environment and differential selection has been demonstrated though it would be a handy way of accounting for racial differences in blood group distribution. One ambitious work recently published has attempted to explain regional differences on the basis of a differential susceptibility of individuals of various blood types to plague, smallpox and syphilis and the known or supposed world histories of these diseases (Vogel, et al, 1960). More solid data have been derived from actual study of the incidence of various disease entities in persons of different blood groups. It seems fairly well established on the basis of numerous studies, in some cases carried on in different parts of the world or among different races (Buckwalter, 1957), that peptic ulcer is more common in persons of group O, gastric carcinoma, pernicious anemia and diabetes mellitus in persons of group A (Roberts, 1959). But this represents a slender selection from the total studies published on the subject, many of which seem mutually contradictory. A constant hazard in these investigations is the difficulty of obtaining adequate control series since a slight unsuspected bias in the choice of controls may vitiate the study. A more hidden difficulty which many of the workers seem somewhat unaware of is the fact that the serologically established types A and B are combinations of AA and AO, and BB and BO genotypes respectively. Since the maintenance of polymorphism demands that heterozygotes shall have different and opposite overall selection coefficients from homozygotes, this leaves the data seriously confounded. Likewise by poor fortune the disease entities so far established as having some relation to blood groups are ones of comparatively late incidence in life, which would not appear to affect an individual's genetic contribution very severely.

Another semi-environmental effect which has been established is that incompatibility in the ABO sytsem has a protective effect against erythroblastosis due to Rh incompatibility (Cohen and Glass, 1959). This introduces the possibility of difference in ABO selection correlated with the genetic environment as represented by the heterozygosity of a given population in regard to Rh factors. Inconsistent results between different workers may in some cases be due to other effects of genetic environment whereby selection in the ABO types differs according to the genetic background of one or another population.

Other factors which have been investigated are differences in fertility of various genotypes (exclusive of "combination effects" such as incompatibility) and possible differences in viability of various genotypes in the embryonic and fetal periods. These investigations usually have gone hand in hand with incompatibility studies since they generally use the same data. These results again are inconsistent and sometimes controversial and not always easy to interpret even after they are established. One of the most active workers has been Matsunaga who, with his co-workers, has analyzed a large series of Japanese families. In addition to defining additional incompatibility situations, by examination of data on childlessness and abortion rates in various classes of matings, he has shown a certain amount of differential fertility; he finds in his series that A x A matings have increased fertility and that in general O fathers are relatively infertile (Matsunaga, 1956, 1959). He also showed evidence for heterozygote advantage of AB (the only genotype which can be identified as a heterozygote on the basis of serological data only). He was able to find 35 families in which both parents were AB; a somewhat easier task in Japan than in most other countries, since the B gene and AB genotype are relatively common there. The 87 children of these families were 65 percent AB rather than the expected 50 percent (Matsunaga, 1954). Though the series is small and the results perhaps exaggerated by a chance factor, it appears to be proved that in this case the AB genotype fares better prenatally than the homozygous types. Unfortunately the heterozygous AO and BO genotypes cannot be serologically distinguished from the AA's and BB's. The bulk of Matsunaga's data did not include blood groups of children, merely blood groups of parents and number of children. Chung and Morton (1961) found an excess of heterozygous children in compatible matings and therefore consider that heterosis is at work. No excess of abortion was noted in these groups, so they believe that some homozygotes AA and BB may be eliminated at very early stages.

It is doubtful that the reader is interested in a recapitulation of all the contradictory results which have been obtained in this field. Perhaps the matter may be closed by quoting Chung and Morton, whose bibliography totalled 82 titles and who concluded, "In an area fraught with many pitfalls, some of them unexpected, it would be well to regard the evidence for the effects other than incompatibility as only preliminary."

Note should be made of evidence for balanced polymorphism in the M-N blood group system. Not only are all known human populations heterozygous for M and N, but considerable evidence indicates that MN offspring are in excess over the expected frequency in heterozygous matings, indicating prenatal selection in favor of the heterozygote in the MN system (Morton and Chung, 1959). In the absence of further evidence at the present time for man, evidence for selection in blood group systems of other animals is of interest.

The most carefully studied is the blood group polymorphism in chickens investigated by Briles and his associates (1957) which involves at least 21 alleles at one of the known loci. Briles noted that even under intensive inbreeding it is difficult to obtain populations which are homozygous for any single blood group, and that in populations in which the blood group heterozygosity has been reduced there occurs both reduced hatchability of eggs and reduced viability of chicks, making the colonies difficult to maintain. This appears to indicate that in this species there is strong selection in favor of heterozygous blood group genotypes. Perhaps the great efflorescence of blood group diversity here is encouraged by the fact that the practice of laying eggs effectively removes any opportunity for disadvantageous incompatibility reactions. It might be noted also that if hatchability of the human zygote were as easily quantified as in the chicken, some of the difficulties of blood group study would be solved.

Thus the results of the studies of blood group selection are presently quite disappointing in view of the number of pages that have been published, so we find ourselves, like various reviewers before us, trying to suggest what is wrong. The necessity for large bodies of data is a rigorous one, and has resulted in limitations such as that on much of Matsunaga's work, in which the records available gave blood type of both parents but in regard to children stated only the number born. Many workers have done nobly in extracting what information they could from such not very suitable data. Of course someday large bodies of data tailored to the problem must be obtained which means much more complete family records.

Another very serious problem, one of those so basic that it is liable to be overlooked, is that we have no means of serologically distinguishing the heterozygote OA and OB from the homozygote AA and BB. The solution of the incompatibility problem would not have been so easy had it not involved a situation in which the A child was known to be OA. It would be a happy event if some immunologist were to break the iron curtain of dominance and develop a means for distinguishing heterozygote from homozygote. Lacking this, we must make what effort we can on a genetic basis. It is possible of course to infer from the theorems of population genetics what percentage of A's are AA's in a given population, without knowledge of the families of the persons involved but we cannot identify individuals. Knowledge of the families will permit some sorting, however. We know that an AA individual cannot have either an O or a B parent, or an O or a B child; correspondingly for BB's. This would make it possible to declare some A's to be OA's and sort out a more nearly pure AA series. Of course this does not tell us if an A child of A parents is OA or not and it is unlikely that we can wait around for the next generation to enlighten us. One is tempted to suspect from the number of demonstrated blood-group-influenced diseases related to the stomach that here we are dealing with an actual effect of the A substance on the tissue so that in this case A and OA are properly combined. But it is more probable that the overall effects of blood group on survival are heterotic in nature and that the evidence is likely to be degraded or lost if we sort by phenotype only. Of course, as Morton and Chung have suggested, it is possible that nearly all of the selection effects of the blood groups are prenatal and are not going to be found by studies of adult diseases. Perhaps we should consider also that the balanced polymorphism of the blood groups may owe its equilibrium in part to differential resistance to various infectious diseases which the advent of antibiotics has taken virtually out of the realm of study. In any event the problem is not likely soon to lose its interest for the clinician, the geneticist, or the anthropologist.

BIBLIOGRAPHY

BRILES, W. E., *et al.*: The B blood group system of chickens. I. Heterozygosity in closed populations. Genetics, *42:* 631–648, 1957.

BUCKWALTER, J. A., *et al.*: Ethnologic aspects of the ABO blood groups disease association. J.A.M.A. *165:* 327–329, 1957.

CHUNG, C. S. and N. E. MORTON: Selection at the ABO locus. Am. J. of Human Genetics, *13:* 9–27, 1961.

COHEN, BERNICE H. and BENTLEY GLASS: The relation of the ABO and Rh blood groups to differential reproduction. Am. J. of Human Genetics, *11:* 414–417, 1959.

MATSUNAGA, EI: Reproductive fitness of AB children from AB x AB mating. Sapporo Med. J., *6:* 165–168 1954 (English summary).

————: Selektion durch Unvertraglichkeit im ABO-Blutgruppen-system zwischen Mutter und Fetus. Blut, *2:* 118–198, 1956.

————: Selection in ABO polymorphism in Japanese populations. J. of Med. Education, *34:* 405–413, 1959.

MORTON, N. E. and C. S. CHUNG: Are the MN blood groups maintained by selection? Am. J. Human Genetics, *11:* 237–251, 1959.

ROBERTS, J. and A. FRASER: Blood groups and disease. Brit. M. J., *15:* 129–133, 1959.

VOGEL, F., *et al.*: Uber die Populationsgenetik der ABO Blutgruppen. Acta Genetica, *10:* 247–294, 1960.

WATERHOUSE, J. A. H. and L. HOGBEN: Incompatibility of mother and fetus with respect to the isoagglutinin A and its antibody. Brit. J. Soc. Med., *1:* 1–17, 1947.

8

Adaptability

Human Biological Variation as an Adaptive
Response to the Environment*

PAUL T. BAKER

(*Editor's Note*) Since the time of the Greeks it has been
considered common sense that geographically widely
separated groups of mankind are racially different because they are exposed to different environmental
stresses. But it is only recently that some investigators
have tried to determine the relevance of a given human
biological feature to a given environmental variable.
On closer examination even such an "obvious" correlation as skin color and intensity of sunlight proved difficult to explain in a scientifically acceptable fashion.
The general conviction among biologists is that traits
that vary among human populations ultimately have
adaptive significance. If no indication for selection of a
trait exists today, it is probably safe to assume that the
trait was originally established by selection. Nevertheless, the possibility remains that an adaptive response to
a given environmental stress, such as heat, may vary
from one population to the next. The result is that
different phenotypes may result by adaptation to the
same selection pressure. In addition to this "flexibility"
of response by different gene pools within the same
species, there is another kind of "flexibility." It is non-
genetic and is a characteristic of the individual organism
rather than of the population. This kind of non-genetic
response, often referred to as "adaptability" (instead of
adaptation), means that regardless of the individual's
genetic constitution he is able to survive, aided most
probably by cultural means, a wide range of environmental stresses. Man has certainly experienced new
environmental conditions during and since the Pleistocene at a far greater rate than he could have genetically
adapted to them.

*From *Eugenics Quarterly*, vol. 13, June, 1966, pages 81–91.
By permission of the author and the publisher.

These considerations, more fully discussed by Baker, have recently stimulated a series of interdisciplinary studies which have undertaken the task of delineating the processes which produce population differences in response to common stresses. The characteristic approach in these studies has been to test the functional (usually physiological) significance of a given trait by eliciting and then measuring a response from individuals under laboratory or natural conditions. Once variation within the population and differences among populations in stress response have been shown, the arduous task of determining whether genetic variation is involved begins. As Baker points out, what this piecemeal, controlled approach lacks in terms of explaining the sorting criteria the layman employs to distinguish races is compensated for by scientific clarity.

M AN, as any other animal species that still survives, is adapted to his environment. This statement only signifies that at this point in time, as measured by numbers and energy exchange, man is a successful animal on this planet with no immediate prospects of extinction. Of course, the statement implies much more, since the parameters of the physical and biological environments within which we exist are greater than for any other animal; and if we logically add that distillate of human behavior called culture to the environmental parameters, then the varieties of environment to which groups of men are adapted is truly prodigious compared to other species.

When we inquire into the sources of the great adaptability of our species, two concepts are generally evoked—culture and race. Both of these represent gross generalizations in the semantic sense and consequently represent the poorest of scientific exploratory tools.

Culture can be a useful abstraction when employed for the broad categorization of nonbiologically transmitted human information, but it can never serve as a complete explanation for any unit of human behavior inasmuch as it is biological organisms that are behaving. Thus the accumulated information on how to sew an Eskimo parka is a product of Eskimo culture, but the adaptive value of the parka in arctic cold also depends on the motor skill of the maker and the physiological responses of the wearer.

Race is an equally unsatisfactory conceptual tool. I would not disagree with Dobzhansky's contention that there exist conglomerates of morphological and genetic traits that permit a valid taxonomic subdivision of man (Dobzhansky, 1962).

Such a classification, however, has limited research use and is often badly abused when the results of a study on one small segment of a race is extrapolated to the whole group without a known basis in physiological functioning. To exemplify valid use and abuse of race as a research tool, cases from environmental physiology may be cited. It has been shown that because of more melanin in the skin of an American Negro, it absorbs more solar radiation than does white skin (Baker, 1958). Since in most classification systems "Negro" always means a high skin melanin, we may generalize that Negroes in a nude condition will absorb more heat from the sun than whites. On the other hand, to cite a possible abuse, it has been found by several investigators that the fingers of American Negro soldiers are, with all other conditions constant, "colder" in ice water than are the fingers of American white soldiers (Adams and Covino, 1958; Iampietro et al., 1959). This appears to be the result of lower warm blood circulation in the Negro hands; but since the causes of this circulatory difference are unknown and may be unrelated to the traits associated with race, it is pure speculation to say that most classificatory "Negroes" would have colder fingers in ice water. Also, since the mechanisms are unknown and no such studies have been performed on U.S. Negro females, it cannot even be stated with more than a low degree of probability that American Negro females would test lower than American white females.

From these considerations it appears to me that if we wish to understand how man has adapted to his varied environments and what role his biological variability has played in this adaptation, we must deal in specifics rather than in abstractions such as culture and race.

The Sources of Man's Adaptation to the Environment

Man owes his adaptive structure to the evolutionary process, but in many ways it seems to have exceeded in complexity that of any other animal. He, as all other animals, may adapt to a new form of environmental stress by mutational change acted upon by selection with subsequent changes in gene frequency. Indeed, as recent studies have shown, this has probably been more common than had been assumed. However, the enormous range of adaptive mechanisms that man has available are primarily the consequence of the increasing somatic and behavioral plasticity that seems to have occurred throughout the mammalian evolutionary process, culminating at the moment in man.

One of the secular trends in mammalian evolution was the rise in adaptive phenotypic plasticity that increasingly allowed animals to vary their pattern of functioning and behavior in response to the information provided by the environment in which they developed. Man's culture-creating capacity might be considered the inevitable end product of this increasing plasticity. The most apparent aspect of increasing plasticity was the increasing ability to learn, and the most important single attribute for the development of culture is man's enormous learning capacity. In biological terms this capacity might simply be conceived of as his great ability to pattern his behavior in response to environmental challenges. Of equal consequence for adaptation to diverse environments is man's functional and morphological adaptive plasticity. The functional and morphological plasticity of man is probably most familiar to us in its short-term manifestations. For example, temperature and altitude acclimatization are well-documented examples of modification in the functioning of man that increase his performance capability in the face of new environmental stress. Other examples would be the increase in muscle fibre size that accompanies exercise or the psychological process of accustomization that allows the organism to ignore distracting stimuli in the environment. Perhaps of similar import, but less well studied, are the long-term adaptive changes that occur in human beings when they develop under particular types of environmental stress. For example, children, when they must exist in a caloric deficient environment, can do so for prolonged periods of time by a cessation of growth which, if the deprivation period is not of excessive length, will later be recouped (McCance and Widdowson, 1951). In the same vein, man has the capacity to store calories in the form of fat when he has available "more than adequate" calories. Those stored calories can later be used during periods of short calorie supply. Other examples include the increased size of the lungs and the heart that occurs in individuals who grow up in a high-altitude environment with its low oxygen pressure (Monge, 1948).

Less is known of the possibilities of long-term improvements in physiological function, but possible examples include the increased tolerance for certain drugs over long exposure.

Thus, if we look closely at the problem of studying human adaptability, we see that man has such a large variety of environmental stresses to which he adapts and such a large variety of mechanisms available to him for adaptation that we are probably dealing with a fairly unique set of interactions in each human population that is studied. More than with any other animal, we must take great care to identify properly the stresses to which a given human population has been exposed and to consider all of the parameters of adaptation man has available to solve the problem of survival in a given environment.

Given the uniqueness of each adaptive pattern, we may still believe that the limitations of the human germ plasm are such that similar partial solutions to adaptive needs will be found over broad population isolates. That such is indeed the case for cultural adaptation seems to be demonstrated by the independent inventions of such material culture items as house forms and agriculture. Biologically, the instances are even more impressive, since the existence of morphological and genetic traits that are clustered enough to permit racial classification indicates a common genetic response to selection. Even the fact that man conforms as well as any species to Allen and Bergman's rules suggests that he has responded to similar environmental stresses by similar adaptive responses (Harrison *et al.*, 1964).

In the remainder of this paper, we will overview some small part of the knowledge so far available on man's adaptive responses. Because our knowledge is more precise in this area, the discussion will be limited primarily to physical and biological environmental stresses; and since our primary goal is to examine the role of man's biological variation in his adaptive structure, the discussion will also be strongly oriented to the biological responses even though these must always be considered in the cultural context.

While the sources of cultural adaptation to stresses remain obscure in the problems of understanding human learning and culture transmission, the sources of biological adaptation can be conceived even though we still do not have available the methods required to partition the biological components of adaptation precisely. As implied earlier in the paper, the sources of biological adaptation may be arbitrarily categorized into at least four interrelated types: psychological accommodation, physiological acclimatization, developmental acclimatization, and genetic adaptation. The functional differentiation between genetic and the other types of adaptation are apparent. However, the psychological accommodation, physical acclimatization, and developmental acclimatization are more arbitrary, since all are part of adaptive plasticity. The differentiation is based on the length of time involved and the discipline differences in perspective.

Theories of Genetic Adaptation

The problem of the relationship between the variability in the genetic structure of human populations and their adaptive significance may be approached from two perspectives: (1) the theoretical relationship established by genetic evolutionary theories, and (2) the demonstrable adaptive value of specific genetic variation in man. Until the end of the 1940's most anthropologists were concerned with the search for nonadaptive inherited traits even though they recognized that many traits might be functional. Indeed, the old goal was to establish a taxonomy of man based on nonfunctional morphological variation so that migration and population admixture could be reconstructed much as the archaeologist reconstructs culture history from pottery designs.

Since this era the geneticist has forcefully pointed out that the body of evolutionary theory derived from genetic studies on other animals does not permit such an interpretation of human variation. Thus, studies of the way human genetic variability relates to human adaptation are essentially confined to the past 15 years.

As will be seen, the well-established relationships remain meager; and it is possible that if the accumulated genetic theories were less conclusive, a majority of human biologists might still hold the view that most genetic variation in man is and was without adaptive significance. Let us, therefore, examine first the nature and strength of this theoretical structure.

Evolutionary Theory and Genetic Adaptation

At the base lies the simple mathematical theorem generally referred to as the Hardy-Weinberg theorem that points out that the gene randomization process that occurs in bisexually reproducing higher animals will not within itself change the frequency of genes in a population. Of course, as Sewall Wright showed mathematically, the size of the population and the frequency of a gene in a finite population is related to the gene's chances of survival (Wright, 1943). Thus, in very small populations pure chance can lead to the loss of a gene with a fairly low frequency, while a gene with a very high frequency may completely replace its heterozygous partner. Since this is a purely statistical concept, the probability of these occurrences is strictly determined by population numbers and gene frequencies.

Aside from these statistical models the only possibilities for modifying gene frequencies in a population are (1) mutation and chromosomal abberations; (2) gene flow (in or out of the population); and (3) selection (any nonchance phenomena that lead to the greater or lesser reproduction of a gene). Mutational and chromosomal abberations cannot be evoked as an explanation for the major part of genetic variation in human populations since they are at least similar in kind and frequency for all groups. Without selection or drift to fix variants, no population variation would develop.

Gene flow is meaningless in the overall problem since we are asking the question, "How did differentiation in genetic structure occur within our species?," which, by definition, is or was a breeding unit. Coon (1962) argues that modern man has a history of racial variation that precedes the *sapiens* form, but even if this proves true, there was genetic overlap. Furthermore, the reasons for the initial variation in genotype must fit into our scheme of genetic evolutionary theory.

Thus, only two explanations remain—the Sewall Wright genetic drift explanation, or selection. Drift first presented an attractive explanation since man in his hunting and gathering days was a thinly spread animal in very small bands. If we assume that he was then endogamous, there existed a perfect situation for drift effects. Undoubtedly, drift did have some effect. It has been demonstrated, fairly conclusively, to be the cause for some of the variation in other species, and at least one example has been presented with strong evidence for man (Giles, 1965). However, drift is a very unsatisfactory explanation for the major variations in human population genotypes. For one thing, if early man was endogamous, he should have rapidly formed different species as other endogamous animal populations did. More importantly, the genetic drift theory is a probability theory; so that while the probability of two populations' developing a difference in the frequency in one gene due to drift is fairly high, the statistical probability of developing multiple gene differences is progressively lower. Indeed, on the basis of this theorem, the probability of two populations' developing a high frequency difference in even 100 genes over the period of time that our species existed as hunters and gatherers is so low that it may be classified as bordering on the impossible. Even the few major morphological characteristics on which broad racial classifications are based seem to relate to quite a large number of genotype differences, so that one must at the present state of knowledge conclude that drift is an unsatisfactory explanation for most of the genetic differences between human populations.

By a process of elimination we are, therefore, left with the conclusion that most group differences in population genotypes are the result of selection. Since selection acts by increasing the frequency of those genes that improve adaptation while it decreases those which lower adaptation, one is further forced to the conclusion that genotypic differences in human populations represent adaptive responses to the environment.

This does not mean that the genotype of a group is adapted to the environment in which it is now found. Because of the long generation time for man and the rapid changes he has produced in some aspects of his environment through culture formation, a given present-day gene may not have had any adaptive value to a population for even thousands of years. Once the environment to which a gene has adapted is modified, the persistence of that gene is governed purely by the intensity of selection against it and its dominance characteristics. The sicklemia gene found among U.S. Negroes is an excellent example. Although it is quite clearly maladaptive in the recent environment of the U.S. Negro, selection has not yet eliminated this gene, which was quite adaptive in the malarial environment from which many U.S. Negro genes were derived (Allison, 1955).

The conclusion that population differences in genotypes arose through selection also must not be viewed as proof that any given phenotypic characteristic of a group is or has been adaptive to an environment. As pointed out earlier, the phenotype is for man almost always subject to environmental patterning through the various forms of genetic plasticity. Equally important, most genes affect multiple phenotypic products, while most phenotypic characteristics have multiple gene determinants. Therefore, even when a close relationship exists between genetic inheritance and phenotypic characteristics, the adaptive value of the gene need not be related to any one aspect of the phenotype. As an example, eye color may be cited. The exact inheritance pattern is not known, but it appears to be quite closely related to the genes involved in skin color variation. In such a situation the variation in eye color and skin color may both have adaptive value, but it is equally possible that only variation in one provides adaptive value while the other tags along as a product of the pleiotropic effects of the gene.

The net product of the widely accepted theories that have been outlined is a scientific posture quite different from the two widely popular views. These views assume either (1) that variation in the genetic structure of human populations (race) is of prime importance to a group's ability to function in modern culture, or (2) that it has no significance to man's ability to live in any given culture. Instead, we are inclined to accept the following as a set of hypotheses to be tested:

1. Population differences in genotype including gene frequency differences are the product of environmental adaptation (including culture as a part of the environment).

2. The longer a population has lived in a set environment, the greater the probability that their genotypic eccentricities are a product of adaptation to that environment.
   Subhypothesis
   A. Ecologically stable populations will be more likely to show genetic adaptation than ecologically unstable units.
   B. Genetic differences are more likely to be related to the stable stresses of the environment such as climate and disease than to the more changeable stresses such as those produced by culture.
3. Many phenotypic variations in man are not the product of genetic adaptation.

Evidence for Genetic Adaptation

When we turn from theory to the demonstrable evidence for population differences in genetic adaptation, the findings are thin. This does not necessarily imply a poor theory. Instead, it may at this time be attributed to (1) the relatively small number of studies that have been undertaken with the preceding hypotheses, and (2) our lack of knowledge concerning man's genetic system and the degree to which it is involved in man's enormous structural, functional, and behavioral diversity.

Each year a considerable number of new genes are identified in man, and very often they are found to be unequally distributed in human populations. This immediately suggests that they have some adaptive value in those populations where a high frequency exists. Occasionally, such an assumption is supported by strong presumptive evidence, such as the sicklemia-malaria chain (Allison, 1955). In other instances, such as the many links between the abnormal hemoglobins and infectious disease, a direction for future research is indicated (Motulsky, 1960). However, for the majority of identified genes, even those such as the long-known genes underlying the ABO blood types, it has not been possible to even suggest an acceptable adaptive explanation for frequency differences. Perhaps the most striking fact is that biochemical investigators have demonstrated such a wide genetic diversity in man without more than lightly touching on the wide morphological diversity in human populations that was known to have some major genetic determinants before the biochemistry of blood was considered.

At the opposite side of the problem the newly rekindled interest in the sensory and physiological functioning of non-Western groups is also demonstrating an increasingly large variety of differences in human populations. True, these differences are not of the magnitude that the 19th century scientist conceived or the 20th century "racist" imagines, but the number is great and the differences are often of significant adaptive value to populations in their present or recently past environments. For this increasing list of traits, one of the major problems is the differentiation between the responses related to genetic variation and those produced by adaptive plasticity. For example, it is quite clear that the warmer temperatures of the Eskimo hand when exposed to cold enhanced his adaptation to the environment in which he lived (Coffee, 1955). On the other hand, the extent of genetic causation in the warmer hand temperatures is not clear. Despite a prodigious literature, the degree to which the different sources of biological adaptation are involved is not clear. It has been demonstrated that psychological accommodation to cold increases the temperature of the fingers when exposed to cold (Fox, 1963). Presumably, this is because anxiety is reduced by repeated exposures. It has also been shown that an acclimatization or training effect occurs, which further produces warmer hands by greater blood flow in most subjects (Egan, 1963). This still does not appear to account for most of the variation. Yoshimura's and Iida's work (1952) showed that northern and southern Japanese have a difference in response after training, so probably there is a developmental factor. It has also been suggested that there is a genetic factor, since U.S. Negro and white soldiers manifest vastly different responses even though they both came from the south (Iampietro et al., 1959). Also, Meehan (1955) showed a striking similarity in twins. Thus, one is inclined to assume a genetic component even though no specific genes have been identified.

It would be most surprising if any specific genes were found associated with the differences in hand temperature upon extreme cold exposures. From what is known of the mechanisms involved, gene action would be indirect, involving such links as hand size, the size of arterial anastomoses, forearm size and insulation, neural pathways, and even brain functions. When attempts at genetic analysis have been made on these possible intermediates, they have consistently yielded the same type of partial genotype causation answer. This is easily explainable by the multiple genes involved in each of these phenotypic characteristics, plus, of course, all the levels of plasticity.

As the preceding discussion has emphasized, evidence for genetic adaptation has been emanating from two sources, but the two sources are at this point not making a great deal of contact. The geneticist wishing to test the hypothesis that genetic variation is the product of adaptation, must trace the known gene through the almost imposssible chain that ties it to morphology, function, and behavior; while the psychophysiologist or environmental physiologist has the equally difficult task of tracking the behavior or function with demonstrable adaptive value through the chain of its environmental determinants to the genetic core. In these two lines of inquiry it is not surprising that the most conclusive cases have contained the simplest links. Thus, the adaptive nature of genotype and gene frequency variation have been best demonstrated between simply inherited hemoglobin types and the diseases that attack hemoglobin, and the best case for demonstrating a genetic component in adaptive behavior or function is where the function is closely associated with morphology, such as climate tolerance and body morphology (Hammel, 1964).

Probably the greatest danger to the understanding of human adaptation comes from the fact that these simple relationships are the easiest to establish and, therefore, lead to the conclusion that they are the most important ones. Indeed, this has happened with geneticists concentrating their efforts on the study of infectious disease while the environmental physiologist has concentrated on temperature. In such important environmental stress areas as nutrition, culture, sensory and motor requirements, altitude and radiation very few attempts have been made to link adaptive behavior and function to genetic factors. Yet, there is no theoretical reason to doubt that selection due to these forms of stress was at least as significant in producing genetic variation as was temperature and infectious disease.

Behavioral and Somatic Plasticity as Adaptation

It is surprising to find that despite an extensive literature on man's adaptive capacity in the presence of stress there does not exist a commonly accepted terminology that differentiates the nature or the types of adaptive responses. If for the moment we ignore the vast literature that deals with intelligence as an adaptive response and deal only with the more specific functions studied by the physiologist, we find that the areas of terminological agreement are still too few. If we use Prosser (1964) as a guide, physiologists would accept the concept of a stress and a response to it on the part of the organism. The responses that enhance the organism's functioning in the presence of stress are *adaptive responses*; these are divided into genetically determined *adaptive variations* and environmentally induced responses called *acclimation*, or *acclimatization*. The geneticists would also point out that acclimatization responses are built into the genetic structure; or, as Prosser states it, "the genotype determines the 'capacity' of an organism to adapt." To the physiologist the concept of acclimatization appears adequate to cover all of the non-genetic changes in man that enhance adaptation. However, the terminological problem may very well prevent the physiologist, psychologist, medical scientist, geneticist, anthropologist, etc. from realizing that they often are involved in the study of very closely related facets of the same problem.

In the majority of psychological studies, for example, an improvement in the human organism's adaptation to the environment is called adjustment, accommodation, or perhaps adaptation. If the word "acclimatization" appears, it must be rare, indeed. In the field of human growth and development the language of the evolutionary geneticist or physiologist is even more alien. The studies of psychological development use the language of psychology, while in the area of physical growth the concept of growth as an adaptive process is so alien that almost no terminology exists. It was with the terminological confusion in mind that a three-way breakdown in adaptive phenotypic plasticity was suggested earlier in this paper.

It may be logically argued that there is no essential difference in the mechanisms that enhance adaptation through psychological accommodation, physiological acclimatization, and developmental acclimatization. All are based on the inherited plasticity of man; and all depend upon environmental stress, which feeds back through the human nervous system to enhance the functioning of the organism in the presence of a given stress. There is, perhaps, a time factor difference, since the three categories of adaptation require progressively longer developmental time. However, the major point is the reminder that whether one is studying the changes in pain threshold or the effect of altitude on the growth of human lungs, all may be viewed as part of man's enormous adaptive capacity and may be profitably considered within the framework of evolutionary adaptational theory.

Perhaps the most difficult aspect of studying phenotypic plasticity is the process of distinguishing between adaptive and maladaptive responses to stress. In most cases the critical question is, "adaptive to what?" The physiologist often has no problem. If he has exposed individuals to a high heat stress, then any response that reduces the strain on the temperature regulation system and enhances work performance is adaptive. On the other hand, it is not so clear to the psychologist that a reduction in the pain sensation with chronic exposure represents a reduction of strain, and the situations in which it would enhance performance must be carefully defined.

For this reason, the psychologist has been quite sparing with the label "adaptive," and in sensory systems such as hearing a considerable difference of opinion is found on whether a given change in response to a sound should be called "masking," "fatigue," or "adaptation." Most of this problem is not meaningful when the researcher is considering adaptive responses in relation to a specific stress. For a hungry hunter in the woods, identification of the sounds of a food animal among the myriad sounds of the forest is adaptive and would be fixed by evolution whether it conforms to the psychologist's definition of fatigue, masking, or adaptation. Indeed, it appears that the precise reason why the terminology of adaptation is so confused is the lack of evolutionary and selection concepts in its usage by the psychophysiologist and even most other physiologists. Until very recent years, the search has always been for the universal changes that improved performance or function. Individual differences were ignored when encountered, and the testing of different human populations was seldom attempted. This contrasts strangely with the psychology of tests and measurements where consideration of the individual and group variation has been paramount, while the hopes of establishing the underlying reasons for the variation were minimal.

Population Variation in Adaptive Responses

As noted in the section on genetic adaptation, two methods are available for the discovery of population differences in adaptive capacity. The one involves relating known gene frequency variations to the adaptive requirements of the environment. The second involves the actual measurement and comparison of the functional capacities of human populations in the presence of a given stress. Once a population difference has been established in functional capacity, the difficult problem of sorting out the genetic from the different forms of plasticity sources-of-adaptation begins. But first there must be the test for functional differences. In those cases where functional differences have been investigated, the population differences have usually proven more substantial than anticipated. Thus, Motulsky (1960) showed that different populations show enormous differences in death rates from common infectious diseases. The environmental physiologist has also discovered a quite broad variation in population responses to physical environmental stresses such as temperature and altitude. Even in the area of nutrition it is now widely accepted that the nutritional needs of different human populations are not uniform (Grande, 1964).

Of course, knowledge in these areas is quite fragmentary, and often the adaptive significance of population variation is not apparent. Hopefully, the Human Adaptability Project of the International Biological Program will provide the stimulus for a rapid expansion of information in these areas. I would, therefore, like to end this brief overview with a special emphasis on the study of population differences in sensory and motor capabilities. The historical and travel literature is replete with comments on the special sensory and motor skills of primitive populations. Yet, our scientific knowledge on the subject is negligible. The few studies that have been made have suggested that there may be dramatic differences in the visual (Mann, 1966) and auditory (Rosen et al., 1962) characteristics of different populations.We have essentially no knowledge about the possibilities of other sensory differences or motor skills. I would not presume at this time to suggest whether there exist population genetic differences, but I would be surprised if there did not exist significant population variations in most of the sensory and motor characteristics. Certainly, the testing of populations would be an important contribution to our knowledge of how human biological variability contributes to adaptation.

Conclusions

Many readers of this article may at this point feel that they have been exposed to a great deal of theory and generalities about how man's biological variation is related to his adaptive capacity but to very little firm data. The author is sympathetic to this view and refers the reader to *The Biology of Human Adaptability* (Baker and Weiner, 1966) for a survey of factual knowledge on this subject as viewed by geneticists and human biologists. *The Handbook of Physiology* section entitled "Adaptation to the Environment" (Dill et al., 1964) provides a comprehensive coverage from the viewpoint of physiology.

I have not attempted a summarization of this information for two major reasons: (1) the mass of material is too great for an article of this length; and (2) the information is too fragmentary to construct an overall pattern at this time. The purpose, therefore, has been, not factual summary, but, instead, to provide a progress report on the scientific productivity of studying human biological variability as the product of adaptation in the evolutionary sense.

Viewed in terms of an interim report what conclusions can be reached? In my opinion, the following seem justified.

1. The concept that most genotypic differences in human populations is the result of adaptation to differing environments has emerged as a dominant theory.

2. The phenotypic variation in the behavior, physiological function, and morphology of human populations may very often be "caused" by adaptation. Thus the search for the causes of racial variation, differences in the physiological and psychological functioning of groups, as well as cultural variations can be profitably pursued from the framework of evolutionary adaptation.

3. The phenotypic adaptations of man contain a high environmental patterning component. Thus, geneticists would do well to broaden the base from which they search for genetic adaptation, while psychophysiologists and environmental physiologists would profit in their understanding of the sources of human adaptability by the design of studies that would allow the demonstration of developmental acclimatization and genetic adaptation.

Finally, I must note that popular questions such as whether race differences in intelligence exist, and if so, are they cultural or genetic in origin, are not meaningful questions at the present state of adaptational theory or evidence. At this time we cannot even state with certainty the degree of genetic versus environmental patterning involved in the presumably adaptive variation in hand temperature; therefore, to debate seriously the genetic versus environmental patterning involved in man's total adaptive behavioral capacity (a common definition of intelligence) in a variety of environmental settings is inappropriate as a scientific endeavor.

References

ADAMS, T., and B. G. COVINO, 1958. Racial variations to a standardized cold stress. *J. Appl. Physiol., 12:* 9–12.

ALLISON, A. C., 1955. Aspects of polymorphism in man. Cold Spring Harbor Symposium, *Quant. Biol., 20:* 239–252.

BAKER, P. T., 1958. Racial differences in heat tolerance. *Amer. J. Phys. Anthrop., 16:* 287–305.

———, and J. S. WEINER (eds.), 1966. *The Biology of Human Adaptability*. Oxford University Press, Oxford and New York.

COFFEE, M. F., 1955. "A Comparative Study of Young Eskimo and Indian Males with Acclimatized White Males." *In* Ferrer (ed.), *Cold Injury*. J. Macy Foundation, New York.

COON, C. S., 1962. *The Origin of Races*. Alfred A. Knopf, New York.

DILL, D. B., E. F. ADOLPH, and C. G. WILBUR (eds.), 1964. *Handbook of Physiology*, Sect. 4, "Adaptation to the Environment." American Physiological Society, Washington, D.C.

DOBZHANSKY, T. H., 1962. *Mankind Evolving*. Yale University Press, New Haven and London.

EGAN, C. J., 1963. Local vascular adaptations to cold in man. *Fed. Proc.*, *22:* 547–551.

FOX, R. H., 1963. Comment following "Local vascular adaptations to cold in man" by C. J. Egan. *Fed. Proc.*, *22:* 952.

GILES, EUGENE, 1965. Anthropological significance of recent New Guinea genetic studies. *Amer. J. Phys. Anthrop.*, *23:* 326.

GRANDE, FRANCISCO, 1964. "Man Under Caloric Deficiency." *In* D. B. Dill et al. (eds.), *Handbook of Physiology*, Sect. 4, "Adaptation to the Environment." American Physiological Society, Washington, D.C.

HAMMEL, T. H., 1964. "Terrestrial Animals in Cold: Recent Studies of Primitive Man." *In* D. B. Dill et al. (eds.), *Handbook of Physiology*, Sect. 4, "Adaptation to the Environment." American Physiological Society, Washington, D.C.

HARRISON, G. A., J. S. WEINER, J. M. TANNER, and N. A. BARNICOT, 1964. *Human Biology*. Oxford University Press, New York and Oxford.

IAMPIETRO, P. F., R. F. GOLDMAN, E. R. BUSKIRK, and D. E. BASS, 1959. Responses of Negro and white males to cold. *J. Appl. Physiol.*, *14:* 798–800.

MANN, IDA, 1966. *Culture, Race, Climate and Eye Disease*. Charles C Thomas, Springfield, Ill.

MCCANCE, R. A., and W. M. B. WIDDOWSON, 1951. The German background studies of undernutrition, Wuppertal, 1946–49. *Med. Res. Counc. Spec. Rep.* (London) *275:* 1–20.

MEEHAN, J. P., 1955. Individual and racial variation in a vascular response to a cold stimulus. *Milit. Med.*, *116:* 330–334.

MONGE, CARLOS, 1948. *Acclimatization in the Andes: Historical Confirmation of "Climate Aggression" in the Development of Andean Man*. Johns Hopkins Press, Baltimore.

MOTULSKY, A. G., 1960. "Metabolic Polymorphisms and the Role of Infectious Diseases in Human Evolution." *In* G. W. Lasker (ed.), *The Processes of Ongoing Human Evolution*. Wayne State University Press, Detroit.

PROSSER, C. L., 1964. "Pespectives of Adaptation: Theoretical Aspects." In Dill et al. (eds.), *Handbook of Physiology, Sect. 4, "Adaptation to the Environment."* American Physiological Society, Washington, D.C.

ROSEN, SAMUEL, M. BERGMAN, D. PLESTER, A. EL. MOFTY, and M. H. SATTI, 1962. Presbycusis study of a relatively noise-free population in the Sudan. *Ann. Otol.*, *71:* 727–743.

WRIGHT, SEWALL, 1943. Isolation by distance. *Genetics*, *28:* 114.

YOSHIMURA, H., and T. IIDA, 1952. Studies on the reactivity of the skin vessels to extreme cold, Part 2: Factors governing individual reactivity on the resistance to frostbite. *Jap. J. Physiol.*, *2:* 177–185.

Terrestrial Animals in Cold:
Recent Studies of Primitive Man*

H. T. HAMMEL

(*Editor's Note*) In the following paper Hammel presents some of the specific studies dealing with the topic of human response to the environment that were discussed by Baker in the previous article. After a discussion of the difficulties involved in identifying climatic variation, Hammel shows that subjects from different populations have physiologically different reactions to cold stress. The point is that in any climate there will be times during the year when a human being will have to contend with low temperatures. For the species as a whole, there evidently are a number of physiological mechanisms available that compensate for heat loss. Hammel suggests that reliance on different kinds of technologies has prevented a pan-species specialization to one kind of cold response. For example, perhaps the reason the Eskimo and the Bushman have physiologically different cold-stress responses is because they depend on entirely different technological devices to aid in cold protection. Obviously the survival value for the individual of a cold response is independent of whether it is technological or physiological and if the latter, whether it's phenotypic or genetic. A knowledge of how man living under primitive conditions today reacts to common environmental stresses may lead to a better understanding of the evolution of population differences.

THE regions on earth are few, if any, where a naked man would not experience a chill during some period of the year if he were to rest eight hours at night without fire or protective cover. The critical temperature of the modern European or American is between 27 and 29 C (8). This means that for the resting naked man in still air, shivering will eventually be required to balance heat production with heat loss for environmental temperatures below 27 to 29 C. Not even the warmest climates of the earth have air temperatures as high as this every night of the year. Notwithstanding these elemental facts, primitive man has found his way into all climates of the earth. A partial description of the types of adaptations which have enabled primitive man to cope with the potential or real cold stresses in all climates on earth is the content of this chapter.

Descriptions of Environments Wherein Primitive Man Experiences Diurnal, Seasonal, or Continual Cold Exposure

The climates of the earth have been classified by Köppen according to the values of the climatic elements, especially temperature and precipitation [taken from Haurwitz & Austin (25)]. Köppen distinguishes 11 principal climatic types which can be combined in five climatic groups denoted by capital letters. A small letter, f, s or w, indicates the absence of a dry period (f), or the presence of a dry period in summer (s) or winter (w). The climatic groups in Table 1 are arranged according to geographical latitude.

They are separated from each other by the values of the extremes of the monthly mean temperatures or by a combination of precipitation and temperature. The climatic groups A, C, and D may be called the "tree climates" because trees can grow only in regions with these climatic types. The mean temperature of the warmest month is chosen as the boundary between the tree climates and the polar climates, E. Where the mean temperature of the warmest month is above 10 C, one of the tree climates A, C, or D exists; where the mean temperature of the warmest month is below 10 C, the polar climate E is found. In the polar climate it is practical to separate the climates ET which still permit the growth of a tundra vegetation, from the climates EF which are characterized by eternal frost.

The boundaries between the climates A, C, and D are determined by the mean temperature of the coldest month. The tropical rainy climates, A, are separated from the warm temperate rainy climates,

TABLE 1. *Principal Climatic Types.**

MAIN ZONES	SYMBOLS	SUBDIVISIONS
A. Tropical rainy climates	1. Af	Tropical rain forest
	2. Aw	Savanna
B. Dry climates	3. BS	Steppe
	4. BW	Desert
C. Temperate rainy climates	5. Cw	Warm, with dry winter
	6. Cf	Warm, moist in all seasons
	7. Cs	Warm, with dry summer
D. Cold snow-forest climates	8. Df	Snow forest, moist in all seasons
	9. Dw	Snow forest, dry winter
E. Polar (snow) climates	10. ET	Tundra
	11. EF	Perpetual snow and ice

*From Petterssen (36).

C, by the temperature 18 C of the coldest month. The lowest mean temperature of the coldest month in the warm temperate rainy climates is —3 C or above. Where the mean temperature of the coldest month is less than —3 C, the cold snow forest climate, D, prevails. The temperature 18 C has been chosen as the boundary between the A and C climates because this temperature was considered by Köppen to be the optimum for human activities. The value —3 C, according to Köppen, is the highest temperature at which a snow cover can persist for an appreciable period during the winter season.

The dry climatic types B are distinguished from the tree climates by a combination of the temperature and the precipitation, for the effects of precipitation, especially on the vegetation, depend not only on the amount of precipitation itself but also on the evaporation. The observations of evaporation are still far too scanty to be of direct use in a study of the distribution of climatic types, but the effect of the evaporation can at least roughly be taken into account by forming an expression that depends not only on the precipitation alone, but on the precipitation and temperature. Köppen chooses as the condition for a dry climate that the annual precipitation in centimeters $r < 2.0\,t + 14.2$, where t stands for the annual mean temperature in degrees centigrade. If the annual mean temperature is 25 C, for example, a climate would be classified as dry if the annual precipitation were less than 64.2 cm, while with a lower annual mean temperature the climate would be designated as one of the tree climates.

In the driest parts of regions that have a dry climate, even the steppe vegetation with its grasses cannot exist and deserts are found.

According to Köppen, the boundary between the steppe BS and desert climate, BW lies where the precipitation drops to half the value it has at the limit between dry and moist climates, or where the annual precipitation $r < t + 7.1$.

Köppen's classification is based mainly on the effect of climate on plant growth because vegetation cover of the earth is of the greatest economic importance to civilization. Temperature and precipitation are chosen as the two principal elements of the classification, although it is, of course, impossible to characterize a climate completely with a few figures referring to temperature and precipitation. It is not implied that extremes of temperature, annual range and diurnal variations in temperature, or other climatic elements such as evaporation, humidity, radiation or wind are not also important; but at least it is possible in this manner to find expressions that permit the combination of regions with the same climatic effects and that facilitate the differentiation between regions where the effects on plants, animals, and human life are different.

As a first approximation of the thermal environment, the mean temperature at the earth's surface as a function of the latitude is given in Table 2.

The Northern Hemisphere as a whole has a higher annual mean temperature than the Southern Hemisphere. On the yearly average

TABLE 2. *Mean Temperatures, C, of the Latitude Circles.**

LATITUDE	YEAR	JANUARY	JULY	RANGE
90° N	−22.7	−41.1	−1.11	40
80° N	−18.4	−32.2	2.11	34.2
70° N	−10.8	−26.3	7.28	33.6
60° N	−1.11	−16.1	14.1	30.2
50° N	5.83	−7.3	18.1	25.2
40° N	14.1	5.0	24.0	19.0
30° N	20.4	14.4	27.3	12.8
20° N	25.3	21.8	28.0	6.2
10° N	26.8	25.8	26.9	1.5
Equator	26.2	26.4	25.6	1.0
10° S	25.3	26.3	23.9	2.4
20° S	22.9	25.4	20.0	5.4
30° S	16.6	21.9	14.7	7.2
40° S	11.9	15.6	9.0	6.6
50° S	5.78	8.11	3.4	4.7
60° S	−3.29	2.67	−9.11	11.2
70° S	−13.6	−3.05	−23.0	19.5
80° S	−27.0	−10.8	−39.5	28.7
90° S	−33.1	−13.5	−47.8	34.5

*From Haurwitz & Austin (25).

each latitude of the Northern Hemisphere is warmer than the same latitude in the Southern Hemisphere. The latitude effect upon the annual mean temperature is least in the tropical and subtropical belts and increases toward the poles. The yearly averages show that the warmest latitude is not at the equator, but at 10° N. Only during January is the equator the hottest latitude. In July, on the other hand, the warmest parallel of latitude is north of 20° N.

From the point of view of cold exposure of the unclothed primitive man, it is more relevant to consider the minimum temperatures of the annual and diurnal cycles. The annual range of the temperature, i.e., the difference between the mean temperatures of the warmest and of the coldest month, is greater at higher latitudes and, at one and the same latitude, greater over the continents than over the oceans. A belt of an annual temperature range of 3 C girdles the earth at the equator with a width of approximately 15° N or S over the oceans and approximately 10° N or S over the continents of Africa and South America. Because of the greater proportion of ocean to land mass south of the equator, the increase in annual range in temperature with latitude is less in the Southern than in the Northern Hemisphere. Over the northern Pacific Ocean, there is a regular increase of annual range from less than 3 C at the equator to more than 30 C at the Arctic Circle. Much more striking, however, is the great increase of the annual temperature range toward the interior of the continents, especially over the large continental masses of North America and Asia. Over eastern Siberia, for example, at the Arctic Circle, the annual temperature range is more than 60 C.

The diurnal variation of temperature is also influenced by latitude and continental land masses. Since the diurnal temperature variation is an effect of the daily period of the incoming solar radiation, the greatest temperature ranges should occur at low latitudes where the sun reaches a high position in the sky at noon. In many instances this is the case, but the latitude is by no means a dominant factor. Regional differences in the daily periods of cloudiness, water vapor, and dust content, which affect not only the amount of solar radiation received but also the long wavelength outgoing radiation, often mask the effect of latitude. The diurnal temperature range at maritime stations is generally less than at continental stations.

PHYSIOLOGICAL VERSUS TECHNOLOGICAL ADAPTATIONS. The tropical rain forest and the tropical savanna climates are the warmest climates of the earth, yet it is apparent that even these do not at all times of the day or year provide environmental temperatures above the critical temperature of the modern American or European. The mean temperature for the coldest month of equatorial Africa is 25.6 C. The annual mean of diurnal range of temperature at six equatorial coast and island stations is 5.3 C and at three continental stations within the equatorial belt is 8.3 C. There is, therefore, little doubt that the warmest climates on earth produce environmental temperatures during the night which may be 5 to 10 C below the critical temperature of modern man.

Early primitive man, before technology, must have possessed adaptations for his frequent exposure to the cold in his environment which enabled him to span the nightly sleeping periods at air temperatures of 20 C or even less. There are only three main types of physiological adaptations possible under these circumstances. The rate of heat loss must be reduced and the rate of heat production must be increased or body heat content will be lost. The rate at which heat is lost from the body may be reduced by only three physiological adaptations: (a) reduction of the surface area exposed to the environment, (b) growth of a hairy coat of insulation, or (c) reduction of the temperature gradient from the skin surface to the environment by dropping the skin surface temperature. The latter can be accomplished only by loss of heat content from at least the shell or peripheral layers of the body. An increase in the resting rate of heat production may be accomplished by either a specialized form of neuro-muscular activity, namely, shivering, or by a general increase in the metabolic rate of some or all the body organs. The latter is referred to as non-shivering thermogenesis. Two types of nonshivering thermogenesis have been described in mammals. One involves increased activity of the thyroid and the adrenal medulla; the other results from the ingestion of foodstuffs, especially protein. Both serve to increase the resting metabolic rate with or without acute cold exposure.

In the event that the rate of heat loss exceeds the rate of heat production within the body, heat content will decrease with time. The loss of heat content is a self-limiting process, i.e., the rate of loss of heat content diminishes to zero as the loss of heat from the shell reduces the skin temperature to a level for which the rate of heat loss from the surface balances the rate of heat production.

We can only surmise that no one of these types of physiological adaptations was adopted exclusively without the others. What is more likely is that more than one type was acquired to enable primitive man to adapt to his environment. We also can assume that these adaptations were slowly modified or lost as his technology evolved.

Even before the advent of technology into the culture of man, he could, like other endotherms, select microenvironments within the climate where the cold exposure would be reduced. Caves must have offered some relief from the cold as well as other advantages. The microenvironment within the cave could be characterized by reduced air movement, reduced long wave radiation loss to the sky, protection from rain, and elevated air and wall temperatures from heat stored within the rock from daily solar radiation. The sleeping environment of the family group could also be modified by huddling of its members, thus reducing the body surface of each individual exposed to the gross environment.

For reasons difficult to discern, early man could not or did not achieve an adequate or optimum adaptation to the cold of his environment. With his wit he employed his hands to fashion protective garments from skins of mammals slain for food or he learned to erect a small shelter of boughs and skins or brush. Perhaps the caves were insufficient in number throughout the tropical savannas over which he ranged, or perhaps he wandered for unknown reasons beyond the bounds of his place of origin into climates with minimal temperatures below those for which he was adapted. His origins were at a time when advancing glacial ice from the polar regions may have forced him, even in his tropical home, to abandon total dependence upon physiological adaptations and invent means for moderating his thermal environment during the sleeping period. Few will doubt that he had the wit to accomplish this, for he learned to employ the heat from fire to achieve a thermal comfort unknown before.

ADAPTATIONS TO WHOLE-BODY EXPOSURE VERSUS EXPOSURE OF EXTREMITIES. Man's origin must have been in a tropical savanna or hot steppe climate where his only exposure to cold would have been that to his entire body. It is inconceivable that man could have originated in the Arctic where he would have to adapt his unclothed extremities to subfreezing temperatures. The only adaptations of pre-technological man were concerned with heat exchange between the whole body and an environment with temperatures never lower than 15 to 20 C. Only with an advanced technology could man, possessing knowledge of the use of fire, skin and fur clothing, and warm shelters, enter the cool snow-forest or polar climates. Any adaptive responses of the extremities to severe cold exposure would have to be superimposed upon adaptive responses of the whole body to moderate cold exposure possessed by the Arctic or sub-Arctic man.

CURRENT METHODS FOR ASSESSING COLD ADAPTATION IN PRIMITIVE MAN. Studies of cold adaptation in primitive man have been limited almost entirely to thermal and metabolic measurements. A review

(43) of the cellular responses in cold acclimation contains no references to such studies in man. Also few in number are studies of the role of the pituitary-thyroid-adrenal axis in cold adaptation in primitive man (40).

Measurement of the basal metabolic rate (BMR) of Europeans living in warm, temperate, and cold climates and similar measurements of other races and cultures exposed to a variety of climates have been made to obtain evidence for warm or cold adaptation in man. Although there is general agreement that the BMR is lower by a few per cent in persons living in warm climates, the cold-climate studies have yielded no clear-cut conclusions about the effect of cold climates upon the BMR (46). However, it may not be inferred from this that cold adaptation does not occur in primitive man because the BMR is determined without thermal stress. Determinations of metabolism during cold exposure should also be known before the occurrence of cold adaptation in cold-exposed races of man can be established.

Measurements of oxygen consumption, and skin and rectal temperatures during cold exposures of varying degrees and for varying times are thought to be a more reliable way to obtain evidence for cold adaptation of the whole body. For this, some investigators prefer to use an acute exposure of moderate severity for a short period where there is no possibility for a steady state to occur (1, 2, 37, 38, 45). Others prefer to employ only moderate cold exposure for times up to 8 hours so that the heat loss and heat production have time to equilibrate and the body heat content approaches a steady state, at least, in the control group (12, 13, 19-21, 23, 27, 29, 41, 42).

Evidence for cold adaptation of parts of the body, especially the hands and feet, has been sought by methods which can show group differences in the amount of blood flowing to the appendage. Only indirect methods have been employed for this such as finger or hand venous occlusion plethysmography (7, 28), finger or toe temperature (3, 14, 26, 28, 30, 32, 34, 35, 50), and hand or foot calorimetry wherein the amount of heat output is measured during the period of cold exposure of the appendage (14, 18, 26, 28).

Discussion

SUMMARY OF RESULTS OF PHYSIOLOGICAL STUDIES ON PRIMITIVE MAN. A comparison of most of the ethnic groups discussed in this survey may be made in terms of the average metabolic response of each group as a function of the mean body temperature. Three distinct patterns of response to moderate whole-body exposure to cold are found: (a) the urban European or American unexposed to chronic cold starts an 8-hour period of cold exposure with a metabolic rate at or near a basal level and increases it markedly as his body temperature falls; (b) the Central Australian aborigine starts with a metabolic rate near basal which slides slowly downward as his rectal and skin temperatures fall to values a little lower than those of urbanized white controls; and (c) the Alacaluf Indian starts with a high metabolic rate which declines slightly and is accompanied by a rectal temperature falling no lower than the rectal temperature of the white control, the skin temperatures of the trunk falling a little more and the foot temperature a little less than those of the white man.

The response of the Alacaluf Indian may be called metabolic acclimatization. The responses of the Eskimos and the Old Crow Indians were in some ways intermediate between the responses of the Alacaluf Indians and the unacclimatized urban white man. The initial metabolic rate was intermediate but, unlike the Alacaluf's response and like the unacclimatized white man's response, the metabolic rate of both the Arctic Indians and the Eskimos increased slightly as the body temperatures of the Arctic Indians (except the foot temperature) fell more than those of the control whites, and the rectal temperature of the Eskimos fell slightly more than that of the whites while the average skin temperature fell less. Rennie et al. (37) found similar results for the metabolism and rectal and skin temperatures for Alaskan Eskimos exposed nude to air temperatures down to 23 C for 3 hours. The response to cold of the Arctic Indian and the Eskimo may represent a fourth pattern of response in which some shivering is added to increase further the metabolism. Metabolic acclimatization also seems to be characteristic of the European exposed to moderate cold for a few weeks.

The response of the Andean Indian to moderate cold shows still another possible pattern in which the initial metabolism is similar to the European standard and the metabolism increases to an extent similar to the European control but accompanied by an extraordinary loss of heat from the core. Such a pattern may be designated as hypothermic acclimatization and lacks the insulative aspect seen in the Australian aborigine. The response of the Bushman of the Kalahari Desert, the tropical Australian aborigine and the nomadic Lapp herder was intermediate between the response of the unacclimatized white man and that of the Australian aborigine of the Central Australian desert, and like the latter group their response to cold may be termed insulative-hypothermic acclimatization.

A comparative study by Adams & Covino (1) of the metabolism and body temperatures of American Negroes, Caucasians, and Alaskan Eskimos exposed nude for 2 hours to an air temperature of 17 C revealed differences in metabolic rate and average skin temperatures which are similar to the differences already described for the Kalahari Bushmen, white Americans, and eastern Arctic Eskimos, respectively. The resting control metabolism of the Eskimos was 54 kcal per m² per hour per degree C compared with 37 to 39 kcal per m² per hour per degree C for both the white and Negro Americans. During the second hour of cold exposure, all three groups increased their metabolic rate; the Eskimos had the highest rate and the Negro the lowest, although the white subjects increased their metabolic rate above the control level more than the Eskimos did. The average skin temperature of the Eskimo was about 1 C above that of white and Negro subjects for the second hour.

An effective whole-body conductance for the transfer of heat from the core to the skin surface may be calculated by dividing the heat loss from the skin surface by the difference between the rectal temperature and the average skin temperature. The heat loss from the skin surface may be roughly calculated by adding to the rate of heat production the rate of loss of heat content from the core and shell, and subtracting about 8 percent of the rate of heat production to account for the heat of vaporization from the respiratory tract which does not pass through the skin surface. Where data were available, the average body conductance over the final one-half to one-third of the night of cold exposure was calculated for each of the ethnic groups in this survey. These body conductances along with the percentage of total adiposity as calculated from skinfold thicknesses by the method of Allen et al. (4) are given in Table 3. Although these results may not be comparable with results obtained by direct calorimetry, they will serve for comparing different groups measured in a similar way. The body conductance of the Central Australian aborigine is about 6 kcal per m² per hour per degree C both summer and winter during the latter half of a night of moderate cold exposure, whereas the body conductance of the unacclimatized European is between 7.5 and 8 kcal per m² per hour per degree C even though the total adiposity of the aborigine is less, that is, 17 percent of body weight as compared with 25 percent for the European controls.

A fairer comparison of the body conductances of the aborigines and Europeans and the other ethnic groups would be to compare conductances recalculated assuming the same thickness of subcutaneous fat for all of the ethnic groups. Assuming a planar model and

TABLE 3.

ETHNIC GROUP	REF.	NO.	SEASON	TOTAL OF TEN SKINFOLDS LESS 40 MM, MM	% TOTAL ADIPOSITY (4)	TOTAL BODY CONDUCTANCE, KCAL/M²/HR/C†	$K_{3.0MM}$, KCAL/M²/HR/C	AVERAGE RECTAL TEMPERATURE DURING LATTER HALF OF WARM NIGHT, C	COLD NIGHT, C	DIFFERENCE, C
Central Australian aborigines	41	6	Winter			6.0	5.2		35.6	
Central Australian aborigines	20	7	Summer	30.4	17.3	5.5	5.8		35.7	
Tropical Australian aborigines	20	9	Summer	51.0	22.4	5.9			36.1	
Kalahari Bushmen	21	10	Winter	7.0	7.7	7.6	6.8	36.6	35.7	0.9
Alacaluf Indians	19	9	Winter	39.0	19.5	7.2	6.9	36.8	36.2	0.6
Arctic Indians	27	9	Fall	17.9	13.0	10.6*	9.4	36.2	35.7	0.5
Arctic Indians	13	8	Spring	26.5	16.3	8.5*			35.5	
Andean Indians	12	8		24.5	15.3	9.7	8.9	36.5	35.1	1.4
Eskimos	23	10	Winter	17.9	13	10.2	9.1	36.2	35.7	0.5
Whites in Australia	41	4	Winter	53.6	22.3	7.6	7.3	36.1 (2)	36.2	−0.1
Whites in Australia	20	6	Summer	74.0	27	7.4	7.3		36.0	
Whites in Kalahari	21	4	Winter	79.3	28	7.1			36.3	
Whites in eastern Arctic	23	3	Winter	49.4	22	8.2	8.5	36.1 (2)	36.1	0.0
Whites in western Arctic	27	7	Fall	59.2	24	8.9	8.7	36.3	36.1	0.2
Average white						7.9	8.0	36.2	36.1	0.1
Korean diving women	38	8	Summer	39.8	19.7	7.7	7.4			
Korean nondiving women	38	4	Summer	44.2	20.8	7.0	6.8			
Korean men	38	7	Summer	29.2	16.8	8.8	8.1			
American white women	38	10	Summer	69.4	26.2	7.5	7.7			
American white men	38	8	Summer	55.8	23.4	9.2	9.1			

*Not corrected for loss of body heat content; such a correction will increase body conductance by a few per cent.

†The expression $kcal/m^2/hr/C$ is equivalent to $\dfrac{kcal}{m^2\ hr\ C}$.

a fat conductivity of 0.000488 cal cm/cm² sec C (24) and using
3.0 mm as a reference thickness of subcutaneous fat, the recalculated
conductance $K_{3.0mm}$, is:

$$\frac{1}{K_{3.0mm}} = \frac{1}{K} - \frac{1}{175/(t - 3.0)}$$

where K is the uncorrected conductance of each ethnic group and t
is the measured thickness of subcutaneous fat in mm (Table 23:3).
The recalculated conductances for the aborigines and the other ethnic
groups are given in table 3.

The lower body conductance of the aborigine, despite his leaner
body, clearly supports the view expressed by Professor Hicks and his
collaborators (17) in their pioneer work with the aborigines to the
effect that the aborigines have a more effective regulation of heat
loss by means of vasoconstriction in the skin in response to cold.
Similarly the tropical aborigines showed the same low body conductance, although their adiposity was the same as the Europeans.
This indicates that less vasoconstrictor control was shown by the
tropical aborigines to achieve the same conductance as by the Central
Australian group exposed to more cold.

The body conductance of the Kalahari Bushmen was found to be
7.6 kcal per m² per hour per degree C. Although this value was no
lower than a normal value for a European, when the unusual lean-
ness of the Bushmen who have practically no subcutaneous fat is
taken into account, the comparable lower conductance of the Bushmen indicates a greater vasoconstriction than is possible for the
European. Therefore, it is fair to conclude that the Bushmen of the
Kalahari Desert exhibit insulative-hypothermic acclimatization similar
to that shown by the aborigine of the Central Australian Desert.

The body conductance of the Alacaluf Indian appears to be a little
less than that of the unacclimatized European when the somewhat
thinner subcutaneous fat layer is taken into account. The other natives
of the American continents all show higher body conductances, but
this is partly due to less subcutaneous fat. Rennie *et al.* (37) found
that Alaskan Eskimos, nude for 3 hours in a 23 C environment, had
a body conductance of about 16 kcal per m² per hour per degree C
during the last hour, whereas the control Europeans had a conductance of about 10 kcal per m² per hour per degree C. These values
are higher than those in Table 3. The difference in conductance between the European and Eskimo can be accounted for only partially
by the difference in the fat layer, since the Eskimos in the study by
Rennie *et al.* had only 2 mm less fat and those in Hart's study 3.1

mm less. There is good indication that the Eskimos maintain warmer skins by more peripheral circulation than unacclimatized Europeans.

Minimum body conductances for Korean diving and nondiving women and for Korean men plus values for European men and women are given in Table 3 for comparison. These values were obtained by Rennie *et al.* (38) for the third hour of immersion in water at or below the critical water temperature for each group which ranged from 30 C for the Korean diving women to 33 C for American men and women. At the critical temperature, maximum vasoconstriction was obtained without shivering. They conclude that no differences existed in minimum tissue conductance between Korean men and women that could not be accounted for by subcutaneous fat. Furthermore, the effect of subcutaneous fat on minimum tissue conductance is the same for the two ethnic groups, although for the same thickness of subcutaneous fat the Korean men and women have a lower tissue conductance than do the American men and women. They suggest that the lower conductances or higher insulation of the Korean women may be the reason women were chosen originally for the diving occupation. The only evidence for cold acclimatization among the diving women was their ability to withstand colder water immersion without apparent shivering. The fact that Koreans as a whole have a lower body conductance than Europeans for the same skinfold thickness suggests greater vasoconstriction, although not to the extent observed in the Australian aborigines.

Table 3 reveals another interesting difference between all of the primitive ethnic groups and Europeans as pointed out by Hart *et al.* (23). Whenever measurements of metabolism and body temperatures were repeated throughout a night of warm comfortable sleep, it was seen that the rectal temperatures during the latter half of the cold nights were 0.5 C to 1.4 C lower than during the latter half of the warm nights. This difference was true for all ethnic groups except the Europeans who, on every occasion, had the same rectal temperatures for both warm and cold nights. The Alacaluf Indians had an average rectal temperature of 36.8 C during the warm night and 36.2 C, the same temperature as the Europeans, for the cold night. On the other hand, the Andean Indians had a rectal temperature when warm similar to the European temperature and dropped to 35.1 C during the cold night. The latter Indians had the lowest rectal temperatures of any primitive group investigated. There appears to be no comparative significance to the difference between the average skin temperature during warm and cold nights for each group.

EFFECTS OF DIET, PHYSICAL FITNESS, AND ACCLIMATIZATION TO OTHER STRESSES UPON RESPONSES TO COLD; THE CONCEPT OF COLD ACCLIMATIZATION. Many authors show a remarkable caution about characterizing a unique response to cold as cold acclimatization unless they can show that the different response to cold of the group possessing it was clearly caused by cold exposure and by no other cause. This may be an ultra conservative view of acclimatization or adaptation. There is no a priori reason why a response to a stress should evolve as a direct and exclusive consequence of stress exposure. A more essential feature of an adaptive response is that it confers an advantage upon the population possessing it. Furthermore, after the adaptive response has been acquired, the one time stressful exposure may no longer be stressful, although to revert to the unadapted condition would again result in stress from the same environmental exposure. From this, one may reason that an adaptive response produced by a cause or means unrelated to the stress may even yield a greater and more lasting advantage than one produced as a direct result of the stress. The reason for this is that an adaptive response acquired by a means unrelated to the stress would be developed and sustained in the absence of chronic or frequent intermittent stress, whereas an adaptive response acquired as a direct and only result of the stress may not develop so quickly or be sustained in the absence of chronic or frequent stress or after the stress has been minimized by the adaptive response to the exposure.

The elevated resting metabolic rate of the Eskimos, Arctic Indians, Alacaluf Indians, and cold-exposed Norwegians may have resulted from causes other than actual or possible cold exposure. Rodahl (39) has shown that the natural diet of the Eskimo, consisting of a higher percentage of meat and fat, is one factor contributing to the higher BMR of the Eskimo. He found that the average daily food intake of male Eskimos at four localities in Alaska contained 148 g protein, 139 g fat, and 307 g carbohydrate equaling 3100 calories, whereas the daily food intake of infantrymen in Alaska contained 109 g protein, 128 g fat, 408 g carbohydrate equaling 3200 calories (40). The average BMR of the Eskimos on their native diet was 41.7 kcal per m^2 per hour or 8 percent above the DuBois standard BMR for white Americans. When the Eskimos were placed on white man's diet containing 73 g protein per day for 3 days, Rodahl found that their BMR dropped to 8 percent below the DuBois standard. This drop of 16 percent in the BMR he attributes to diet. At the same time he found that a group of white controls (consuming 60 g protein per day) had an average BMR of 37.8 kcal per m² per hour or 8 percent below the DuBois standard for men of their age. In this connection, it should be mentioned that the Sage (Aub-DuBois) standards and the Mayo (Boothby-Sandiford) standards are generally about 6 percent higher than the Harris-Benedict standards and the Krogh standards (10). When five whites consumed 500 g meat per day containing 137 g protein, Rodahl found that their BMR increased by 13 percent. On the other hand, McClellan *et al.* (31) found that two white men on an exclusive meat diet for one year showed no significant elevation of their basal metabolic rate when tested in the Sage calorimeter by direct and indirect calorimetry. The BMR of the two men, when on a mixed diet, ranged from 80 percent to 91 percent of the DuBois standard, not unusual for well-trained subjects. After meat for 6 weeks, their BMR increased by 5 and 7 percent. Another subject, Dr. DuBois, on an all-meat diet for 10 days showed a 6 percent higher BMR than at the beginning. The BMR's of the two men at the end of the year of eating only meat were at or below those found at the beginning. During this time the basal nitrogen excretion varied from 0.5 to 0.8 g per hour. When tested for the specific dynamic action (SDA) of a 300 to 500 g all-meat meal, the two subjects showed an extra heat from the 3rd to 5th hours, inclusive, which ranged from 14.6 to 25.0 percent of the basal heat production. There was a suggestion, although not conclusive, that the SDA effect of meat was greater by a few percent at the end of the year of meat diet than before when the diet was mixed. The SDA of fat was determined by a meal of about 200 g fat during the year of exclusive meat diet. This raised the heat production about 14 percent.

Hart *et al.* (23) have shown that a number of factors may have some effect upon the metabolism of the Eskimo. The average metabolic rate of ten hunter Eskimos of the eastern Arctic was 49.0 kcal per m² per hour over the latter half of a warm comfortable night. These Eskimos were provided with white man's diet for about a week during the tests, although they supplemented their diet with foods exchanged with other Eskimos in camp. The average metabolic rate of eight Eskimos from the western Arctic who had been living on white man's diet for approximately 12 months was 39.7 kcal per m² per hour during a warm comfortable night. These Eskimos were at a hospital in Edmonton, although none was suffering from active tuberculosis nor from any metabolic disease. They were more sedate than the Eskimo hunters whose resting metabolism was 25 per cent higher.

Adams & Heberling (2) have shown that the thermal and metabolic aspects of metabolic acclimatization to cold may be produced by an increase in physical fitness alone. The responses of five white infantry-men wearing shorts only and exposed to 10 C air temperature for 50 min were compared before and after a 3-week period of physical training which increased their physical fitness significantly. Their metabolic rate generally was higher after physical training. In the resting but nonbasal state before cold exposure their rates were 38 kcal per m² per hour and 48 kcal per m² per hour before and after training (difference not significant). For the last 30 min of cold ex-posure, their rate was significantly higher after physical training by 15 kcal per m² per hour than it was before training. After training their average skin temperature was about 1 C higher during the con-trol period and during cold exposure than before training. On the other hand, their rectal temperature after training was 0.5 C lower than before training during the entire control and exposure period. Although these differences in heat production and skin temperatures are characteristic for the type of metabolic acclimatization seen in the Eskimo and the cold-exposed Norwegian youths, they differ from the type of metabolic acclimatization described for the Alacaluf Indian whose skin temperatures (except on the feet) were lower, rectal temperature was the same or higher, and warm and precooling metabolic rates were markedly higher than in control white subjects.

ASSESSMENT OF SURVIVAL VALUE OF PHYSIOLOGICAL ADAPTATIONS TO COLD. It may be stated again that the essential feature of an adaptive response to cold is that it confers an advantage upon the population possessing it. Hart et al. (23) conclude that the general response to cold in the Eskimo does not confer any marked advan-tage over white control subjects insofar as their all-night exposures to moderate cold are concerned. They note that the Eskimos certainly did not show the "adaptive" ability of the Australian aborigines to sleep while the body cooled without an increase in metabolic rate. They point out that to do so would lead to an increased risk of frozen extremities in an Arctic environment. Perhaps the adaptive value of metabolic acclimatization in an Arctic environment where meat is abundant lies in the reduced risk of dangerous hypothermia, cold discomfort and pain in parts of the body, without regard to the energy cost. It is not difficult to imagine that the metabolic acclimatiza-tion seen in moderate cold exposure would confer a distinct advantage upon individuals possessing it if, as seems probable from similar studies on cold-acclimatized rats (22), the capability for increased heat production can be sustained for a longer period and at a higher level under conditions of severe cold exposure. It is not necessary that metabolic acclimatization be a direct consequence of and have no other cause than cold exposure in order for it to confer advantage upon individuals or populations possessing it. Metabolic acclimatization will confer just as much advantage whether it is caused by cold exposure, by modified physical fitness, or by diet.

There are clear advantages to be derived from the other major type of cold acclimatization as seen best in the aborigines of the Central Australian Desert and in the Bushmen of the Kalahari Desert. In a tropical environment or in a subtropical desert environment where materials for making fire are available to moderate the cool winter sleeping environment so that cold exposure never need be more than moderate, the response to cold characterized by insulative-hypothermic acclimatization has some distinct advantages. In a land where food is never abundant and starvation may frequently or even occasionally threaten the population, the saving of even a few percent in the daily energy expenditure may be important for survival. The total energy requirement for 8 hours at night was 20 percent higher for the European controls than it was for the Central Australian aborigines per kilogram lean body mass or per square meter of surface area. Assuming the Europeans and the aborigines would have the same energy requirements during their active hours, the saving in energy by the aborigines at night under conditions of moderate cold exposure would be about 5 percent of the total daily energy requirement. The fact that this amount of energy or more may be saved by other means, such as smaller body size and less activity, does not lessen the advantage of sleeping without shivering through insulative-hypothermic acclimatization. The ambient temperatures of the semi-desert environment of the Central Australian aborigines or the Kalahari Bushmen are never so low as to freeze appendages of the inhabitants. Since the moderate loss of heat content during the night generally is restored by the high flux of solar radiation of the day, a metabolic type of acclimatization caused by dietary meat, physical fitness, or in any other way would be an unnecessary extravagance. Furthermore, metabolic acclimatization would be a disadvantage in these desert people for not only are they acclimatized to cold, but also they may be fully acclimatized to heat (47). Any elevation in the basal or resting metabolic rate as seen in the Alacaluf Indians or Eskimos would impose an additional stress upon the aborigines or the Bushmen exposed to the sun's radiation and the high daytime temperatures of the desert where water is limited.

ROLE OF COLD ADAPTATION IN DISTRIBUTION OF PRIMITIVE MAN OVER THE EARTH. The physiologist's reward for exploring the responses of men to thermal stress is to find a unique response. His findings, however, may have even greater meaning to the physical anthropologist if they assist him in unravelling the climatic factors in the evolution of human populations (5) or in showing that climatic adaptation is a cause for racial differentiation (9). Assuming that the few and limited studies of the responses of primitive ethnic groups to moderate cold exposure give license for speculation, perhaps the story of man's adaptation to cold would go as follows.

Wherever the place or places of origin of man, it was at a time and in a climate where he exposed his unclothed body to ambient temperatures between 20 and 25 C many nights during the year. Presumably, there was a time when the early homonids had no fire, made no protective garments of fur, and constructed no abode of any sort; nor could they always retreat to a more moderate environment within a cave. It seems very probable that they passed over the low periods of thermal exposure by an insulative and hypothermic type of response similar to that still seen today in the Australian aborigine. We infer that man was already a hairless or nearly hairless being as a result of factors unrelated to energy exchange between his body and his environment or, if hairlessness had some thermal advantage, as a result of the need to facilitate evaporative heat loss from the perspiring skin surface during prolonged periods of activity under the sun and through the peak thermal load of the day. For whatever reason the body hair and its insulation was lost, compensation was achieved through increased insulation of the body shell and by moderate hypothermia which enabled early man to span the low thermal period each night.

With the advent of fire, man could move into climates where nocturnal temperatures would frequently fall to the freezing point. Without fire these climates were intolerably cold to the uncovered hairless body. With fire to moderate the nightly environment of these climates, the insulative-hypothermic response to cold remained entirely satisfactory. But with fire alone man was unable to extend his range much beyond the subtropical zone, for in the winter season of the temperate zone, even the increased heat production of daytime activities was not sufficient to balance the heat loss.

Only with the use of the protective insulation provided by the fur of game animals was it possible to enter the temperate zone. Furthermore, by judicious preparation of the finest furs fabricated into a glove-like enclosure of the entire body combined with an understanding of the physical properties of snow as a house building material, primitive man was even able to enter the polar regions of the earth.

A new feature of the microenvironment achieved through the use of garments was that the chronic aspects of cold exposure were gone. Furthermore, with the use of clothing in the temperate zone in winter or in the Arctic, there was no longer a need to maintain a dual acclimatization to cold after sundown and to heat during the day. In time, the chronic warm microenvironment surrounding the body had its effects upon the populations of men wearing clothing. Those populations that became Europeans lost their habituation to cold. There was no longer any tendency to tolerate chronic cold exposure. With fire, housing, and clothing, they were amply protected over all periods of the day and night through all seasons and, especially, during the extreme cold of winter. After losing a familiarity with moderate cold exposure, they were no longer able to rest or sleep comfortably while their body shell and core were cooling. Sleep was comfortable or possible only if the sleeping environment were sufficiently warm to relax all the vasoconstrictor tone of peripheral arterioles, thus increasing all skin surface temperatures from foot to head to above 33 C .

Too little is known about the physiological responses to cold of the descendants of those populations invading the vast Asiatic land mass to speculate critically about the interaction of climatic adaptation and the evolution of human populations. The work on Koreans and especially Korean diving women immersed for 3 hours in neutral to cool waters, suggests, at least in this group, a continued habituation to cold. One would like to know, however, whether the insulative-hypothermic reaction of the Korean diving women would also appear during an all-night exposure to moderate cold before linking this group's cold adaptation to man's ancestral type adaptation.

Most of the descendants of those populations that pressed over into the American continents who are still residing in cold or frigid zones display another type of adaptive response. For whatever reason it may be, they have a high resting or basal metabolic rate. Where food and oxygen are abundant, these groups can well afford the higher energy cost of living and they gain some modest advantage therefrom. More heat may be channeled into the hands when acutely exposed to severe heat loss, or we may guess that a greater capacity to produce heat during a period of acute, severe cold exposure may result when starting from an elevated base line. The major adaptation, however, of the high Arctic populations must clearly be a technological adaptation. Thus through the use of animal furs, warm houses, and fire, they too have lost the habituation to cold of the ancestral type man. When exposed to moderate cold at night, their shell does not become highly insulative and they commence to shiver, although less than is the pattern of the European-type response.

On the other hand, those indigenous Americans living in cool but not frigid zones have not been compelled to retain or redevelop a high level of thermal technology and thus have not mitigated entirely the chronic aspects of the cold stress of their environment by suitable garments and housing. They retain a degree of cold habituation which implies greater shell cooling and insulation along with the elevated resting metabolic rate which has been characterized as metabolic acclimatization.

Large gaps will occur in any present account of the variety of man's responses to cold and their significance. Already mentioned has been the lack of studies of primitive groups still to be found throughout Asia. Also to be mentioned are groups found throughout the Americas. For example, a physiological study on Indian tribes living in the semiarid tropical savannas of equatorial Brazil would make a significant contribution to the story of loss or gain of insulative or metabolic acclimatization as a race of people pass from Arctic to equatorial to sub-Arctic climates.

References

1. ADAMS, T., AND B. G. COVINO. Racial variations to a standardized cold stress. *J. Appl. Physiol.* 12: 9–12, 1958.
2. ADAMS, T., AND E. J. HEBERLING. Human physiological responses to a standardized cold stress as modified by physical fitness. *J. Appl. Physiol.* 13: 226–230, 1958.
3. ADAMS, T., AND R. E. SMITH. Effect of chronic local cold exposure on finger temperature responses. *J. Appl. Physiol.* 17: 317–322, 1962.
4. ALLEN, T. H., M. T. PENG, K. P. CHENG, T. F. HUANG, C. CHANG, AND H. S. FANG. Prediction of total adiposity from skinfolds and the curvilinear relationship between external and internal adiposity. *Metabolism* 5: 346–352, 1956.
5. BARNICOT, N. A. Climatic factors in the evolution of human populations. *Cold Spring Harbor Symp. Quant. Biol.* 24: 115–129, 1959.
7. BROWN, G. M., AND J. PAGE. The effect of chronic exposure to cold on temperature and blood flow of the hand. *J. Appl. Physiol.* 5: 221–227, 1952.
8. BURTON, A. C., AND O. G. EDHOLM. *Man in a Cold Environment.* London: Arnold, 1955.

9. COON, C. S. *The Story of Man* (2nd ed.). New York: Knopf, 1962.

10. DuBois, E. F. *Basal Metabolism in Health and Disease.* Philadelphia: Lea & Febiger, 1936, p. 160.

12. ELSNER, R. W., AND A. BOLSTAD. Thermal and metabolic responses to cold exposure of Andean Indians native to high altitudes. Tech. Rept. No. AAL–TOR–62–64 Arctic Aeromedical Laboratory, Ladd AFB, June 1963.

13. ELSNER, R. W., K. LANGE ANDERSEN, AND L. HERMANSEN. Thermal and metabolic responses of Arctic Indians to moderate cold exposure at the end of winter. *J. Appl. Physiol.* 15: 659–661, 1960.

14. ELSNER, R. W., J. D. NELMS, AND L. IRVING. Circulation of heat to the hands of Arctic Indians. *J. Appl. Physiol.* 15: 662–666, 1960.

17. GOLDBY, F., C. S. HICKS, W. J. O'CONNOR, AND D. A. SINCLAIR. A comparison of the skin temperature and skin circulation of naked whites and Australian Aboriginals exposed to similar environmental changes. *Australian J. Exptl. Biol. Med. Sci.* 16: 29–37, 1938.

18. GREENFIELD, A. D. M., AND H. SCARBOROUGH. An improved calorimeter for the hand. *Clin. Sci.* 8: 211–215, 1949.

19. HAMMEL, H. T., R. W. ELSNER, K. LANGE ANDERSEN, P. F. SCHOLANDER, C. S. COON, A. MEDINA, L. STROZZI, F. A. MILAN, AND R. J. HOCK. Thermal and metabolic responses of the Alacaluf Indians to moderate cold exposure. Tech. Rept. No. 60–633, Wright Air Development Division, 1960.

20. HAMMEL, H. T., R. W. ELSNER, D. H. LeMESSURIER, H. T. ANDERSEN AND F. A. MILAN. Thermal and metabolic responses of the Australian Aborigine to moderate cold in summer. *J. Appl. Physiol.* 14: 605–615, 1959.

21. HAMMEL, H. T., J. A. HILDES, D. C. JACKSON, AND H. T. ANDERSEN. Thermal and metabolic responses of the Kalahari Bushmen to moderate cold exposure at night. Tech. Rept. No. 62–44, Arctic Aeromedical Laboratory, Ladd AFB, 1962.

22. HART, J. S. Climatic and temperature induced changes in the energetics of homeotherms. *Rev. Can. Biol.* 16: 133–174, 1957.

23. HART, J. S., H. B. SABEAN, J. A. HILDES, F. DEPOCAS, H. T. HAMMEL, K. LANGE ANDERSEN, L. IRVING, AND G. FOY. Thermal and metabolic responses of coastal Eskimos during a cold night. *J. Appl. Physiol.* 17: 953–960, 1962.

24. HATFIELD, H. S., AND L. G. C. PUGH. Thermal conductivity of human fat and muscle. *Nature* 168: 918–919, 1951.

25. HAURWITZ, B., AND J. M. AUSTIN. *Climatology.* New York: McGraw-Hill, 1944.

26. HILDES, J. A., L. IRVING, AND J. S. HART. Estimation of heat flow from hands of Eskimos by calorimetry. *J. Appl. Physiol.* 16: 617–623, 1961.

27. IRVING, L., K. LANGE ANDERSEN, A. BOLSTAD, R. ELSNER, J. A. HILDES, Y. LOYNING, J. D. NELMS, L. J. PEYTON, AND R. D. WHALEY. Metabolism and temperature of Arctic Indian men during a cold night. *J. Appl. Physiol.* 15: 635–644, 1960.

28. KROG, J., B. FOLKOW, R. H. FOX, AND K. LANGE ANDERSEN. Hand circulation in the cold of Lapps and North Norwegian fishermen. *J. Appl. Physiol.* 15: 654–658, 1960.

29. LANGE ANDERSEN, K., Y. LOYNING, J. D. NELMS, O. WILSON, R. H. FOX, AND A. BOLSTAD. Metabolic and thermal response to a moderate cold exposure in nomadic Lapps. *J. Appl. Physiol.* 15: 649–653, 1960.

30. LE BLANC, J., J. A. HILDES, AND O. HÉROUX. Tolerance of Gaspe fishermen to cold water. *J. Appl. Physiol.* 15: 1031–1034, 1960.

31. MCCLELLAN, W. S., H. J. SPENCER, AND E. A. FALK. Clinical calorimetry: prolonged meat diets with a study of respiratory metabolism. *J. Biol. Chem.* 93: 419–434, 1931.

32. MEEHAN, J. P., JR. Individual and racial variations in a vascular response to a cold stimulus. *Military Med.* 116: 330–334, 1955.

34. MILLER, L. K., AND L. IRVING. Local reactions to air cooling in an Eskimo population. *J. Appl. Physiol.* 17: 449–455, 1962.

35. NELMS, J. D., AND D. J. G. SOPER. Cold vasodilatation and cold acclimatization in the hands of British fish filleters. *J. Appl. Physiol.* 17: 444–448, 1962.

36. PETTERSSEN, S. *Introduction to Meteorology* (2nd ed.). New York: MCGRAW-HILL, 1958.

37. RENNIE, D. W., B. G. COVINO, M. R. BLAIR, AND K. RODAHL. Physical regulation of temperature in Eskimos. *J. Appl. Physiol.* 17: 326–332, 1962.

38. RENNIE, D. W., B. G. COVINO, B. J. HOWELL, S. H. SONG, B. S. KANG, AND S. K. HONG. Physical insulation of Korean diving women. *J. Appl. Physiol.* 17: 961–966, 1962.

39. RODAHL, K. Basal metabolism of the Eskimo. *J. Nutr.* 48: 359–368, 1952.

40. RODAHL, K. Human acclimatization to cold. In: *Transactions of the Fifth Josiah Macy Jr. Conference on Cold Injury*, edited by M. I. Ferrer. New York: Macy, 1958, pp. 177–252.

41. SCHOLANDER, P. F., H. T. HAMMEL, J. S. HART, D. H. LE MESSURIER, AND J. STEEN. Cold adaptation in Australian aborigines. *J. Appl. Physiol.* 13: 211–218, 1958.

42. SCHOLANDER, P. F., H. T. HAMMEL, K. LANGE ANDERSEN, AND Y. LOYNING. Metabolic acclimation to cold in man. *J. Appl. Physiol.* 12: 1–8, 1958.

43. SMITH, R. E., AND D. J. HOIJER. Metabolism and cellular function in cold acclimation. *Physiol. Rev.* 42: 60–142, 1962.

45. WARD, J. S., G. A. C. BREDELL, AND H. G. WENZEL. Responses of Bushmen and Europeans on exposure to winter night temperatures in the Kalahari. *J. Appl. Physiol.* 15: 667–670, 1960.

46. WILSON, O. Adaptation of the basal metabolic rate of man to climate—a review. *Metabolism* 5: 531–542, 1956.

47. WYNDHAM, C. H., AND J. F. MORRISON. Heat regulation of Masarwa (Bushmen). *Nature* 178: 869–870, 1956.

50. YOSHIMURA, H., AND T. IIDA. Studies on the reactivity of skin vessels to extreme cold. II. Factors governing the individual difference against frost-bite. *Japan. J. Physiol.* 2: 177–185, 1952.

9

Genetic Drift

Factors Governing the Genetics
of Primitive Human Populations*

D. CARLETON GAJDUSEK

(*Editor's Note*) Whereas students of human evolution
agree that no one evolutionary force can be held responsible for all of the genetic variations within and
among human populations, there is a difference of
opinion regarding the relative importance of each force.
The disagreement depends in part on whether the subject population is a large civilized one or a small primitive isolate. The dynamics of on-going evolution in the
small population isolate is particularly important to the
anthropologist because most of the evolution of *H.
sapiens* may have occurred when the constituent populations were quite small and quite isolated. Under such
conditions the cultural and historical "accidents" can
have significant influence on the size and quality of the
breeding population. It is perhaps unfortunate that these
considerations make every such population a unique
case requiring unique analyses if we want to know
(1) how a given population arrived at its particular
genetic constitution, and (2) how the genes within the
population got to their present distribution relative to
genealogical, social, and demographic factors. The general, theoretical approaches of population genetics must
be supplemented by data and methods from other disciplines for an adequate evolutionary understanding of
any specific case. The problem is perhaps most dramati-
cally illustrated when an effort is made to understand
the distribution of genes in islands of the Pacific. Here
the geneticist turns historian and anthropologist through
necessity. These disciplines are sensitive to variables

*This is the initial section of an article of the same title
from *Cold Spring Harbor Symposia on Quantitative Biology*,
Vol. XXIX, 1964, pp. 121–127 and 134 with pertinent references. Copyright © 1960 by the Biological Laboratory, Long
Island Biological Association, Inc. By permission of the author
and the publisher.

which can "bias the gene pool" in one direction or another and therefore must be recognized by the student of evolution.

DURING his million or more years on earth man has lived only a small portion of this time, certainly no more than 10,000 years, in cities, towns, and villages. Most of his sojourn as a species on earth has been spent, undoubtedly, as a member of a small hunting or food-gathering band or in small shifting hamlets or scattered dwellings as a primitive hoe or digging-stick agriculturalist. It would, furthermore, appear unlikely that his human horizons from birth to death ever brought him face to face with as many as one thousand members of his species—more likely the upper limit of his close intimate contact with other human beings has been only a few hundred individuals. The small, nomadic or semi-nomadic bands or primitive agricultural communities rarely attained a population of over one hundred individuals, and contacts with outside groups were probably infrequent, dangerous, and never free-and-easy.

From all we can learn in studies of primate social organization and of the social structure of the few remaining hunting, food-gathering, and primitive agricultural peoples who still exist today, it would be plausible to surmise that a similar situation prevailed when prehominid species were evolving to establish the purine and pyrimidine sequences in the human chromosomes which characterize modern man (Washburn, 1961).

It was civilization that permitted much denser population than would be possible for "uncivilized" societies in the same territory. Not until man discovered civilization did the flood of humankind cover the continental plains, hills, and river valleys, to alter the prevailing evolutionary pattern of extremely small breeding pools operating on extremely non-random mating principles. Only then did extensive random population mixing and chance in mating, with approach of gene distributions to near-equilibrium patterns, become as important factors in human genetics as they now appear to be (Haldane, 1961).

Investigation of mating patterns in primitive modern communities of man or of those of other primates indicates that selection of mates from among the biologically eligible partners is neither random nor unrestricted. Rigidly restrictive practices, rules, and taboos governing mating partner selection apply, and have applied, from the distant past. A male probably had, during the millions of years of evolution which immediately preceded the appearance of *Homo sapiens,* no more than a few dozen sexually mature females to choose from in his life-span—more often, under a dozen, and even among these there was probably a marked ranking or ordering of their availability to him (Washburn, 1961; Aberle, Bronfenbrenner, Hess, Miller, Schneider, and Spuhler, 1963).

Migrations, murders and suicides, warfare, and massacres, splitting and fragmentation of communities and bands, or amalgamations and sudden mergers of groups, sudden social changes in mating practices and prohibitions—even very transient ones—and such natural accidents and catastrophes as earthquakes, floods, typhoons, volcanic eruptions, droughts, famines, and plagues all have a major influence in determining the genetic composition of small groups. The phenomenon of gene pattern being dependent upon a single pregnant female progenitor or very small number of progenitors or "founders" may, time and again, be repeated in the history of a given small group as the result of historical events such as these. The descendant population contains only the relatively few genes that the founders brought with them until replenished by later immigrations and mutation. Ernst Mayr (1963) has used the term "founder principle" to summarize these phenomena of funneling and associated variability among internally rather homogeneous groups derived from different "founders" which results from this small number sampling (Dobzhansky, 1955, 1963; Mayr, 1963; Goldschmidt, 1962). Furthermore, different assortments of genes produce phenotypes that may react in a similar manner to a given selective pressure (Mayr's selective equivalence of genotypes [1963]). This phenotypic equivalence, together with the indeterminacy of genetic recombination, may produce a wide genetic variance within the band which is the source of a great element of chance in human evolution (Wright, 1956; Mayr, 1963). Thus, unpredictable accidents select breeders possessing a random sample of only a small fraction of the total genetic variation of the parental population, and one such accidental sample may differ markedly from another.

I am thus stressing nothing fully new—you have all worked with models for "drift"—but rather contending that these diverse effects loosely called "genetic drift" have been major contributors to human evolution, as they more recently have been to the currently noted gene patterns in isolated populations. Random genetic drift and the factors usually summarized under this term are not sampling effects precisely determined by population size, because the effective size of sampling pool varies for each funneling event. The nets of kinship, mating rules, and the ties of psychological and social patterning by cultures serve to reduce the effective breeding pool size of small groups far below the figure obtained by simple enumeration of group members usually used in "drift" calculations. In fact, some smaller number determined by each historical accident which leads again to funneling of the gene source for the next generation through but a few individuals of the band renders meaningless any mean or average or effective group size estimate used over many generations in such computations. The hopeful application of mathematical techniques, derived from R. A. Fisher's work and from Sewell Wright's (1955) model for "random genetic drift" to man has long been made with full appreciation that cultural factors play a dominant role in human breeding patterns. In large populations with extensive mixing and unrestricted mating and near attainment of equilibrium, as encountered in agriculture and with some dense populations of lower animals in nature, these techniques are adequate. For human evolution and genetic analysis in primitive groups of man such mathematical models as usually applied are unrealistic predictors of variability. When exact historical data of the precise matings which gave rise to any pattern of gene distribution in small groups are known, no mathematical calculations which might predict the extent of possible "drift" are any longer entertained. The historical facts "explain" fully the pattern observed (Glass, 1956; Roberts and Harrison, 1959; Coon, 1962).

But human populations are historical, and man everywhere has a complex cultural and biological heritage. Only, when we do not know his history, we merely acknowledge its existence and proceed to calculate, using equations derived from concepts of selective advantage and fitness, mutation, and "drift," the predictable genetic pattern we would now observe if the population had sprung from a hypothetical group of founders; or we extrapolate back to hypothetical progenitors from the existing pattern we have observed. Yet, these equations represent processes easily overwhelmed by historical changes and accidental, or natural events which would fully account for the current pattern.

Our dilemma in describing human societies and their genetic structure and attempting to reconstruct their origins lies in our uncertainty about the sort of explanation we should regard as sufficient. R. A. Fisher (1958), who recognized this philosophico-historical problem clearly, has himself most aptly phrased it for human evolution:

> While genetic knowledge is essential for the clarity it introduces into the subject, the causes of the evolutionary changes in progress

can only be resolved by an appeal to sociological and even historical facts. These should at least be sufficiently available to reveal the more powerful agencies at work in the modification of mankind. . . . Generalized description should, however, never be regarded as an aim in itself. It is at best a means toward apprehending the causal processes which have given rise to the phenomena observed. Beyond a certain point it can only be pursued at the cost of omitting or ignoring real discrepancies of detail, which, if the causes were understood, might be details of great consequence. Alternatively, somewhat different states and events are subsumed under generalized and abstract terms, which, the more they are made comprehensive, tend to possess the less real and definable content. Finally, any purely descriptive general picture of events in time is in its nature fatalistic and allows no place for intelligent and corrective intervention.

The problem of the direction of our curiosity when confronted with the phenomenon of a strange genetic pattern in a population isolate, and of the nature of the questions we ask and what we should accept as adequate solution of them is crucial to my argument. I shall use an example from observation of a different game than that of gene sorting by history, chance drawings, and natural selection. Should we come upon a Grand Master of chess before a board on which his checkmate is imminent, with a novice at the game the impending victor, we would rightly be astonished and with legitimate curiosity ask how he got into such a mess. If in reply we were given a dissertation on the theory of chess, problems in strategy, and a general statistical treatment of the unlikelihood of this situation having ever arisen, we would, I venture to assert, be less satisfied than with a card on which the coded moves in the game to this point were recorded. With this information, all curiosity about the unlikely state of the board is answered, unless we now have further questions to ask such as "Who is the novice?" or "What prompted you, Grand Master, to reply as you did in your fourth move?"

I believe that the analogy here of various types of interest in the state of a chess board with the problem of the nature and direction of our curiosity about the genetic pattern of populations is cogent. In our interest in the nature of man and our wonder as to how he got to his current genetic destinations, we should ask what type of information will assuage our curiosity, satisfy our interests, and what types of answers we should find acceptable solutions to our queries. For many problems only the specific history and no general theory will provide the desired solution.

This aspect of the problem of knowledge has been long the subject of inquiry by devotees of the philosophy of history. Although a general theory of the necessary decline of a complex civilized culture after reaching its climax and of the associated victory over it by surrounding underdeveloped groups may satisfy our desires for generalization, it does little to still our curiosity and answer our interests about the historical events that led in a given culture to a given state of affairs. A general theory of history neither answers the legitimate specific questions we ask nor does it provide a means of answering them; it does not replace the need for a specific, detailed historical account of the unique and discrete situation that has aroused our interest. Similarly, in our desire to know more about ourselves, to ask of man whence and whither, we needs must face the problem that any general theoretical treatment which explains the causal processes will do little to account for our specific route to our current genetic composition or to predict its future course. Viewing our disappointment with his solutions, the theoretician can do little other than chide the nature of our intellectual inquiry and declare our curiosity misdirected to trivialities rather than to causal generalities . . . at best an unsatisfactory dogma.

If, as the result of my remarks, I am asked why then do we not see yet a further genetic variability in the populations of scattered islands of the Pacific, the oases of Australian deserts, or the jungles and mountains of South America and New Guinea than we do—why does man not vary from island to island as do dogs from kennel of one breed to kennel of another—I think that the accompanying chart of accidental and deliberate voyages in the South Pacific, consisting of only the better documented canoe and small unpowered craft voyages and not those of Polynesian myth, will serve to emphasize at what order of magnitude we must allow for unsuspected contact and genetic mixing possibilities (Denning, 1963; Simmons, Gajdusek, Brown and Riesenberg, 1964). For the populations of the Saharan oases, in contrast, we are not surprised to accept extensive mixing throughout the last few millenia, for we have a good record of human ebb and flow across North Africa. For these other areas we lack much of the history. Yet these islands of mankind *are* remote and infrequently visited, and unusual, unpredictable genetic differences *do* appear. Thus, the Polynesian population of Rennell Island today shows the extraordinarily high blood group B incidence of 57%, although ancient Polynesia was supposedly B gene free, as is most of modern Polynesia (Simmons and Gajdusek, 1964). This is a far higher incidence of the B gene than that found in adjacent Melanesian or further Micronesian populations or in any Asian or European

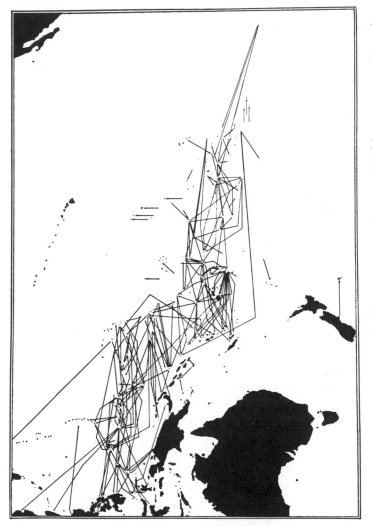

FIGURE 1. *Map of the South Pacific showing accidental and deliberate voyages in native canoes and small unpowered craft. Adapted from Dening, 1963 and Simmons, Gajdusek, Brown, and Riesenberg, 1964.*

peoples with whom they may have mixed. Now, should anyone inquire how one could possibly explain such founder variance or genetic heterogeneity as shown by the 1000 Rennellese, or other similarly extraordinary gene concentrations or discontinuities in gene patterns in the South Pacific, I refer them again to the same chart. It provides ample evidence for the possibility of enough intermixing and crossing to account for any desired dilution of widening variance just as well as it does for any unusual concentration of "unlikely" genes or gene systems to produce "improbable" degrees of variance (Simmons, Gajdusek, Brown, and Riesenberg, 1964).

As an example of the sort of past history we have learned to expect from isolated populations in the South Pacific, I turn to Micronesia. The Micronesians of the southwesternmost Caroline Islands on the remote, widely separated, tiny islands of Tobi, Sonsorol, Merir, and Pulo Anna trace their origins in their legends to Ulithi, some 650 miles to the northeast when a canoe sailed to Yap and then to these southwestern islands which were found uninhabited. By 1908, when the German South Sea Expedition arrived, Merir legends accounted for 23 successive chiefs (Eilers, 1936). In the reign of the fourth chief, "Papuans" (at least, dark-skinned, curly-haired Melanesians in canoes with double outriggers which Micronesians do not use) arrived from over 700 miles away, fought for 20 days with the Merir people, killed almost the entire population, and left. The island was repopulated from Pulo Anna and Sonsorol. Such hostile visits from Papuans from Jobi (Sofi or Gobi) and Larera on the north coast of New Guinea occurred again in the reigns of the 14th and 16th chiefs and in that of the 20th chief five Papuan women castaways arrived on Merir. In 1908 the Germans found a 15 year old boy on Sonsorol whose grandmother was one of these Papuans. Early in the 19th century 30 Papuans arrived on Sonsorol, captured several Sonsorolese, and then attacked Pulo Anna, Merir, and Tobi. Tobi was later resettled from Merir. A decade or two later, Papuans and people from Ternate Island near the Celebes reached Pulo Anna via Sonsorol. They fought, took many prisoners, and fled. One of the prisoners taken was an adopted Papuan who had previously arrived at Pulo Anna by canoe. Further evidence for such migrations lies in the fact that, when Europeans discovered many isolated Micronesian islands, strange Malay-speaking individuals, probably from distant Indonesian islands, were already in residence on two, while on others the people pointed to descendants of New Guineans living as part of their groups. S. H. Riesenberg (personal communication) of the Smithsonian Institution tells that the Melanesian peoples of the

Takar-Saar coast of New Guinea, which comprises the Jobi region and Sarmi on the mainland, and the coastal islands of Kumamba, Wakde and Jamna, from where these Papuans apparently came, are, interestingly, the only New Guineans who use a loom for weaving, a distinctly Micronesian trait.

Many studies have revealed remarkable differences in genetic pattern among neighboring human populations in the same environments: among adjacent Australian aboriginal tribes (Birdsell, 1950; Simmons, Graydon and Gajdusek, 1958; Simmons, Tindale and Birdsell, 1962), Micronesian Islanders (Kidson and Gajdusek, 1962), New Guineans (Curtain, Kidson, Gajdusek and Gorman 1962; Simmons, Graydon, Zigas, Baker and Gajdusek, 1961), American Indian groups (Kraus and White, 1956), Eskimos (Blumberg, Allison and Garry, 1959), and within small religious isolates of Europeans and Americans such as the Dunkers (Glass, Sacks, Jahn and Hess, 1952), the Hutterites (Steinberg, 1962), and the Amish (McKusick, 1964).

Last year J. Guiart, R. Kirk and I initiated an intensive long-term study of the population of Tongariki, a group of some 350 people living in three villages on the small island we had picked because of its extreme isolation and expected minimal genetic mixing among the New Hebridean islands (Gajdusek, 1964). We found to our surprise that many members of one of the villages were descendants of two Queensland aboriginal children who had been brought back to the island by returning Tongarikians after the repatriation to the New Hebrides of "black-birded" (kidnapped) islanders late in the last century from forced work in the Queensland sugar cane fields. This unlikely aboriginal Australian-New Hebridean crossing had given rise to a significant portion of the current Tongariki population; but, even today, these descendants were largely restricted to residence in one of the three villages on the island hardly five miles in maximum diameter. Furthermore, among children of a pure Australian aboriginal woman and a Tongariki man three siblings had developed familial periodic paralysis, an hereditary disease not previously reported in the Australasian populations (Gajdusek, Kirk, and Guiart, 1964).

We further learned of the attack on the island by Samoans in a war canoe late in the last century, just prior to the first arrival of Europeans. As the Samoans finally fled, a Samoan girl was captured, and today many Tongarikians trace their descent from her. This same canoe left a man on the island of Epi and finally landed on the island of Ambryn to found there a currently surviving Samoan-speaking community. Without the linguistic and the anthropological skill of

J. Guiart in tracing patiently the ethno-history of these peoples, we should have remained ignorant of these two "unlikely" events in population mixing on Tongariki which have been based upon only one or two new arrivals, but have contributed significantly to the current gene pattern on the island.

In the present era of molecular biology and biochemical genetics it is not surprising that, when faced with any unusual or remarkable pattern of gene distribution, the modern population geneticist should rush to discover the selective advantages of one enzyme or protein molecule over its allele-determined alternative, or to determine the selective disadvantage of the heterozygous and homozygous quantitative deficiencies in an enzyme. However rewarding this type of inquiry may be, with large populations of civilized mankind or with huge populations of lower organisms, I doubt the wisdom of such an attempt in dealing with the peculiar gene distribution patterns we encounter in small groups of primitive man, or even in population isolates of high inbreeding in the civilized world. These are not the proper places to look for effects of small selective advantages or small increases in fitness or fertility. It is in these very communities that strange historical accidents based upon natural catastrophe, faddish and changing social customs, and peculiarities in accidental encounters with members of other groups, determine far more the survival and distribution of a gene than its more easily grasped interaction with long-term forces such as malaria, filariasis, prevalence of tuberculosis, intensity of sunlight, or other biochemically determined selective advantages or disadvantages. Thus, destruction of those households or dwelling units on one side of a small island by a lava flow, tidal wave, typhoon, or earthquake can, in very small groups of very small numbers of breeding adults, very markedly determine the genetic composition of the next generation, as can canoe accidents or even such an event as the killing of a man and his brothers by a wounded beast on a hunt. The survivors after a volcanic eruption or a tidal wave may be just those biologically weaker outcasts who were forced to the periphery by their more able competitors, and who were destined for extinction in the operation of natural selection over many centuries in a large population. On this remaining group, not the fittest of the fit, selection then continues to exert its effects.

Similarly, we look immediately to biochemical causes for any selective disadvantage we suspect to be associated with a disease or anomaly. Yet leprosy, tinea imbricata (Schofield, Parkinson and Jeffrey, 1963), and other skin disorders may be far more a cause of late mating and limited fertility, even in the most primitive group, from the repugnance they arouse, than from any physiological limitation they impose upon reproductive ability or survival of the individual. Albinos may be sought and cherished in one community, rejected or destroyed in another. A mildly disabling disease or anomaly may determine extent of exposure to enemy attack in a group of warriors or even, by confining the sufferer to a house or bush shelter at the time of attack, determine his survival, whereas his more hardy companions are exposed as frontline warriors to major hazard and danger of death. Peculiar traits, such as the economic position of clansmen and other relatives, or the very fact of relationship, can far outweigh, in retaliatory murder, vendetta and revenge killings, rapes, or kidnappings, any genetic, biochemically-determined advantage which an individual may bear. Physiological advantage which brought the more hardy and able group on a small island to the best harbor site may also cause their annihilation when a large war canoe from distant islands picks the sheltered harbor for night landing and attacks the harbor settlement. Similarly, changes in cultural pattern which even in primitive groups may occur quickly, may suddenly render disadvantageous or without significant advantage a trait which previously served as a decided advantage, and such changes can often occur several times within the span of a human lifetime.

These events, biasing the gene pool fortuitously one way, then another, may average out over dense populations living under diverse environmental hazards and subject to diverse accidents. However, in small, virtually closed groups with breeding pools dependent upon but a few breeders for the next generation they are decisive, far outweighing even major biochemically-determined advantage. They frequently leave the genetic fate of the future community once again in the genetic laps of a few new "founders" who have been so selected by the vicissitudes of tempest, cataclysm, madness, or fad.

A castaway washed adrift on an island, or seeking shelter from his own or enemy group in a new small community or band, or kidnapped or captured in warfare, or spared after a headhunting raid, or welcomed as a visitor, God, or hero, if permitted to survive and join the group—as often may happen—may bear, by virtue of his lack of incest-taboo-limited mating possibilities in the new group, a great reproductive advantage over any of his hosts. This may lead to his markedly shifting the genetic pattern of the next and subsequent generations, producing an ultimate result which we might easily mistake for "hybrid vigor." This certainly has been the case many times over when civilized visitors have settled in primitive communities. Even in the baboon pack the shift of an old leader to another strange pack wherein he suddenly enjoys extreme mating privilege may occur.

In most primitive bands the next generation is often supplied in large part by only very few of the men and women of the previous generation. The marked variations in fertility among individuals in human communities is dependent upon the birth order, kinship and social status, training in infancy and childhood in social and sexual roles, and ascribable more to difference in individual temperament and disposition than to chance. Far more often than not the individuals in the privileged reproductive roles are determined by psychological and economic factors, rather than by biochemical advantages as naively sought at the level of disease resistance and physiological adaptability.

With civilized societies, although a small fraction of the reproducing adults may account for the major portion of the offspring of the next generation, there are still a great many such favored breeders, and natural selection operates quite as expected upon their mixed offspring. One favored breeder has little effect on the composition of the next generation. However, in small primitive bands half the community or more may stem from one single breeding male—with polygamy or special social license often assisting him—and thus, the accidents of temperament and fad, of economic advantage, or the vicissitudes of warfare and vendetta may completely alter the genetic pattern of a small community from generation to generation, eliminating by accident genes which have every biochemical advantage and reason for survival, or leaving at high frequency genes which in a large population would soon be eliminated because of selective disadvantages associated with them. Even in bands of Japanese and Indian macaques only dominant males are in a position to achieve fertile mating, and bachelor bands of the unsuccessful competitors are found.

The problem may be looked at in yet another way: small communities are never in genetic or evolutionary equilibrium, and changes causing major shifts in the composition of the genetic pool are likely to occur at far shorter intervals of time than the span of generations required for even approximate attainment of equilibrium patterns of gene distribution. These changes themselves shift the available chromosome and gene combinations which may be brought into the newly required equilibrium, and in human affairs one may expect within a few generations, at the most, further shifts in both the socio-environmental conditions that must be met and the pool of chromosomes which are undergoing natural selection to meet them optimally.

Thus, *Homo sapiens* has arrived at his genetic destinations by whim and misadventure, driven before the storms of natural selection which have shifted often in their course and their kind. His races have arrived at different current genetic locations by diverse routes from the genetic habitats of prehominid ancestors. The various genetic courses taken by his groups have been determined by their encounters with accidents and with others of their kind, and by the seas and the weather en route; and all along the exercise of choice—free will, if you wish—has left to him crucial decisions in the nature of purposeful "self selection" which have been determined more by the individual ethno-environmental patterning ("programming") of his nervous system than by his genetic endowment. The prevailing winds and tides have directed all his groups along approximately the same channel or course, as small craft before a hurricane, but the sea before him has been vast and the possible routes many. His courses have been varied and his genetic destinies diverse. Natural selection has operated only with "self selection" and accident to determine these routes and havens. Tempests of the future and his purposeful reactions to them could sweep him from all his varied gene shelters into one Maelstrom, or herd him into one fiord along varied routes, or force him into one harbor—or they may scatter his races far and wide and increase the genetic gulf between them. It is our inability to foresee the cataclysms, or men's willed and varied responses to them, that prevents our predicting his future genetic course with any certainty.

Small number sampling effects have undoubtedly been determining influences in human evolution. They should lead us to expect more genetic diversity among the various small population isolates of mankind than the number of founders and ultimate population size alone would lead one to predict. These effects arise from sampling diversity in the selection of small numbers of original progenitors, and a further "founder variance," the result of further small number sampling from within the small group of progenitors and their descendants is brought about by nonrandom operation of historical accident and psychological whim within the group. They have repeatedly offered to the forces of natural selection only small and unique arrays of those genotypes which they deliver to an evolving population and not an "infinite" collection of the fittest gene combinations possible. It is failure to find the expected diversity among primitive islands of mankind that calls for explanation, more than its presence (Coon, 1962; Neel, Salzano, Junqueira, Kiter, and Maybury-Lewis, 1964).

The theme of this paper is, then, that of the indeterminate results which we should expect from the operation of natural selection in human evolution in small population isolates; a diversity of outcome in excess of that which we should estimate from the number of original progenitors of each population derived from the same foundation stock. As a corollary, we should see in the homogeneity of genetic patterns in different distributional pockets of mankind derived from small numbers of "founders" not so much the consequences of natural selection pressing for one genetic goal as an indication of the lack of isolation and of the extent of inter-marriage in the recent past. Without this repeated cross-fertilization, and even to a large extent in spite of it, small primitive populations of mankind should be expected to show a marked "founder variance" produced by the indeterminate direction of natural selection which has augmented the frequency of any relatively fit array of genotypes which happened *first* to appear in a given population.

Variation in response has been found with animals in which several daughter populations of a single parental population were exposed to the identical selection pressure. Furthermore, Dobzhansky (1963) has shown in experimental populations of Drosophila, derived from small numbers of founders of two racial origins, divergent results in replicate experiments from apparently identical populations kept in identical environments. This, he believes, stems from the marked disproportion which exists between the number of new gene combinations possible and the number of individuals who make up the experimental population following interracial hybridization. Rather than waiting for the fittest of all possible genetic combinations to appear, natural selection begins to act on whatever genotypes arise in the first generations, a very small sample of all the possible gene combinations. This disproportion between the number of potential genotypes and the population size in interracial hybridization inevitably produces heterogeneity of genotype distribution in the early progenitors. Furthermore, the diversity of outcome now reflects in magnified form, as a result of the small number of founders, the variance that existed in the parental stock. A similar situation prevails with man; with each new splitting or fragmentation of community, new migration, or catastrophic reduction of numbers, the survival of a primitive human population isolate is again returned to a few critical founders. The more these differ one from another genetically the wider the possible diversity of outcome, since the next generation will be derived from but a small finite selection from among all the diverse gene systems in the original founding stock.

In summary, when faced with unusual incidences of genetic traits in small primitive human isolates, the geneticist should first turn to discovery of the human history of his group, rather than to the indirect prediction of the progenitors from assumed genetic advantages or to a search for the selective advantages. This entails the use of the historical record, study of myth, legend, folklore and religion, archaeological and paleontological data, comparative linguistics and all hints which may be derived from comparative ethnography and from the observations of botanists, zoologists, and geologists pertaining to man in the region under study. He should search for similar data in surrounding populations and study current kinship patterns, marriage practices, and other behavior relative to reproduction and survival. Reconstruction of past breeding patterns may occasionally be aided by gene markers found also in adjacent populations. Only when, through history, we know the genetic material on which natural selection has exerted its force, can the outcome of the action of these selective forces be interpreted. The vicissitudes of history caused by social, psychological, and natural events operating in small bands have contributed greatly to the determination of the evolutionary course that has led to man.

References

ABERLE, D. F., U. BRONFENBRENNER, E. H. HESS, D. R. MILLER, D. M. SCHNEIDER, and J. N. SPUHLER. 1963. The incest taboo and the mating patterns of animals. Amer. Anthrop. *65:* 253–265.

BIRDSELL, J. B. 1950. Some implications of the genetical concept of race in terms of spatial analysis. Cold Spring Harbor Symp. Quant. Biol. *15:* 259–314.

BLUMBERG, B. S., A. C. ALLISON, and BARBARA GARRY. 1959. The haptoglobins and haemoglobins of Alaskan Eskimos and Indians. Ann. Hum. Gen. *23:* 349–356.

COON, C. S. 1962. The origin of races. Knopf, New York. 724 p.

CURTAIN, C. C., C. KIDSON, D. C. GAJDUSEK, and J. G. GORMAN. 1962. Distribution pattern, population genetics and anthropological significance of thalassemia and abnormal hemoglobins in Melanesia. Amer. J. Phys. Anthrop. *20:* 475–483.

DENING, G. M. 1963. Polynesian navigation. Part 2. A table of accidental and deliberate voyages in the South Pacific. J. Polynes. Soc. *71:* 137–153.

DOBZHANSKY, T. 1955. A review of some fundamental concepts and problems of population genetics. Cold Spring Harbor Symp. Quant. Biol. *20:* 1–15.

———. 1963. Biological evolution in island populations, p. 65–74. *In* Man's Place in the Island Ecosystem. A Symposium. Ed.: F. R.

Fosberg. Tenth Pacific Science Congress, Honolulu, 1961. Bishop Museum Press.

EILERS, A. 1936. Westkarolinen. Part I. Songosor, Pur, Merir. Part II. Tobi, Ngulu. In: Ergebnisse der Südsee Expedition 1908–1910. Friederichsen, De Gruyter and Co., Hamburg, pp. i 405, ii 351.

FISHER, R. A. 1958. The genetical theory of natural selection. Second Revised Edition. Dover, New York, 291 p.

GAJDUSEK, D. C. 1964. Journal of a Trip to the Shepherd, Banks and Torres Islands and to Espiritu Santo and Efate in the New Hebrides, 1963. NINDB, Natl. Inst. Health, Bethesda.

GAJDUSEK, D. C., R. L. KIRK, and J. GUIART. 1964. Familial periodic paralysis with complete heart block in a family of New Hebridean (Melanesian) Australian aboriginal crossing. First report in aboriginal Australasians. Program and Abstracts of the Amer. Pediat. Soc., 74th Annual Meeting, p. 137–138.

GLASS, B. 1956. On the evidence of random genetic drift in human populations. Amer. J. Phys. Anthrop. *14:* 541–555.

GLASS, B., M. S. SACKS, E. F. JAHN, and C. HESS. 1952. Genetic drift in a religious isolate; an analysis of the causes of variation in blood group and other gene frequencies in a small population. Amer. Nat. *86:* 145–160. Reprinted in Yearbook of Phys. Anthrop. 144–158, 1952.

GOLDSCHMIDT, E., Ed. 1962. The genetics of migrant and isolate populations. Proceedings of a Conference on Human Population Genetics in Israel held at the Hebrew University, Jerusalem. Williams & Wilkins Co., Baltimore, 369 p.

HALDANE, J. B. S. 1961. Natural selection in man. Progress in Medical Genetics. Grune and Stratton, New York *1:* 27–37.

KIDSON, C. and D. C. GAJDUSEK. 1962. Glucose 6-Phosphate dehydrogenase deficiency in Micronesian peoples. Aust. J. Sci. *25:* 61–62.

KRAUS, B. S. and C. B. WHITE. 1956. Micro-evolution in a human population: a study of social endogamy and blood type distributions among the Western Apache. Amer. Anthrop. *58:* 1017–1043.

MAYR, E. 1963. Animal species and evolution. Harvard University Press, 797 p.

McKUSICK, V. A. 1964. Distribution of certain genes in the Old Order Amish. Cold Spring Harbor Symp. Quant. Biol. Vol. 29.

NEEL, J. V., F. M. SALZANO, P. C. JUNQUEIRA, F. KITER, and D. MAYBURY-LEWIS. 1964. Studies on the Xavante Indians of the Brazilian Matto Grosso. Amer. J. Hum. Gen. *16:* 52–140.

ROBERTS, D. F., and G. A. HARRISON. Ed. 1959. Natural selection in human populations. Symposia of the Society for the Study of Human Biology, Pergamon Press, London, *2:* 76 p.

SCHOFIELD, F. D., A. D. PARKINSON, and D. JEFFREY. 1963. Observations on the epidemiology, effects and treatment of tinea imbricata. Trans. Roy. Soc. Trop. Med. Hyg. *57:* 214–227.

SIMMONS, R. T., and D. C. GAJDUSEK. 1964. Blood group genetic survey of Rennell and Bellona Islands (B.S.I.P.) and certain northern New Hebridean islands. Oceania, in press.

SIMMONS, R. T., D. C. GAJDUSEK, P. BROWN, and S. RIESENBERG. 1964. Blood group genetic survey of Micronesians on the Caroline Islands. Am. J. Phys. Anthrop., in press.

SIMMONS, R. T., J. J. GRAYDON, and D. C. GAJDUSEK. 1958. A blood group genetical survey in Australian aboriginal children of the Cape York Peninsula. Amer. J. Phys. Anthrop. *16:* 59–78.

SIMMONS, R. T., J. J. GRAYDON, V. ZIGAS, LOIS BAKER, and D. C. GAJDUSEK. 1961. Studies on kuru. V. A blood group genetical survey of the kuru region and other parts of Papua-New Guinea. Amer. J. Trop. Med. Hyg. *10:* 639–664.

SIMMONS, R. T., N. B. TINDALE, and J. B. BIRDSELL. 1962. A blood group genetical survey in Australian aborigines of Bentinck, Mornington, and Forsyth Islands, Gulf of Carpentaria. Amer. J. Phys. Anthrop. *20:* 303–320.

STEINBERG, A. G. 1962. Evidence for a Gm allele negative for both Gm (a) and Gm (b). Vox Sang. *7:* 89–92.

WASHBURN, S. L., Ed. 1961. Social Life of Early Man. Aldine, Chicago, 299 p.

WRIGHT, S. 1955. Classification of the factors of evolution. Coldspring Harbor Symp. Quant. Biol. *20:* 16–24.
———. 1956. Modes of Selection. Amer. Nat. *90:* 5–24.

10

Culture and Microevolution

Blood Groups and Ancestry:
A Test Case from the New Guinea Highlands*

FRANK B. LIVINGSTONE

(*Editor's Note*) In this article Livingstone describes research done among New Guinea tribesmen in which blood group frequencies give no information about the relationships of neighboring tribes. That is to say, the blood grouping data are difficult or impossible to interpret in terms of what is known about the language similarities and relative geographical position of the tribes. Livingstone states that for populations which are very small, separated by only a few miles and difficult to delineate in terms of endogamy, it appears that genetic drift has obliterated any effect from common ancestry. While this is no general indictment against the use of blood grouping to determine "population paternity," it is an indication that the method cannot be indiscriminately applied. This paper should also serve as a reminder that human groups, regardless of the parameters used to identify them, seldom even approach the tidiness of the theoretical population.

THE blood group genes constitute the major source of data for genetic anthropology. Mourant's (1954 and 1958) summaries indicate the overwhelming mass of data that have been collected over the years for these genetic systems, and the collection continues today at an accelerated rate. In many publications there is little attempt to explain the data so that the work appears to be data collection for its own sake; a situation which closely approaches that which has filled libraries with masses of anthropometric measurements. Of course, many studies on blood groups have contributed significantly to the elucidation of our theories on the nature of human genetic diversity. However, many attempts to explain the similarities in blood group

*From *Current Anthropology*, vol. 4, No. 5, pages 541–542. By permission of the author and the publisher.

frequencies which have been obtained are in the form of assertions of common ancestry or migrations. This is true both for farreaching studies which claim to find Berber strains in England or American Indians in the Pacific and for smaller microevolutionary studies which are restricted to a single geographic region.

If the blood group genes are "relatively stable" and hence give some indication of distant common ancestry, then presumably within a small area and among closely related peoples they should also be correlated with common ancestry. The purpose of this paper is to attempt to test this assumption in one small area, the Eastern Highlands of New Guinea. The blood groups of this area have been examined by Kariks, Kooptzoff, Steed, Cotter, and Walsh (1960:225–236) and by Simmons, Graydon, Zigas, Baker, and Gajdusek (1961:639–664). The paper by Watson, Zigas, Kooptzoff, and Walsh (1961:25–41) does not give the results by language groups, so it has not been used. For the same human populations, the linguistic relations have been examined by Wurm, and for many of the languages he has calculated the percentage of cognates they share with neighboring languages. These data on the percentage of shared cognates have been obtained mostly from Gajdusek, Zigas, and Baker (1961:599–627), but also from Watson et al (1961) and from Wurm (1961:14–23). In some cases the percentage of cognates had to be estimated from dates of separation which were given, but these cannot be wrong by more than one percent. In addition, geographical distance between linguistic communities was estimated from the map given in Gajdusek and Zigas (1959:442–469). In Table 1 the absolute value of the difference in blood group gene frequencies for the ABO, MN, and Rh blood groups, the mean difference for all blood group genes, the mean difference using only two genes from each system, the mean of the maximum gene frequency difference for the 3 loci, the percentage of shared cognates, and the distance between the various language pairs are shown. Since the Keiagana blood group sample was quite small but much cognate data was available for this language, this sample has been combined with that of the Kanite, a mutually intelligible language. Although the ABO and Rh blood groups of these two languages were not significantly different, the MN blood groups of these two groups were significantly different at the .01 level; so this could reduce the significance of the results. This and other problems will be discussed after the results have been given.

Correlation coefficients were computed between the various blood group differences and linguistic differences, between the blood group and geographical differences, and between the geographical distance

TABLE 1. Ancestry and Blood Group Differences in the Eastern Highlands, New Guinea.

ABSOLUTE VALUE OF THE DIFFERENCE IN GENE FREQUENCY

TRIBES	O	A	B	Ms	Ns	NS	CDe	cDE	cDe	AVE. MAX.[3]	AVERAGE[1]	TOTAL AVERAGE	FREQUENCY DISTANCE OF COGNATES	(MILES)
Fore-Gimi	.145	.130	.015	.010	.028	.039	.026	.034	.007	.073	.039	.048	.46	25
Fore-Usurufa	.108	.079	.029	.120	.089	.030	.003	.031	.034	.087	.054	.058	.19	16
Fore-Bena	.109	.080	.029	.009	.049	.041	.137	.118	.019	.098	.049	.066	.33	47
Auyana-Usurufa	.105	.002	.107	.118	.129	.011	.007	.010	.003	.082	.042	.055	.76	10
Auyana-Agarebi	.020	.117	.097	.024	.072	.047	.084	.008	.076	.091	.062	.061	.49	28
Auyana-Tairora	.049	.030	.018	.027	.084	.056	.045	.047	.002	.060	.030	.040	.33	14
Auyana-Gadsup	.050	.039	.011	.092	.129	.037	.046	.049	.003	.076	.039	.051	.46	29
Gadsup-Gimi	.092	.010	.082	.104	.061	.043	.082	.062	.021	.093	.057	.062	.32	59
Gadsup-Tairora	.001	.009	.007	.065	.045	.019	.001	.002	.001	.025	.017	.017	.35	20
Gadsup-Agarebi	.070	.156	.086	.068	.057	.010	.130	.057	.073	.118	.075	.079	.69	11
Auyana-Gimi	.142	.049	.093	.012	.068	.080	.036	.013	.024	.086	.045	.057	.32	35
Agarebi-Gimi	.162	.166	.004	.036	.004	.033	.048	.005	.052	.085	.049	.057	.32	53
Agarebi-Tairora	.069	.147	.079	.003	.012	.009	.129	.055	.074	.096	.061	.064	.35	25
Gimi-Tairora	.093	.019	.075	.039	.016	.024	.081	.060	.022	.071	.040	.048	.20	50
Gahuku-Asaro	.046	.047	.002	.007	.071	.063	.004	.004	.009	.042	.022	.028	.71	19
Gahuku-Benabena	.016	.049	.033	.040	.045	.005	.044	.054	.010	.049	.032	.033	.58	23
Keiagana-Fore[2]	.100	.078	.022	.065	.078	.014	.036	.041	.005	.073	.038	.049	.34	10
Keiagana-Gimi[2]	.045	.052	.007	.075	.050	.025	.010	.007	.002	.046	.028	.030	.34	22
Keiagana-Usurufa[2]	.008	.001	.007	.055	.011	.044	.039	.010	.029	.034	.024	.023	.23	8
Keiagana-Benabena[2]	.009	.002	.007	.056	.029	.027	.101	.077	.024	.055	.032	.037	.60	37
Keiagana-Gahuku[2]	.025	.051	.026	.016	.016	.032	.057	.023	.034	.047	.030	.031	.48	47
Keiagana-Tairora[2]	.048	.033	.082	.036	.034	.001	.091	.067	.024	.070	.041	.046	.14	28
Keiagana-Auyana[2]	.097	.003	.100	.063	.118	.055	.046	.020	.026	.088	.045	.059	.29	13
Correlation coefficient with cognate frequency r =	−.1924	+.0973	+.0140	+.0244	+.2580	−.0862	−.0378	−.1127	−.0095	+.0029	+.0132	+.0067		−.2131
Correlation coefficient with geographical distance r =	+.2419	+.0712	+.0110	−.2294	−.4319	+.1340	+.3849	+.3451	+.1304	+.1656	+.1562	+.1657		

[1] This is the average difference of the A, B, Ms, NS, cDE, cDe genes.
[2] The Kanite have been included in this sample of Keiagana.
[3] This is the average of the maximum gene frequency difference for each of the three loci.

and linguistic distance. These are shown at the bottom of Table 1. Only one of these correlation coefficients is significantly different from zero at the five percent level; that between geographical distance and the Ns gene is significantly less than zero, which means that the farther apart the languages are, the closer are their Ns frequencies! Because of the problems involved in the Keiagana-Kanite sample, these correlations were also run excluding comparisons involving this sample, and the results were the same, i.e., none of the blood group differences was correlated with language differences.

If it is assumed that differences in language are a measure of how far in the past different populations were members of the same speech community and hence also members of the same breeding population, then these results indicate that there is absolutely no correlation between blood group gene frequency differences and closeness of common ancestry. In this small area of New Guinea with perhaps a similar environment throughout, there is also no correlation of the blood group differences with geographical distance. Of course, there are many problems connected with these data. The language groups are almost certainly not the breeding populations of this area, but this concept is hard to apply to this area in any way. The locus of marriage choice is the small exogamous patrilineal clan, and each of these clans has a different group of clans with whom they exchange women. These differences are mostly a function of distance. Hence the group which appears to conform most closely to the concept of breeding population is quite small and has fifty percent gene flow in each generation. In addition the samples for the blood group determinations are quite small so that much of the variation is sampling variation, but the frequencies among these tribes do differ significantly. These significant differences may be due to gene drift which has undoubtedly played a large role and seems to have overwhelmed in the time since separation any similarity due to common ancestry. I am also not sure that the test of these differences by the correlation coefficient is the best statistical test available. But in any case these results strongly contradict many explanations of blood group differences and should indicate more caution in using common ancestry as such an explanation.

References

GAJDUSEK, D. C. and ZIGAS, V. 1959. Kuru, *The American Journal of Medicine*.

GAJDUSEK, D. C., ZIGAS, V., and BAKER, J. 1961. Studies on Kuru. III. Patterns of Kuru incidence: demographic and geographic epidemiological analysis. *American Journal of Tropical Medicine and Hygiene.*

KARIKS, J., KOOPTZOFF, O., STEED, M., COTTER, H., and WALSH, R. J. 1960. A study of some physical characteristics of the Goroka natives, New Guinea. *Oceania.*

MOURANT, A. E. 1954. *The Distribution of the Human Blood Groups.* C. C. Thomas, Springfield.

MOURANT, A. E., KOPEC, A. C., and DOMANIEWSKA-SOBCZAK, K. 1958. *The ABO Blood Groups.* Blackwell, Oxford.

SIMMONS, R. T., GRAYDON, J. J., ZIGAS, V., BAKER, L. L., and GAJDUSEK, D. C. 1961. Studies on Kuru. V. A blood group genetical survey of the Kuru Region and other parts of Papua-New Guinea. *American Journal of Tropical Medicine and Hygiene.*

WATSON, J. B., ZIGAS, V., KOOPTZOFF, O., and WALSH, R. J. 1961. The blood groups of natives in Kainantu, New Guinea. *Human Biology.*

WURM, S. A. 1961. *The linguistic situation in the Highlands Districts of Papua and New Guinea. Australian Territories,* Dept. of Territories, Canberra.

Population Distances: Biological, Linguistic, Geographical, and Environmental*

W. W. HOWELLS

(*Editor's Note*) A broad definition of anthropology after the somewhat pompous one which reads "anthropology is the study of man" is the more meaningful "anthropology is the study of race, language, and culture." This definition, at least, indicates the major subjects considered to be in the realm of the discipline. It doesn't, however, indicate whether it refers to the piecemeal product of specialists or whether race, language, and culture really are to be thought of as such closely integrated aspects of a whole that any dissection is artificial. The fact is that few anthropologists have ever taken on this problem directly. While convinced that the proper study of man demands a holistic approach, the methodological problems involved in carrying it out have prevented most anthropologists from making the attempt. That is why the following article by Howells is particularly interesting and important. The need for a multivariate approach is greater as it becomes increasingly evident that genetic and phenotypic variation in man can ultimately be affected by exceedingly complex and subtle interactions among ecological, demographic, socio-cultural, and biologic variables. It may be pointless to advocate cooperation among workers in these various areas until analyses are available that adequately deal with the problems which prompt an interdisciplinary effort. The author experiments with new analytic techniques using data collected many years ago. While continued data gathering is no doubt essential, we may have arrived at a period in the study of micro-evolution when the emphasis should be strongly on the side of developing adequate kinds of analyses.

*From *Current Anthropology*, vol. 7, No. 5, pages 531–540. By permission of the author and the publisher.

IN the early days of physical anthropology, population ("racial") differences were assigned entirely, if seldom explicitly, to differences in *genetic origin*, that is, to ancestral "pure races," modified only through mixture. It was Boas who demonstrated for man the possibility of *environmental response*; and biologists were simultaneously recognizing that such shifts could involve either *phenotypic plasticity*, a pure environmental effect on an unchanged gene pool, or actual Darwinian *adaptive selection*.

Partly because of this, and partly because of their own clear genetic basis, blood groups took primacy of interest away from anthropometry in both descriptive and genetic studies. Here, also, the original assumption was one of stability in population blood group differences, differences whose origin was not explained except by mutation. Only a decade ago did the probable action of selective agents on blood factors, and still more recently the importance of *genetic drift*, become generally acknowledged. In addition, however, to evidences in some regions of long-time stability and in others of drift, there are also strong signs of nonrandom trends in the ABO system in the decline or loss of gene B, and perhaps of A, in small isolated or marginal populations (America, Oceania, Switzerland—see Benoist 1964 for a West Indian example). This suggests that still other factors, more familiar from mathematical population genetics, may be of real significance in man: *population size* and effectiveness of isolation, i.e., *rate of gene flow* (as distinguished from the mere fact of hybridizing).

We have become theoretically sophisticated as to the factors italicized above, but we are still by no means advanced methodologically in applying them to the materials of physical anthropology, which are normally derived from a complex historical situation. We gather data first and ask questions afterwards, an old anthropological habit learned from justly revered masters, who adopted it because of the rush of ethnic and ethnographic change. Our publications are apt to consist of a report of the data followed by a discussion section in which these evolutionary factors are browsed among and ruminated, but are not or cannot be submitted to test.

Livingstone (1963), using material from the Eastern Highlands of New Guinea, determined intergroup distances or differences in miles, blood group frequencies, and language and got low correlations among these three distances, especially the last two. Thus, if language is used as the index of common ancestry, the latter was *not* reflected in blood group likenesses, which should therefore, Livingstone concluded, not be incautiously used as a measure of community of genetic origin. That genetic drift may have been important in this case appears from Giles, Walsh, and Bradley (1965; see Cavalli-Sforza *et al.* 1965; Gajdusek 1965), who showed its significance in differentiating blood types of two clearly related and ecologically similar villages, also in the Territory of New Guinea. Laughlin and Jorgensen (1956) demonstrated the probable effect of drift on morphological characters, using Eskimo crania from Greenland.

One can think of other studies of the effect of one particular factor. Relatively few studies attempt to assess several factors at once. Among these is that of Hiernaux (1956), who used measures of "distance" in anthropometric traits (D^2) and in blood traits (sum of chi-squares) among a number of tribes in Kivu and Ruanda Urundi to gather evidence relating to environmental effects, persisting genetic differences, and gene flow.

This paper is also an attempt to view the operation of several factors, in a case in which controls are not good but which deals with a definable population area, important to Oceanic history: Bougainville in the Solomons. The method is to use biological, ecological, and cultural variables, reducing each one to a single measure of differences between populations and investigating the correlation of these differences.

The Data

The population of Bougainville is "Melanesian" in physique and culture, but cultural and linguistic evidence makes it clear that the existing ethnic differentiation has not been a purely local process, i.e., that distinct immigrant groups are involved, previous analysis suggesting at least three such (Oliver 1954; Oliver and Howells 1960). Environment varies from coastal beaches to hill slopes and ridges to mountainous areas along the central spine. Languages are Melanesian and non-Melanesian, the former being largely confined to the shore and occupying the majority of it (see Fig. 1). There exist two different stocks of non-Melanesian and several families of Melanesian.

Oliver took measurements and made morphological observations visually on over 1,300 males aged 20-49, who were assignable to 18 ethnic groupings, representing most of the island's territory.[1] The

[1]Data on the samples may be found in the previous publications on the material. Several number less than 50, but the deficiency is probably less serious where blood group frequencies are not involved; and the smallest group,

data used here consist of "distances" computed among these 18 groupings in a number of characteristics defined immediately below. These distances are correlated with one another in Table 1. For example, the distance in actual miles, GEOG, is correlated with Penrose's generalized SHAPE distance, r being .24; thus there is a low but positive and significant association between actual distance between groups and degree of difference in one aspect of physique. Correlations between any two kinds of distance are positive even when insignificant. N is 153, the number of possible pairings among 18 groups.

Geographic distance (GEOG). The crude distance, in miles, taken directly from the 1:253,400 (4 miles to 1 inch) map (4 miles series, LHQ Cartographic Coy, Australian Survey Corps 1945), between centers of group areas.

Topographic distance (TOPOG). An attempted adjustment of the crude distances above, with Oliver's advice, to allow for supposed ease or difficulty of actual human travel, according to terrain.

Group boundaries distance (TRIBE). A count of the boundaries between groups (see Fig. 1) necessary to be crossed in going from one population center to another by the most economical or direct route (the same as Hiernaux's [1956] "genetic barriers" or Elmendorf's [1965] "contact interval"). This is an attempt to recognize the element of social access in what is still to a large extent geographical distance. Subdivision of two language areas, Siuai (1-4) and Nagovisi (6-8), has however perhaps disproportionately increased the counts in this region (see below).

Altitude distance (ALT). A scale of 0 to 5 based on rough estimates made from the adjacent map, with help from Eugene Ogan, of mean altitude of a group's territory.

Linguistic distance (LING). A four-step scale (with some interpolation), based on the data of Jerry Allen and Conrad Hurd,[2] proportional to the number of shared cognates between languages and essentially expressing (1) interdialect, (2) interlanguage, (3) interfamily, and (4) interstock (Melanesian *vs.* non-Melanesian) differences.

#16, numbering only 17 men, nevertheless closely resembles its neighbor #15, as other considerations would have made likely. The net effect of variation due to sample size is probably to lower correlations among distances involving physique, while possibly spuriously increasing any evidence of genetic drift.

[2] The survey was conducted in 1963 for the Summer Institute of Linguistics, New Guinea Branch; the report, *Linguistic Survey of Bougainville*, is not yet published, and the material is used here by the kind permission of James C. Dean, Director of the Institute.

Cognate distance (COGN). The actual percentage of shared cognates, from Allen and Hurd's material. This gave correlation results almost identical with LING; since the distribution was rather abnormal, with gaps, the distances were changed to a continuous scale of 25 steps, on the advice of C. F. Mosteller.

Size distance (SIZE). Penrose's size distance (general size independent of proportional differences), based on eight measurements: sitting height, arm length, chest breadth, head length, head breadth, minimum frontal, bigonial, total face height (Penrose 1954; see Oliver and Howells 1960).

FIGURE 1. *Map of Bougainville showing location of populations. Melanesian-speaking groups (14–18) underlined.*

Shape distance (SHAPE). Penrose's shape distance (differences in proportions, with size constant), based on the same eight measurements (Penrose 1954; see Oliver and Howells 1960 for full tabulation of these distances).

Morphological observations (SCOPIC). Anthroposcopic, or nonmetric, observations (the term SCOPIC is used to avoid the clumsiness and ambiguity associated with "morphological") of the following (all shown by chi-square to have significant intergroup heterogeneity): hair form, hair texture, head hair color, eye color, height of eye opening, forehead slope, nasal root breadth, nasal tip inclination, frontal nostril visibility, integumental lip thickness, Darwin's point, occipital protrusion. The generalized distance between groups is their

$$D^2 = \frac{(\mu_1 - \mu_2)^2}{\frac{1}{2}\,(\sigma_1{}^2 - \sigma_2{}^2)} \text{ on a discriminator,}$$

standardized mean difference, $(\log L\ gp_1) - (\log L\ gp_2)$, furnished me by Arthur Dempster and programmed by John Chambers.[3] This is a sort of "genetic" distance—the reader may invoke for himself all of the implications of this, especially vis-à-vis blood group data, without further discussion in this abbreviated paper.

[3]Each trait was reduced to two classes only, e.g., 0 to 1, so as to give the proportions of one of these classes: p in group 1, q in group 2. For an individual whose score on trait i is X_i (either 0 or 1):

$$\log L\ gp_1 = \sum_{i=1}^{12} \left(X_i \log p_i + (1 - X_i) \log (1 - p_i) \right)$$

$$\log L\ gp_2 = \sum_{i=1}^{12} \left(X_i \log q_i + (1 - X_i) \log (1 - q_i) \right)$$

$$\mu_1 = \sum_{i=1}^{12} \left\{ \log (1 - p_i) - \log (1 - q_i) + p_i \left[\log p_i - \log (1 - p_i) - \log q_i + \log (1 - q_i) \right] \right\}$$

$\mu_2 =$ same, with p and q interchanged.

$$\sigma_1{}^2 = \sum_{i=1}^{12} \left\{ p_i (1 - p_i) \left(\log p_i - \log (1 - p_i) - \log q_i + \log (1 - q_i) \right)^2 \right\}$$

$\sigma_2{}^2 =$ same, with p and q interchanged.

Results

The values of *r* in Table 1 cover a considerable range, but only a difference on the order of .25 or more can be considered significant statistically. However, the N involved (153) is of respectable size, and there are internal consistencies in the figures. Further, it is primarily the method of approach which is of interest. If we bear all this in mind, Table 1 seems to contain the following information:

(1) The spatial distances (GEOG, TOPOG, TRIBE) are all rather similar in their relationships with other factors. The topographic distances do not represent any real distinction from the crude geographic (although they do appear to be very slightly better related to the biological distances).

(2) The group boundaries (TRIBE) do not seem to represent a distinct isolating factor. The figures do not show whether in fact group isolation or simple distance is the primary agent. Because, however, of a higher degree of subdivision, for this analysis, of the Siuai and Nagovisi areas, increasing somewhat arbitrarily the number of boundaries reckoned here, I think the geographical rather than the group separation is more important. Also, in fact group isolation is anything but complete.

(3) Altitude differences are insignificantly related to spatial distance (.05 to .13). The relation of ALT to other factors may therefore be considered essentially independent of mere geographical distance, an important point *if* altitude is viewed as an environmental factor of consequence. (In any case, the shape of the island plays a part in the low correlation: altitude varies with the shorter, transverse distances, not with the longer longitudinal ones.)

(4) Altitudinal and linguistic distances are moderately well correlated. COGN has a lower *r* with ALT than does LING, which seems to reflect the hierarchical differences in language (Melanesian *vs.* non-Melanesian) between upland and shore, a matter of historical migrations, over and above general linguistic differentiation by local change.

(5) The two linguistic distances are generally similar except for the higher *r*'s of LING with ALT (.32 *vs.* .21), with SHAPE (.43 *vs.* .36), and with SCOPIC (.42 *vs.* 37). These differences are small and conceivably a statistical artifact, but at face value they suggest that altitude, body proportions, and external features are all distributed with some relation to language, and especially to the Melanesian-non-Melanesian distinction.

TABLE 1. *Coefficients of Correlation Among Various "Distance" Measures.*

	GEOG	TOPOG	TRIBES	ALT	LING	COGN	SIZE	SHAPE	SCOPIC
GEOG	—	.92	.60	.13	.58	.57	.13	.24	.22
TOPOG	.92	—	.58	.13	.59	.55	.15	.29	.24
TRIBES	.60	.58	—	.05	.52	.48	.22	.24	.15
ALT	.13	.13	.05	—	.32	.21	.39	.41	.48
LING	.58	.59	.52	.32	—	.71	.31	.43	.42
COGN	.57	.55	.48	.21	.71	—	.30	.36	.37
SIZE	.13	.15	.22	.39	.31	.30	—	.36	.45
SHAPE	.24	.29	.24	.41	.43	.36	.36	—	.28
SCOPIC	.22	.24	.15	.48	.42	.37	.45	.28	—

$N = 153$ (the total of possible pairings of 18 groups).   Levels of significance: for 5%, $r = .16$; for 1%, $r = .22$.

('6) The linguistic distances are well correlated with the spatial distances, six r's varying from .48 to .59. (Livingstone, with a much smaller N, found $r = .21$; Elmendorf [1956] found a good though unmeasured correlation of this sort *within* the Interior Salish.) These values are considerably higher than the LING-ALT r of .32, which would suggest that a Melanesian-shore *vs.* a non-Melanesian-upland distinction, while apparently present, is only a fraction of the whole picture of linguistic differentiation on the island.

(7) The three biological distances are intercorrelated with interesting variation. SIZE and SCOPIC are correlated (.45) more highly than SHAPE and SCOPIC (.28). Since we ordinarily assume these last two aspects to be more "genetic," i.e., less variant from external causes, than size, we might have looked for the opposite trend in r, especially if differences in genetic origin are accepted. (Hiernaux found $r = .63$ between blood group "distance" and D^2— size and shape combined—in a situation where historical genetic differences were an obvious factor.) This leads us to enquire for special causes, such as a genetic connection of size and external features. Oliver (1954) during the course of his work came to believe that the smaller peoples of the southern mountains (especially area 7; see Oliver and Howells 1957) were in fact Negritoid in origin, rather than simply environmentally dwarfed. This special explanation accords logically with the facts above.

(8) All the biological distances are poorly or insignificantly correlated with spatial distances. (Here we have comparative figures: Hiernaux, for the r with tribal boundaries, found .33 for D^2 and .34 for blood group distances, with genetic factors assumed to be causal. On the other hand, Livingstone found $r = .17$ between geographic distance and over-all blood differences. Brooks and Van Arsdale [1964] report $r = .17$ between distance in miles and a biological distance computed from cranial measurements, as well as lower r's for individual cranial measurements. Hanna [1962] found "no significant correlation" between D^2 and distances in miles among seven southwestern U.S. Indian tribes.)

It is SHAPE which consistently has the highest correlations with geographical distances: this accords with the possibility that there is variety in body form on the island independent of what may be traced either to altitude or to a possible Negrito genetic strain in the south of the island.

(9) All biological distances are correlated with altitude (to a degree well above the lowest r between two biological distances them-

selves). Environmental differences might have been expected to cause ALT and SIZE to exhibit the highest r; in fact, it is the lowest in this set, with r for ALT and SCOPIC being a surprising .48. Again, this suggests differences which are primarily genetic, stemming from the presence of a Negritoid population.

(10) Biological and linguistic distances are fairly well correlated, especially in the cases of SHAPE and SCOPIC (the more "genetic" characters?), r in four cells ranging from .36 to .43. (Livingstone found r for cognate distance and blood group difference to be —.01.) This seems to suggest, Livingstone's data notwithstanding, historical associations between genetic features and language.

(11) For SIZE, the high r's are with altitude, shape, and scopic differences—is this a reflection of Negrito associations? It has lower r's with geography and language, as noted; in this connection it should be borne in mind that the size factor is strictly a simple, one-dimensional scale (Oliver and Howells 1960), which need not exhibit, or preserve, distinctive patterns like other aspects of physique or language. Its relatively high r with ALT may therefore reflect in part a real environmental response and not only the presumed Negrito effect. Nevertheless, it should be said that the basic data show no constant, island-wide association of stature with altitude.

The above evidence might be interpreted, with relation to the three main assumed agencies of differentiation, as follows:

Genetic drift. To measure this, one would like several distinct populations, mutually isolated but of common origin and of identical culture and environment. The study of Giles *et al.* (1965) approaches this, but Bougainville offers no such regularities.

Evidence *for:* (10), combined with (6), the correlation between linguistic and biological differentiation, and linguistic differentiation which is to a significant degree local, not introduced;[4] also (7), the low correlation between SHAPE and SCOPIC, two presumably "genetic" systems.

---

[4]Drift in the simplest sense, i.e., random fluctuations over time in related populations of similar size, should correspond with, and correlate with, the linguistic drift envisaged in the model of glottochronology. (Linguistic drift, however, is irreversible; and this model appears not to allow for linguistic "flow," corresponding to gene flow, which would inhibit drift because of contact and exchange between contiguous groups and which must exist—see Elmendorf 1965. Therefore correspondence of linguistic and biological differences with one another and with geographic distance should be compatible with the interpretation of human genetic drift, although these effects are just what Livingstone did not find.)

Evidence *against:* (2) and (8), the poor correlation of all biological distances with geographical distance, and especially the failure of group boundaries to show such a relation.

Genetic differences. To demonstrate these, one hopes to find, in a common environment, population differences in physique which are too systematic to be explicable by drift and which are also associated with cultural differences (the evidence Livingstone did *not* find). If clines—gradients in a biological feature—can be discerned, they are (a) evidence of environmental effect if they correspond to an environmental gradient; (b) contra-evidence of differences in genetic origin or of drift *if* group isolation is complete; (c) positive evidence of genetic differences if, as is usual, gene flow exists; and neutral for drift.

Evidence *for:* in general, (10), the association of biological and linguistic differences, combined with (3), the higher correlation of geographic separation with shape distance than with other physical features; in particular, the several suggestions—(4), (5), (7), and (9)—of upland (especially Negritoid) shore distinctions; also possibly (6), and (11).

Evidence *against:* (7), the poor correlation of SHAPE and SCOPIC, probably more telling here than in the case of drift; also (2), with (8), the poor correlation of geographical separation with biological distance, and (6), the higher correlation of geographical distances with linguistic than with physical distances, suggesting some independence of linguistic intrusions from physical ones.

Environmental effects. To demonstrate these, one would like an originally homogeneous population exhibiting a clearly environmentally related cline; concomitant drift can hardly be excluded.

Evidence *for:* (11), the relation of altitude and size distances; however, (9) allows this to be an original genetic difference.

Evidence *against:* (9), and all the several indicators that the altitude differences in physique are possibly traceable to Negrito ancestry.

Discussion

While this paper is addressed to general principles, we cannot, as I have noted, escape the special case. We should therefore refer briefly to some of the background data, primarily those in Oliver's own (1954) presentation, which is unfortunately not widely distributed. I believe the following are fair statements from that material.

While there is definite patterning in the distributions of body size and form on the island, there are no consistent clines in body measurements, etc., with relation to altitude or other environmental factors. Oliver himself concluded this, and the correlations in Table 1 correspond to what might be expected from examination of the full material. (Correlation of *distances* in altitude and biological factors is not the same as direct correlation of, e.g., altitude and size.) There is therefore no positive evidence of environmental effects.

Of the 18 ethnic groups, 11 correspond to linguistic divisions while the remaining 7 are only subdivisions of 2 other linguistic divisions. Since these subdivisions in both cases show significant physical differentiation (see Oliver and Howells 1957), it is to be expected that the other 11 groups, at least the large ones, would also manifest such internal differences, which are masked in the use of these groups as units. This should not vitiate the evidence relating to environmental or genetic differences; however, the smaller divisions, actual or possible, should better approximate the "effectively small" populations in which genetic drift might occur (Giles *et al.* 1965). We may conclude, then, that the internal differences in the two groups mentioned may be due either to drift or to gene flow from outside; that the general analysis used here is *not* suitable for the proper testing of drift; and that the lack of evidence for the presence of drift therefore does not demonstrate its absence.

There is good specific evidence that the main physical differences on Bougainville are those resulting from original genetic differentiation of populations and gene flow among them. (This also was Oliver's conclusion; however, the present study was not undertaken to prove it.) It is clear that Melanesian-speakers arrived when non-Melanesians were already present, the last of them (the east coast Torau) coming from Shortlands after 1865. Rates of intermarriage across various group boundaries, sometimes considerable, are known in a general way. The full pattern of SHAPE distances (see Oliver and Howells 1960, Table II) accords quite well with all this information, and the analysis here supports it also.

(It is interesting to apply the findings to the question of Oceanic Negritos. Are those of different areas parts of a single original population, as may be argued if "scopic" traits—and size—are taken as the index of ancestry? Or are they quite independent in origin, locally precipitated out of other populations, even non-negroid ones, as an adaptive response to a tropical forest environment, as may be argued if blood traits are taken as the index of ancestry? The evidence in Table 1, as I have interpreted it, seems to favor the first hypothesis.)

So for Bougainville the most definite evidence leads us back, somewhat frustrated, to the conclusion which was the assumption of the early anthropologists: differences are due to pre-existing differences. In the last 50 years anthropologists have been able to demonstrate phenotypic response, genetic drift, or the action of selection, either from carefully selected special cases or from world-wide distributions (e.g., Bergmann's rule, or malaria). But the establishment of morphologically distinctive human populations on a small scale (other than by hybridizing), such as must have been happening constantly and recently, and such as we presume to result from the above factors, has not been caught in the act. Possibly we are also suffering from incomplete assimilation of genetic theory and need an expansion of our formulations beyond the point reached by recent writings on race. If the early idea of human races might be compared to the "big bang" theory of an exploding universe, perhaps we can use a postulate corresponding to the "steady state," in which populations, at least those of moderate size, have constantly been assuming distinctive form, under forces of genetic homeostasis, integration of the genotype, and regulation of variation, which we do not know how to detect or to apply in interpretation.

Historical problems are complex compared to well-controlled experimental studies, and it is difficult in the preceding analysis to point to the most telling evidence. The correlations, where comparable, do not agree with those of Livingstone or Hiernaux. This shows that generalizations cannot be made from special cases, but it does not disparage the evidence; instead it points to the value of historical and cultural information in shedding light on the reasons for the differences found (see also Gajdusek 1965).

Finally, it is interesting to see that visually made physical observations, those termed "scopic" herein, although seldom used recently (except in Germany, in paternity testing; but see also Keiter, in Neel *et al.* 1964), turn out to be decidedly useful in measures of distance.

Comments

J. LAWRENCE ANGEL. *Washington, D.C.* In showing that under precivilized conditions tribal differences in language and in altitude (hence also ecology) correlate clearly with physical differences (including morphological details) which are at least partly genetic in origin, Howells' paper supports a traditional anthropological point of view: that variation between groups has clear historic, microevolutionary, and complex explanations based ultimately on factors of selection, both environmental and social; drift is less important.

Howells stresses that the clashing correlations between genes and language found by Livingstone in New Guinea and Hiernaux in Africa caution generalization; but there is a common fallacy here which both Livingstone and Howells seem not to avoid. Single gene traits such as blood groups change much more easily from accidents of sampling in small populations (the founder effect, one aspect of drift) than do functional or even morphological traits which (a) depend on many gene systems and (b) are subject to stronger and more variable selection. I don't know what Howells would find if Oliver had had the facilities and time to collect blood group data, but I will guess that the blood groups would have varied much more randomly with little correlation with language simply because of population size change.

Size of breeding group is one factor which Howells might have included to clarify the question of drift. In theory, both the founder effect and drift itself should respond most sensitively to this. But Howells is not actually testing microevolution, even though his data are better for this purpose than almost any human data previously set forth. To do this, he would need both a closer control of selective forces than "altitude" suggests (for example, some correlation between specific fertilities and specific physical traits) and above all a really detailed historical picture. It is the lack of time depth which tends to short-circuit analyses of human group relatedness at both physical and social levels. Several microevolutionary studies on skeletal material (including my own on Greece [1951]) which show a close relation between population size and degree and spread of evolutionary change omit detailed social data and most of the precise geographic group and language control of Howells' present approach.

This approach is a landmark on the path toward ideal analysis of micro-evolution, less in its specific results than in its use of multiple computer-worked data from linguistics and geography as well as from physique. When this sort of control can include also social anthropology (like the breeding pattern correlations of Oliver and Howells' 1957 analysis), psychophysical traits (visual discrimination, imagination, emotional restraint, etc.), *and* a hierarchic analysis of the traits used, we will have a real basis for the question of processes of selection. These I believe to be the crucial next steps.

JOSEPH B. BIRDSELL. *Los Angeles, Calif.* At a time when physical anthropologists are primarily concerned with detecting evidences of the existence of evolutionary processes, and subsequently hoping to evaluate their magnitudes and perhaps even to partition out the contributions of the several forces which are always interacting in nature, one can sympathize with Howells' expressed frustration over the conclusions presented in his paper. The number of man-years of cumulative effort and of computer-hours of analysis required to reach these results has obviously been enormous.

A survey of scientific method and progress would reveal two opposing, but often overlapping, types of approach. On the one hand, many workers attempt to achieve greater scientific predictability through refining the methods of analysis, usually through proceeding to higher and higher levels of abstraction. Howells has preferred this approach in his own systematic building toward an understanding of human evolution. It is disappointing, then, to find that this analysis, in its efforts to relate biology to behavior and environment, offers as its best correlation between independent variables a coefficient of correlation of 0.48 (between morphological distance and altitude). This indicates that 77% of the variance between these two factors is still unexplained. With the lowest coefficient of correlation, 0.13 (between size "distance" and geographical distance), the unexplained variance rises to 98%. These values do not produce optimism with regard to the general principles involved in the analysis.

Another type of approach to scientific predictability involves refinement at the data level with the hope that functional interrelationships between the variables involved will show through clearly. With good luck and careful choices, this method may yield successful analyses at a very low level of abstraction. This general approach offers a variety of directions in which progress can be made: The numerical size of the series of basic units can be increased; the data can be refined in terms of their essential homogeneity; best of all, data can be collected in a context which maximizes the opportunity to discover functional relationships where they exist. Some of these considerations will be applied to the discussion below.

When Oliver collected his basic data in 1938–39, he was operating at a high level both in terms of the training then available and the general state of the art upon which it was based. All investigators have personal equations of error, but it may be suspected that these are smaller in Oliver's work than in those of other cultural anthropologists trained by E. A. Hooton to conduct anthropometric field surveys. The data have the advantage of having been collected by a cultural anthropologist with his own commitments to the study of cultural variables. In these terms the raw data should not be faulted.

Viewed in the perspective of a modern statement of evolutionary principles, however, Oliver's data have a number of disadvantages. Tribal populations differ considerably in total numbers. Linguistic evidence confirms a variety of sources of derivation. The island of

Bougainville is not idealized genetic space, either in terms of topography or geometry. It has become amply clear that microevolutionary studies must be based upon the breeding population. This does not mean a congeries of genetic isolates, but a micro-isolate, or minimum breeding unit. Since this problem had not yet been formulated when Oliver did his fieldwork, it is not surprising that the proper analyses cannot be performed now. From the failure to identify the micro-isolates involved in the data, it follows that effective rates of gene flow cannot be determined, even if the details of the mating patterns had been adequately documented. Howells is correct in using dialectical linguistic boundaries to crudely approximate the consequences of breeding behavior; but the average size of the tribal groups on this island is more than 2,000 persons, much larger than where the dialectical tribe can be, and has been, identified with the genetic isolate, as in aboriginal Australia. These raw data, then, are inadequate insofar as they deviate from a design in which basic units are defined by breeding performance, fail to show homogeneity in size and structure, and are not distributed advantageously in a space which lends itself to the critical analyses. They are good data for many purposes, but they do not approximate the conditions to be hoped for in a definitive experiment in nature.

Since Howells has explicitly offered his study as an illustration of methodology, this is where it should be examined most closely. There can be no doubt that summary, single-figure estimates of "distance" can be analytically useful for some purposes. Howells' four measures of spatial distance and two of language differences are certainly acceptable as generalized dimensions; but his three biological, summary measures of "distance," based upon size, shape, and morphological differences, fall into a different category. Even though we are dealing with genetically complex characters, it has never been adequately demonstrated that such figures relate well to the variables of evolutionary biology (if one excepts cases of recent, massive, generalized hybridization). They represent a mathematical simplification of enormously complex and ill-explored aspects of population variation in time and in space. I am aware that mathematical justifications for them can be shown to exist, provided an adequate number of necessary simplifying assumptions are utilized; but the biological validity of most of these assumptions is not only undemonstrated, but is even contradicted by microevolutionary data. Clinal analyses not only point to the virtual independence of population variations, trait by trait, in the same space and among the same people, but also demonstrate that the slopes of the surfaces, both as expressions of rates of change and directions of change, vary from character to character.

If all is not chaos in the world of natural population variations, it is nevertheless much too complicated to allow single summary figures to stand for the realities of biological differences.

Quite aside from questions of validity of biological measures of "distance," there arises the equally important question of the meaning of the differences, should they be granted any validity. Most investigators of microevolutionary phenomena in man would agree that the magnitude and direction of biological differences are not measures of biological relationship. A biologically meaningful framework for interpreting the magnitude of such differences or distance figures has not been specified and tested.

If variations in population data at the simple empirical level present confusing patterns, this is the area where resolution must be successful before we can examine the meaning of summary statements at high levels of abstraction. Micro-isolate variation among Australian aborigines suggests a series of disturbing conclusions: genetic differences between adjacent and interbreeding tribes are systematically larger than have ever been predicted and frequently approach the magnitude of differences found between major racial groups. Variations in cline surfaces for different characters usually appear chaotic. But in one area they visibly cluster and define an emergent adaptive peak. As might be anticipated, different characters show markedly different adaptive responses within the same populations comprising this peak. Such data demonstrate that the mathematical models for the genetics of microevolution are not only too simple, but certainly in some instances altogether misleading in their conclusions. As Ernst Mayr has already suggested, drift should not be viewed alone and in a vacuum, but as acting in a complementary fashion with selective processes. Drift may even accelerate adaptive changes. These basic Australian data, which do represent a definitive experiment in nature, suggest new points of departure for analyzing microevolution through genetics. Unhappily, they also imply a fundamental indeterminacy in present or probable future methods of analysis of microevolutionary processes. We have now reached a point where the data from natural populations must be used to totally redefine the classic mathematical models of evolution.

ALICE M. BRUES. *Boulder, Colo.* To me the most interesting aspect of Howells' work is the evaluation of the relative importance of clinal variation, indicating gene flow, and random variation representing drift effects. A basic question is what factors are best correlated with the degree of reproductive isolation. Language is clearly more strongly correlated than geographic distance. We must consider the complicating factor that while language itself tends to drift with isolation, a linguistic difference, once having developed, may discourage social contact and therefore gene flow. The high correlation of biological differences with altitude suggests possible selective effects; but since the author states that the differences are not systematic with relation to altitude, we might ask what correlation there is between altitude and ecology which might discourage mate exchange between different levels.

From the point of view of estimating drift effects, however, the greatest difficulty is the fact that the measures of biological distance are rather composite, especially the "SCOPIC" distance, which is an average of 12 observations, probably largely independent in their genetic determination. The best evaluation of the effect of drift would be obtained from an examination of the intercorrelations of the different genetic loci subsumed under these composite distances. Are the gene frequencies at the various loci varying in a correlated way, or are their variations random with respect to one another? The latter alternative would indicate active drift.

It would be helpful also if discrimination were made between major linguistic differences, indicating diversity of the original colonizing populations, and lesser differences, indicating linguistic drift *in situ*. Estimates of the total population of tribes would be interesting also.

A. CAPELL. *Sydney, Australia.* Approaching this paper as a linguist, I can ask only certain types of questions, for which not all the necessary data is presented. One important question is whether Austronesian and non-Austronesian languages are spoken by people of the same physical type. Howells' data may help to test the previously accepted theory that Oceanic Melanesian represents a pidginised form of Austronesian grafted onto basically non-Austronesian languages. My own impression is that this is true, but the theory is now being widely controverted. Are there definite physical differences between the speakers of Melanesian languages (in the north) and non-Melanesian (in the south) of Bougainville?

Bougainville may well provide a picture in microcosm of the problem. I am not sure what is meant in RESULTS (6) "a Melanesian-shore *vs.* a non-Melanesian-upland distinction, while apparently present, is only a fraction of the whole picture of linguistic differentiation on that island." What other elements could enter in, seeing that the Polynesians have no footing in Bougainville? There is very little

Melanesian, if any, inland in the south; in the north the admixture is more complicated, but there is still a shore-upland dichotomy.

The anthropologist as well as the linguist will query the value of "Negritoid" as a separate group. There are certainly no "Negritoid" languages anywhere and no basic physical difference that would justify "Negritoid" as a separate group. Hence the statement in (7) that Oliver came to believe that "the smaller peoples of the southern mountain area were in fact Negritoid in origin, rather than simply environmentally dwarfed" needs revision. One would need to examine the vocabularies to show whether there is anything to support such a view.

The paper as a whole is interesting and valuable: the fact that from the special viewpoint of the linguist there are still refinements to be made is not to be considered to indicate a radical disagreement with Howells' results and argument.

CARLETON S. COON. *Gloucester, Mass.* Howells' careful study of Oliver's Bougainville material shows the value of being a professional in both physical and cultural anthropology. His method might be profitably applied to a number of old, carefully documented anthropometric studies now collecting dust because of the unpopularity of racial studies. Some of the older series cover relatively wide geographical ranges, encompassing considerable variations in temperature, annual amount of sunlight, and water vapor pressure. In reworking them it might be useful to add these parameters to altitude as a fuller measure of environmental distance.

In his own stated opinion, Howells' work has principally resulted in a historical reconstruction of the racial and cultural history of Bougainville. This in itself warrants the effort. While, as one might have expected, body size varies with altitude, he tentatively attributes this correlation to the presence of a relatively old Negrito element in the highlands. The high values of r between altitude and the three somatic parameters tend to support this suggestion.

On the other hand, as Oliver has shown elsewhere, nutritional differences between highland and coastal populations favor the latter. Also, since under the dense cloud cover of Bougainville the highlands are colder than the lowlands, Bergmann's second rule—that below a certain temperature threshold mammals of a given species tend to be smaller—might be invoked. In Australoids this threshold is relatively high compared to some other races.

These racial differences in physiological response to environmental factors are likely to yield different results in different parts of the world, tending to complicate or obscure the application of Howells' procedure but they cannot alone invalidate it. It seems eminently worthwhile that his work be repeated on other available series, with the inclusion of other parameters where indicated. Howells is to be congratulated for this fruitful and promising piece of work.

EUGENE GILES. *Urbana, Ill.* Although Howells states that correlations between any two kinds of his distances are positive, I would suspect that COGN, the percentage of shared cognates, decreases as GEOG, the distance apart in miles, increases, leading to a negative correlation, as Livingstone (1963) found. The thrust of Howells' figures and conclusions suggests that COGN is really the percentage of non-cognates. If this, and a similar inversion in the definition of LING, are not amiss, the methodological advances represented in this integration of anthropological data are clear and significant. In particular, the development of a statistical technique for evaluating inter-population variation in non-metrical anthropological observations should find much employment.

It may be worth pointing out this paper as something of an answer to anthropologists who decry the collection and reporting of information not immediately reducible in terms of current theories and practices. While mindless accumulation of data should not be encouraged, the punctiliously gathered and documented material Oliver provides from fieldwork almost 30 years ago would not be available—and, more important, might now be unobtainable—had he waited for the statistical and electronic innovations wielded today by Howells.

The only suggestion I might make would be that Howells need not be too concerned that his results and Livingstone's are at odds. The approach used by Livingstone in studying the correlations between the percentage of shared cognates, blood group gene frequency differences, and geographic distance in populations in New Guinea's Eastern Highlands is open to some question. For example, Livingstone utilized data pertaining to 11 populations but considered only 23 out of the 55 possible combinations. He claimed he calculated interpopulation distances from a map appearing in Gajdusek and Zigas (1959), yet only five of his 11 groups are shown on that map. While the method of choice in comparing interpopulation blood group gene frequencies may be debatable, merely taking the absolute gene frequency differences (when the frequencies of the three alleles in each system—ABO, Rh, and MNSs—must sum to one) can certainly be improved upon. A possible alternative is Majumdar and Rao's (1960:120–21) suggestion that three frequencies summing to one (e.g., $p + q + r = 1$) may be transformed to two by letting

$$x = (2q + p)/\sqrt{3}, \text{ and}$$
$$y = p.$$

If this transformation is made for each population's three allele frequencies, in the ABO, Rh, and MNSs systems, the gene frequency differences between, say, populations 1 and 2 (separately for each blood group system) can be expressed as

$$z_{12} = \sqrt{(x_1 - x_2)^2 + (y_1 - y_2)^2}.$$

If interpopulation differences so defined in blood group gene frequencies are correlated with corresponding interpopulation geographic distances (which can be estimated, like Howells' GEOG, from another Gajdusek map [Gajdusek 1961 or 1962]) for all possible combinations of Livingstone's 11 samples, the resulting r's of .026 for the ABO system, .482 for Rh, and $-.073$ for MNSs, each with an N of 55, are quite different from those reported by Livingstone. Livingstone offers three versions of the "average" correlation between geographic distance and gene frequency differences, .166, .156, and .166. These "average" r's, with which Howells must make comparisons, clearly do not well represent the interrelation of distance and gene frequencies in the Eastern Highlands, and in fact, by implying a low but insignificant correlation between all blood group differences and distance, obscure the absence of correlation between geographic distance and the ABO and MNSs systems on the one hand and the highly significant correlation with the Rh alleles on the other. Obviously, genetic drift may occur at one locus and selection at another at the same time: the increasing evidence for selection at the ABO locus and the lack of evidence for on-going selection at other blood group loci (Morton et al. 1966) suggest that this may well be the case in these genetic markers. Hence Livingstone's data do not necessarily counter all of Howells' expectations as stated in his footnote 4.

J. HIERNAUX. *Brussells, Belgium.* I fully agree with Howells' method of approaching a complex situation. There is need for the study of such situations in biological anthropology, as well as for advances in theory, computerized simulation of evolutionary processes, and study of those rare cases in which there is a reason to believe that a single mechanism might have played a major role.

It might have been of interest had Howells given a general distance such as C_H^2 (or better, D^2) in addition to the SIZE and SHAPE distances, for the latter represent size and shape only in a special statistical sense, a fact which might be misleading if this special sense is not fully understood. For example, two populations, one of which is higher in stature by one standard deviation, but lower in nose breadth, also by one standard deviation, would have a zero size distance which might be biologically inaccurate.

Looking at the correlations between non-biological distances, it seems possible that a consideration of partial correlations would produce some supplementary information of interest.

The relatively high correlations with non-biological distances exhibited by SCOPIC distance merely indicate the need for physical anthropology to work more systematically with anthroposcopic traits. There is a fair probability that a number of them are nearer to a simple genetic mode of determination than any anthropometric variable could be; more twin and family studies on this matter would be welcome.

I. KARVE. *Poona, India.* Howells is right, I think, in interpreting not as a factor leading to biological differences, but as suggesting the possibility that "originally" different stocks speaking different languages came together in a historical accident. There are too many variables for singling out any factor as significant.

The observation that SIZE and SCOPIC are correlated more highly than SHAPE and SCOPIC is very suggestive. I have had the feeling with regard to a series of measurements I had carried out that there was some kind of relationship between SIZE and head shape, perhaps with a biological factor involved. In Maharashtra, the western tribes tended to be mesocephalic to sub-brachy cephalic and smaller-headed (as judged by circumference) and smaller-statured compared to eastern tribal people, who are dolicho cephalic, medium-headed (in circumference), and medium in height. Is there a negative correlation? Smaller circumference and longheadedness? Is there an original biological difference between the two stocks? This department has undertaken further studies on this subject to be published by the end of this year. We would welcome comments and suggestions. An analysis of factors involved in SIZE and SHAPE would help immensely. I found Howells' contribution very stimulating.

The differences, whether SHAPE, SCOPIC, or SIZE, seem to be ultimately biological rather than environmental. The environmental correlation seems to be based on the fact that the two geographical areas are occupied by two different stocks. This opens up anew the vexed question that Boas posed about environmental response, phenotypic plasticity, and adaptation. The kind of change over a generation or two suggested by Boas has no parallel in other studies, nor can it be adequately explained by modern genetic theories. Studies like the present one may ultimately be able to answer the riddle posed by Boas.

B. LUNDMAN. *Uppsala, Sweden.* In my opinion, Howells' elaborate procedure is somewhat out of proportion to the small amount of material to which he applies it. I have devoted a great deal of time and labour to the study of large groups of small isolated populations. In 1945 I collected data on about 15,000 peasants in nearly 300 villages (or small groups of hamlets) in the interior of Sweden. Grouping the 300 units into 40 larger units, I used Czekanowski's (1910) average-difference method to establish six types with regard to stature, morphology, and colour. I found an obvious division into six groups which accurately represented the population history of the region (Lundman 1945, 1956). This division coincides with the results of a still unpublished study of ABO blood groups among 70,000 recruits native to the same region. Considering the difficulties of obtaining definitive results even in such a large scale study, I must conclude that Howells' material is insufficient to provide clear evidence for his far-reaching theories.

PETER A. PARSONS. *Victoria, Australia.* It is good to see a report of research in physical anthropology in which some attempt has been made to ask definitive questions about population structure at the outset rather than after the data have been collected. The approach outlined by Howells may find considerable application in the study of primitive groups.

My other comment concerns the question of genetic drift, which has recently been invoked as an explanation of blood group gene frequencies in certain groups. A major question that should be investigated is the effect on gene frequencies of deviations from random mating, especially as there may be large deviations from random mating in the primitive hominids such that a dominant male could contribute far more genes to subsequent generations than other males. This may still occur in some tribes as an original condition and in others as a derived condition (see Mayr 1963 for discussion). In small populations this would probably lead to greater variations in gene frequencies than strict random mating. The theoretical consequences of such deviations may repay more study.

Reply

W. W. HOWELLS. I was gratified to read these comments and have little to say in specific reply. The important point, evident in all the above, is the deficiencies, in both data and analysis, with which physical anthropologists are faced when they try to get into the realm of population theory with practical efforts. The commentators have put it all better than I did, though the paper itself was meant to be a statement of problems, not of solutions. Particularly useful are the suggestions as to what might have been done, or might be done, in such an investigation.

Angel makes explicit what is implicit in other comments: the different behavior of single gene traits (see also Giles) and polygenic morphological traits, both theoretically and empirically. Blood group projects are now getting past the inventory stage and are being addressed to problems of population genetics and microevolution. How much they can show about processes relating to morphological characters—the real material of most evolutionary studies—and about general changes in genotype is a question which needs continuing discussion. For instance, not long ago, in considering recent human evolution or racial differentiation, we were accustomed to reading of "mutations to" this or that feature, say brachycephaly or facial reduction; or, more circumspectly, "genes for" such traits being passed around over considerable distances. While I do not for a minute denigrate gene flow in this respect, it seems to me that these expressions are inadequate and incorrect for the genotypic changes and reorganizations leading to small-scale differentiation of populations in their morphological aspects. Such traits doubtless change mainly by recombinations, rapid or slow, in the existing genetic materials of regional groups of populations, and it is the processes involved here that we should, and probably can, investigate. Can the use of single-gene traits be directly connected with all this?

In answer to Birdsell: (1) I partly agree with his objection to "summary figures": when these are merely additive, as for morphological traits or blood groups, they have the deficiencies which Giles illustrates in his comment; but when they use continuous and correlated traits (measurements) they are really in a different category of basis and meaning, which is in fact not adequately exemplified by SIZE and SHAPE herein (for an example using multiple discriminant analysis see Howells, 1966). We *must* use such transformations in order to escape from limitations of the trait-by-trait approach, or else stop where we stood many long years ago. Should we really "keep it simple," as Birdsell seems to be suggesting? that an apparent association of 20% (nearer 23%) of the variance in morphological distance with that in altitude is surely not minor, and I do not feel that "predictability" is the best expression of aims in analyses like this. (3) While Bougainville is not idealized genetic space, we are not likely to find such space in working with man and should not expect to; that is one point of my paper. (Birdsell himself, in his Australian work, has doubtless come as close to it as we ever shall.) (4) "Most investigators of microevolutionary phenomena in man would agree that the magnitude and direction of biological differences are not a measure of biological relationship." I agree entirely as to the importance of this proposition; but I think the statement as it stands would make a good topic for debate. Actually, I agree with almost all of Birdsell's points of view, particularly his last sentence.

In answering Capell's queries, I can say that the physical differences do not neatly follow any Melanesian-non-Melanesian division. Northern Melanesian-speakers do differ from southern non-Melanesian-speakers, but there are northern non-Melanesian-speakers who differ from both of these groups (Oliver 1954; Oliver and Howells 1960).

Allen and Hurd divide the non-Melanesian languages into two stocks, Konua (northern) and Nasioi (southern), which have a percentage of shared cognates not substantially greater than either has with the Melanesian languages. I have not worked out physical distinctions between these three linguistic groups, but they do correspond generally with the population differences found by Oliver (and reported in his 1954 publication).

My observation under RESULTS (6), quoted by Capell, is meant to say that Melanesian—non-Melanesian linguistic distribution does indeed array itself by shore vs. upland in part, but the differentiation within these stocks leads to geographic distinctions among them along other axes than the shore-upland one. I was not suggesting the presence of further major elements.

Giles notes something I should have made clear: I treated all group differences as "distances," that is, as quantities increasing with unlikeness, and so in order to arrive at a linguistic distance, I changed the signs of the percentage of shared cognates, which is a measure of likeness. I also changed the signs of Livingstone's correlations, in quoting them, to make them consistent with the others.

Commentators mention the supposedly great amount of labor and computation demanded. I hasten to say this is an illusion. It is true that much of the analysis involved experimenting—the word might be "fiddling"—with the data and with methods of attack, as matters of obvious interest in themselves. And, of course, the linguistic comparisons of Allen and Hurd must have involved a lot of work on their part, but this was something dropped in my lap. Given their tabulation, the linguistic distances, like the altitudinal or geographical distances, were the work of a few hours on my part. To repeat, the work and computation (of course with electronic computers) called only for a quite modest investment of time and money. Much of the experimenting was done by an undergraduate assistant. The work is not to be compared in scale with that carried out in the pre-electronic laboratories of Pearson or Hooton.

In other words, the same analysis could readily be done routinely. The point is, however, that such experiments *should* be made, and other new methods worked out, even if they shoud be laborious. The investment is still small compared to that in collecting data. Furthermore, it is obvious that increased attention should be given both to theoretical considerations and to analytical problems like those pointed out above before starting to collect data in the first place.

References

ANGEL, J. LAWRENCE. 1951. *Cold Spring Harbor Symposia on Quantitative Biology* 15:343–51.

BENOIST, J. 1964. Saint-Barthélemy: physical anthropology of an isolate. *American Journal of Physical Anthropology* 22:473–87.

BROOKS, S. T., and M. VAN ARSDALE. 1964. A computer analysis of the relationship between human measurements and "biological distance." *American Journal of Physical Anthropology* 22:507–08.

CAVALLI-SFORZA, L. L., I. BARRAI, and A. W. F. EDWARDS. 1965. Analysis of human evolution under random genetic drift. *Cold Spring Harbor Symposia on Quantitative Biology* 29:9–20.

CZEKANOWSKY, J. 1910. Verwandtschatsbezeichnungen zentralafrikanischer Pygmäen. *Korrespondenzblatt der Deutschen Gesellschaft für Anthropologie* 41:65–71.

ELMENDORF, W. W. 1965. Linguistic and geographic relations in the Northern Plateau area. *Southwestern Journal of Anthropology* 21: 63–78.

GAJDUSEK, D. C. 1961. Kuru: an appraisal of five years of investigation. Preprint of paper presented at 10th Pacific Science Congress, Honolulu.

———. 1962. Kuru: an appraisal of five years of investigation. *Eugenics Quarterly* 9:69–74.

———. 1965. Factors governing the genetics of primitive human populations. *Cold Spring Harbor Symposia on Quantitative Biology* 29: 121–35.

GAJDUSEK, D. C. and V. ZIGAS. 1959. Kuru. *American Journal of Medicine* 26:442–69.

GILES, E., R. J. WALSH, and M. A. BRADLEY. 1965. Micro-evolution in New Guinea: The role of genetic drift. *Annals of the New York Academy of Sciences* 34:655–65.

HANNA, B. C. 1962. The biological relationships among Indians of the Southwest. Analysis of morphological traits. *American Journal of Physical Anthropology* 20:499–508.

HIERNAUX, J. 1956. *Analyse de la variation des caractères physiques humains en une région de l'Afrique centrale: Ruanda-Urundi et Kivu*. Annales du Musée Royal du Congo Belge. Serie en 8e. Sciences de l'Homme. Anthropologie vol. 3. Tervuren.

HOWELLS, W. W. 1966. *The Jomon population of Japan*. A study by discriminant analysis of Japanese and Ainu crania. Papers, Peabody Museum, LVII/1:1–43.

LAUGHLIN, W. S., and J. B. JORGENSEN. 1956. Isolate variation in Greenlandic Eskimo crania. *Acta Genetica et Statistica Medica* 6:3–12.

LIVINGSTONE, F. B. 1963. Blood groups and ancestry: A test case from the New Guinea Highlands. CURRENT ANTHROPOLOGY 4:541–42.

LUNDMAN, B. 1945. Dala-allmogens antropologi. (English summary: Anthropology of Dalecaria.). Unpublished Ph.D. dissertation, University of Uppsala, Uppsala, Sweden.

————. 1956. Über anthropologische Gauuntersuchungen. *Homo* 17: 174–80.

MAJUMDAR, D. N., and C. R. RAO. 1960. *Race elements in Bengal: a quantitative study*. Calcutta: Statistical Publishing Society.

MAYR, E. 1963. *Animal species and evolution*. Cambridge: Harvard University Press.

MORTON, N. E., H. KRIEGER, and M. P. MI. 1966. Natural selection on polymorphisms in northeastern Brazil. *American Journal of Human Genetics* 18:153–71.

NEEL, J. V., F. M. SALZANO, P. C. JUNQUEIRA, F. KEITER, and D. MAYBURY-LEWIS. 1964. Studies on the Xavante Indians of the Brazilian Matto Grosso. *American Journal of Human Genetics* 16:52–140.

OLIVER, D. L. 1954. Somatic variability and human ecology on Bougainville Island, Solomon Islands. MS.

OLIVER, D. L., and W. W. HOWELLS. 1957. Micro-evolution: Cultural elements in physical variation. *American Anthropologist* 59:965–78.

————. 1960. "Bougainville populations studied by generalized distance." *Actes, VIe Congrès International des Sciences Anthropologiques et Ethnologiques, Paris, 1961*, I:497–502.

PENROSE, L. S. 1954. Distance, size and shape. *Annals of Eugenics* 18: 337–43.

Eskimos and Aleuts:
Their Origins and Evolution*

WILLIAM S. LAUGHLIN

(*Editor's Note*) In a comment on Howells' article
Angel states, "It is the lack of time depth which tends
to short-circuit analyses of human group relatedness at
both physical and social levels." In the following articles
by Laughlin and by Pollitzer *et al.*, the attempt has been
made to eliminate this "short circuit." Evolution is a
process which makes it necessary to consider change
in space *and* in time. Because human generation time
is long, the interpretation of skeletal material must provide information that is at least somewhat comparable
to that gathered on the living. The study of geographically stable populations who are currently living, as it
were, on top of their ancestors' bones, provides distinct
advantages for the investigator. Laughlin deals with
such a situation in the Arctic and subarctic region
stretching from Alaska to Greenland. It is an area that
has been little affected by cultural or technological
change since its initial habitation by man. Moreover,
although there has been internal migration there evidently never were massive displacements of one population by another from outside the area. All of these
factors make it a particularly advantageous part of the
world to document the cultural and biological ways in
which man has been able to cope with a particularly
harsh environment. Laughlin cites the evidence for the
probable North Asian origin of the Eskimo and Aleut
and their gradual dispersion over the vast area which
they now occupy. He then describes the microevolutionary changes these populations have undergone
in that environment.

The anthropologist is at his eclectic best where he is

*From *Science*, vol. 142, November 1963, pages 633–645.
By permission of the author and the publisher.

able to focus on a well defined, but limited geographical area, for the purpose of answering the question: "Where did the inhabitants come from and what changes have they undergone since their arrival?"

E SKIMOS have been known to the European world since A.D. 1000, when Leif Erikson found them on the coast of Labrador. The Greenlandic Eskimos and their relatives the Aleuts and Eskimos to the west and north were by no means newcomers to North America and Greenland. At the time of their discovery by Leif they had been living in the New World for over 4000 years.

In the more than five millennia that have passed since these Mongoloid peoples migrated from Siberia to Alaska, they have worked out a remarkable system of adaptation to a series of diverse environments, ranging from the harsh climate and poorly lighted terrain of the polar regions to the more moderate marine environment of the Aleutian Islands. Their adaptations, physiological and cultural, have enabled them to occupy the entire coast of northern North America, from Alaska to the northeastern coast of Canada, and the entire coast of Greenland. Because of their antiquity, the evolutionary changes in successive groups, and the variations throughout their distribution over a long coastal area, the Eskimos and Aleuts provide a unique opportunity for studying microevolution, population history from the standpoint of genetics, and biological and cultural adaptation. Such studies have been facilitated by the excavation of stratified village sites rich in durable artifacts and in faunal remains and human skeletons, many of them showing direct continuity with living groups. Moreover, studies of the blood groups of living individuals show a basic similarity between Aleuts and Greenlandic Eskimos, as distinguished from American Indians, who are much less Mongoloid. In addition, the linguistic diversity within a single stock provides an invaluable means of tracing the impressive florescence of these energetic and practical peoples.

Linguistic Characterization

The three distinctive languages spoken by members of this stock differentiate them from American Indians and indicate a connection with Siberian Mongoloids that is confirmed by the serological and morphological evidence. The two Eskimo languages and the Aleut language differ to the extent that an individual who speaks Eskimo cannot understand Aleut, but phonologically and grammatically they are quite similar. Rasmus Rask first noted the basic similarity between Greenlandic Eskimo and Aleut in 1819. Inyupik Eskimo is spoken in northern Alaska and Canada as well as in Greenland. The second Eskimo language, Yupik, is spoken in western Alaska, south of Unalakleet on Norton Sound—the area where most of the Siberian Eskimos live—and by the Eskimos of St. Lawrence Island in the Bering Sea. There are at least four dialects of Yupik, and communication between individuals who speak different dialects is difficult. Edward Sapir noted this diversity and formulated a useful working principle (*1*): "The greater the degree of linguistic differentiation within a stock, the greater . . . the period of time that must be assumed for the development of such differentiation." He concluded that the divergence between Aleut and Eskimo and the diversity of dialects within them pointed to southern Alaska as the earliest center of dispersion. Later, a method of dating on the basis of linguistic characteristics (called glottochronology or lexicostatistic dating) was applied by Marsh and Swadesh (*2*), who estimated that the Aleut and Eskimo languages had separated some 3000 years ago. They based this estimate on an assumed retention rate and on the number of words Aleut and the Eskimo languages now have in common. This date has more recently been revised to about 4500 years ago, the subsequent separation of the two major divisions of Eskimo being placed close to 1400 years ago (*3*). The possibility that there was a connection with the Siberian languages Chukchi-Koryak and Kamchadal some 5000 years ago has recently been suggested (*4*). Other linguists, though not necessarily proponents of the glottochronological method, generally agree that the differentiation took place in southern Alaska and that the speakers of Yupik moved from south to north (*5*). These estimates fit well with findings which indicate that, at the time of the exploration of Bering and Steller in 1741, southwestern Alaska was the area of highest population density (*6*). At that time some 7000 Koniag Eskimos lived on Kodiak Island, and 16,000 Aleuts inhabited the Aleutian Islands and the western part of the Alaska Peninsula. A few hundred Eskimos lived in the interior of the Alaska Peninsula, in northern Alaska, and in the Barren Grounds of Canada (*7*).

Anangula

The archeological evidence also points to southern Alaska as the homeland of the Eskimo-Aleut stock. The oldest known site in the

Eskimo-Aleut world, according to dates obtained by the radiocarbon technique, is the lamellar-flake site on Anangula Island, 5 miles off the shore of Umnak Island, opposite the present village of Nikolski on the Bering Sea side. Three dates have been obtained from a cultural level underlying two layers of ash and humus; these are 8425 ± 275 years ago (Isotopes Inc. specimen I-715), 7990 ± 230 years ago (Isotopes Inc. specimen I-1046), and 7660 ± 300 years ago (U.S. Geological Survey specimen W-1180). Prismatic blades from 2 to 12 centimeters long, polyhedral cores from which small blades have been struck, core tablets, retouched blades with chipping on one surface to form scrapers, knives, gravers, and burins, and many refuse flakes make up the bulk of this industry (8). In this unifacial industry, imported obsidian, greenstone, cherts, and other siliceous, fine-grained stone were used. The obsidian apparently came from the Cape Chagak region (chagak is the Aleut word for obsidian) on the north end of Umnak Island, probably the only source of obsidian in the Aleutians. Who made these blades and what they were used for can only be inferred in the absence of human skeletons and faunal remains. However, the location suggests a marine economy. R. F. Black, who is currently investigating the geology of this area, has noted that, whereas a 10-meter depth of ocean now separates Anangula from Umnak, this area would have been dry land 8000 years ago, and that 12,000 years ago Umnak was an extension of the Alaska mainland, having formed, in fact, the end of the Alaska Peninsula and the southern corner of the old Bering Platform. Early migrants from Asia could have walked along the southern edge of the platform and reached the world's richest hunting ground without losing contact with the sea upon which they depended for their principal food supply. St. Lawrence Island, Nunivak, and the Pribilof Islands, like Umnak and Anangula, are remnants of the higher hills on this now submerged platform. The pass (now the strait) that separates Umnak from the Islands of the Four Mountains was never closed during the Pleistocene. People living on the Umnak-Anangula corner of this platform could hunt the annually migrating whales and fur seals, as well as the resident sea otters, hair seals, and sea lions. The founders of Anangula may have been a migrant Bering-platform population who reached the site on foot (see Figs. 2 and 3).

Continuity with the village site of Chaluka is suggested by the presence of unifacial tools fashioned on lamellas or prismatic blades. A similar manufacturing technique and similar materials are involved, though the polyhedral cores have not been found at the Chaluka site. The frequency of occurrence of lamellar tools declines rapidly from the bottom level to the top of the Chaluka site, and the frequency of occurrence of obsidian and greenstone declines as well (9); these matters were defined more fully by the 1962 excavations of C. Turner, G. Boyd, A. McCartney, L. Lippold, and J. Aigner.

This true core and blade industry is more like the lamellar industries in Japan and Siberia between 9000 and 13,000 years ago than like the somewhat later Denbigh Flint complex of Norton Sound (10). M. Yoshizaki, who has excavated at Anangula with McCartney and R. Nelson, suggests that the Anangula materials are most like the tools of the Sakkotsu microblade industry of Hokkaido, the Araya site on Honshu, and the Budun site in Siberia. They seem more clearly Asiatic than tools of the Arctic small-tool tradition, which extended over much of Alaska and provided the base for the Dorset culture of the eastern Canadian Arctic and related cultures of Greenland (11, 12). Both Irving and Yoshizaki place them, with confidence, in a separate province from tools of other Alaskan industries, though there are some similarities to materials of the Campus site at College, Alaska. I infer that the bone artifacts occurred in approximately the same proportion and were of approximately the same kind as those associated with the lamellar tools in the lowest levels of Chaluka, and that the Anangula industry was that of a marine-based people similar to the Paleo-Aleuts of 4000 years ago, a long-headed Mongoloid group. American Indians of comparable antiquity, proto-Mongoloid in appearance, have already been found thousands of miles to the south.

Chaluka

Four thousand years of continuous history are lavishly illustrated in the deep, stratified village site of Chaluka, which now forms the southern margin of Nikolski, a village of some 55 Aleuts. This is one of the few sites in the Arctic or subarctic which contains the requisite materials for interdisciplinary study of evolution, prehistory, and ecology: human skeletons, abundant artifacts, and remains of buildings and of faunas, all superimposed in such a way as to provide a record of several thousands of years of events in one place and evidence of a connection with the living inhabitants. The reasons for the long-term occupation of this site are apparent. There were freshwater lakes, vital for spawning salmon (these lakes may not have existed at the time of initial occupation); an enclosed bay with front reef, which provided protected waters for fishing during storms at sea; large reefs, exposed at low tide, which were rich in invertebrates such as sea urchins, mussels, whelks, limpets, and chiton and in edible seaweeds, kelpfish, and octopus; offshore rocks and islands that provided cliffs for nesting cormorants and puffins, where they were protected from foxes (the Aleuts ate the eggs of these birds); a complex coastline which trapped driftwood, dead whales, and dead sea lions and provided diverse ecological niches attractive to sea

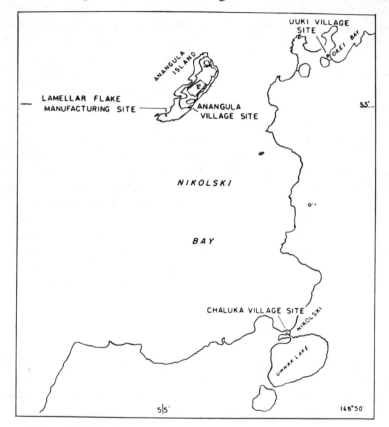

FIGURE 1. *Map of Anangula Island and Nikolski Bay (scale: 1/40,000).*

otters, which like to live in extensive kelp beds. Cod and halibut could be caught from the shore, as well as from boats in the channels and pockets. This site is on a 10-meter beach of the postglacial thermal maximum and thus cannot be older than 5000 years; the water level has probably changed very little during this period. The oldest date obtained by the radiocarbon method, 3750 ± 180 years, is for a sample found above the sterile floor (*13*), and an age of 4000 years has been proposed for the site, on the basis of the lower limits of seven dates obtained by this method.

The earliest Paleo-Aleuts of the Chaluka site used stone lamps, various kinds of harpoons and spearheads, fishhooks, unifacial (lamellar) tools, and ivory and bone labrets for lip decoration. Adze bits and whalebone wedges are evidence of a wood-working industry. Distinctive harpoon heads are fluted or channeled and slotted to receive straight-based bifacial chipped stone points. Stone points have been found embedded in sea lion bones in these strata. The elaborate carving of harpoon heads with circle-dot-and-line designs shows great artistry. The incompletely excavated foundations of houses indicate that these were oval, with coursed masonry; that one entered from the side; that there was a slab-lined hearth; and that ribs and mandibles of whales were used for rafters.

The artifacts in the upper levels include many tools and objects needed for life in a subarctic, marine environment, but none of these represent basically new categories, with the possible exception of barbs for fish spears. Many new types do appear. Two-piece bone sockets to receive long harpoon heads with stone points inserted in a basin rather than a slot are found, still in association with Paleo-Aleut skeletal remains. The forms of fishhook shanks change. The older, elbow shank carved from whalebone is replaced by a curved shank carved from sea otter rib. In general, the artifacts at various levels are of the same categories: lamps, root diggers, splitting wedges, bird-spear side prongs, labrets, weights for fish lines, chipped stone knives, and flaking tools. Recently (only a few hundred years ago at most) four variations appeared at Chaluka: ground-slate ulus, shallow soapstone lamps, single-piece sockets to receive small barbed ivory harpoon heads used in hunting small mammals, and a group of artifacts, including hats, that have been found in mummy caves. The Neo-Aleut skeletal type is associated with these recent artifacts, and this association poses the problem of rapid internal change versus migration.

There is no single change in kind or category of artifact over 4000 years that appears to have made a detectable change in the system of adaptation or in the way of life. While it is entirely possible that such fundamental changes did in fact take place, it is significant that, despite sensitive excavation techniques and the recovery of large numbers of artifacts and faunal remains and of human skeletons in sufficient numbers to show how the people lived, what they lived on, and how they buried their dead, no major change is detectable. The later, bifacial tools have no obvious advantage over unifacial tools.

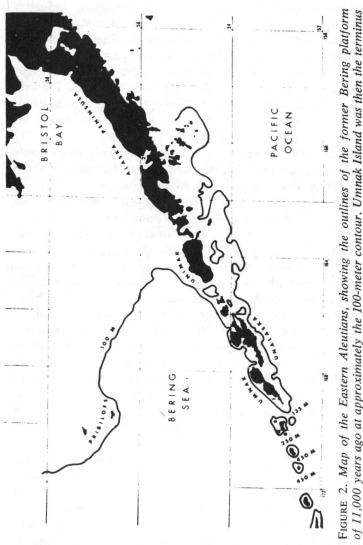

FIGURE 2. Map of the Eastern Aleutians, showing the outlines of the former Bering platform of 11,000 years ago at approximately the 100-meter contour. Umnak Island was then the terminus of the Alaska peninsula. The passes west of Umnak are too deep for a land bridge to have formed at any time during the last glaciation as a result of lowered water levels. Presumably, early populations lived on the platform and withdrew as the water level rose. 1. The Chaluka-Anangula area. 2. Port Moller, the point of division between Aleuts and Eskimos. (Courtesy of R. F. Black.)

Line holes in a few harpoon heads of the lowest levels are gouged out rather than circularly drilled. Such traits may be important time markers, but they have little significance from the standpoint of adaptation.

Faunal Remains

The faunal picture at the Chaluka site explains the rise of a large population in this area and the use of many tools. W. G. Reeder has sketched the basic relations between mammals, birds, fish, and invertebrate remains and is relating these to modern communities. As Scheffer has noted (*14*), "There are in fact no small marine mammals of any kind." Large marine mammals were available, and thus the Eskimos and Aleuts had an unusually rich source of food. In addition, their social habits and their numbers assured them a good food supply. Eskimo culture is primarily adapted to marine hunting but is sufficiently flexible to include means of hunting land animals as well.

The principal faunal remains excavated in 1962 (except for invertebrate remains) are shown in Table 1. The pinnipeds include harbor seals, fur seals, and sea lions. Though Aleuts on the Alaska Peninsula secured important numbers of walrus, sea lion remains are found more often in the Aleutians. More of the sea lion than of the seal skeletal remains are adults. This may reflect the selective use of hides of mature sea lion for making umiaks and kayaks, and the use of sea lion flippers for boot soles. The fur seal now migrate through the Aleutian straits to the Pribilof Islands, some 400 kilometers north of Umnak. Since they do not ordinarily haul up on beaches while in transit, it is probable that they were killed at sea from boats.

Cod and halibut are the principal fish represented in the 1962 excavations, the cod constituting some 80 percent of all the fish remains. Salmon are poorly represented—a finding which suggests that the great salmon runs of the last several hundred years had not started 4000 years ago. Among the bird remains in these deposits, cormorant remains are the most common, with puffin and duck remains less frequent. Albatross remains occur at all levels, perhaps in somewhat greater number at the lower level. Either the habits of the albatross have changed and they formerly nested on Umnak Island, as claimed by Chamisso, or they were hunted down at sea. Sea urchin remains make up a large part of the deposits; apparently the sea urchin was the basic invertebrate in the diet, as the sea otter was a basic vertebrate. The importance of the sea urchin cannot be overestimated. Women, disabled men, and children could gather sea urchins and other invertebrates during the spring, when other food sources were depleted. Thus, starvation was avoided in many communities. The contrast between this situation and that in the central Arctic, where the inhabitants were unable to get food from the sea because of the impenetrable ice barrier, is reflected in the population profiles. The economic productivity of children, disadvantaged women, and elderly or disabled men is a major factor in community adaptation, with both genetic and cultural consequences.

The human skeletons (Figs. 3–7) indicate an evolutionary change in all of southern Alaska—a change in head form from dolichocranial (breadth less than 75 percent of length) to brachycranial (breadth more than 80 percent of length). There are also changes in the occurrence of dental cusps and mandibular tori. One Paleo-Aleut found at the bottom of the Chaluka site displayed vault thickening (hyperostosis cranii) characteristic of some anemias. All the skeletons found in the eastern end of the Chaluka site, with the exception of recent burials, belonged to the long-headed (dolichocranial) Paleo-Aleut type. The most recent inhabitants—those whose remains are associated with knives of ground slate, with shallow stone lamps, and with single-piece sockets and short harpoon heads—are extremely broad- and low-headed. Hrdlicka, who was the first to note that there were two physical types, one of which succeeded the other stratigraphically, termed the earlier type "pre-Aleut" and the later type "Aleut" (*15*). Marsh and I suggested the terms "Paleo-" and "Neo-Aleut" for the physical populations, to indicate the continuity and similarity, and the possible evolution of the later from the earlier population (*16*). Dental studies (*17*) and anthropometric studies of living individuals (*18*) establish a continuity between the most recent skeletons in Chaluka and the present-day inhabitants. Some characteristics of the earlier population appear in the western Aleuts. They are more narrow-headed than the eastern Aleuts, and they differ from them in frequency of occurrence of discontinuous traits. The pressing problem now is that of securing enough skeletons from stratified and dated sites to confirm this apparent evolutionary change and to provide a basis for estimating the rate of change, as well as its extent. Parallel changes on Kodiak Island and along the Kuskokwim River indicate that there was both internal evolution and migration (*19, 20*).

The record for 4000 years of prehistory in the Chaluka site demonstrates that the styles of artifacts change more rapidly than ecological circumstances. The artifacts (harpoons and spears in particular) were necessary for hunting marine mammals, but the particular forms varied considerably. It apparently made no difference, either to the

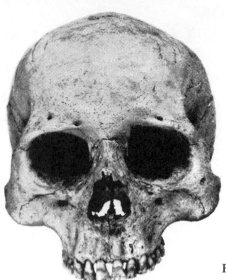

FIGURE 3. *Paleo-Aleut cranium.*

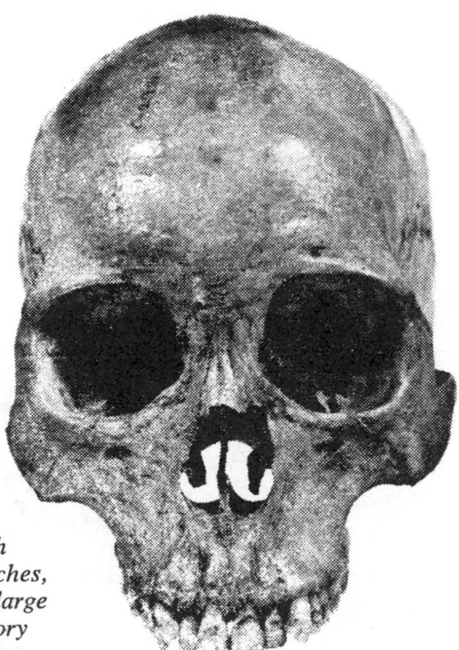

FIGURE 4. *Neo-Aleut cranium, with supraorbital foranina instead of notches, an accessory supraorbital foramen, large infraorbital foramina and an accessory infraorbital foramen, and an accessory zygomaticofacial foramen. Mongoloids characteristically have large or accessory foramina.*

409

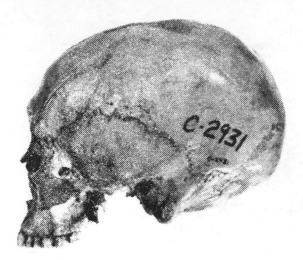

FIGURE 5. *Paleo-Aleut cranium (side-view).*

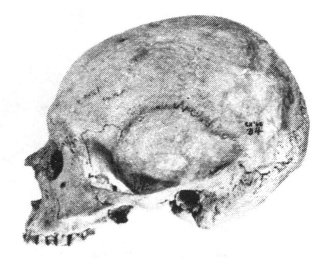

FIGURE 6. *Neo-Aleut cranium (side-view). Crania of Neo-Aleuts are among the lowest and most capacious in the world.*

sea lion or to the hunter wielding the harpoon, whether the harpoon had a fluted, stone-tipped head or a four-barb whalebone head. Cod and halibut were caught equally well with an elbow-shank fishhook and a curved-rib-shank fishhook. The 16,000 Aleuts discovered by Bering and Steller in 1741 were adequate evidence of the faunal wealth of the Aleutians and of the efficiency of their system of exploitation.

Bering Strait Sequence

The time depth for Eskimo sites decreases as one proceeds from southwestern Alaska to the Bering Strait region. Prior to 2000 B.C. the Bering Strait cultures are represented primarily by lithic industries and yield little information about the way of life or the racial characteristics of the people. Giddings has drawn attention to the persistence of tradition in the constituent areas: the Asiatic, Chukchi Sea, and

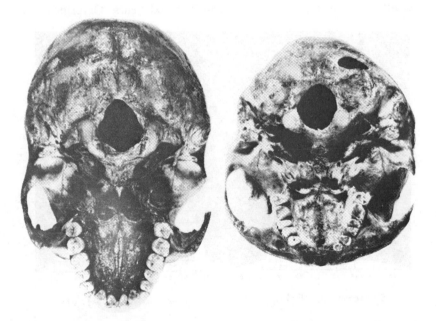

FIGURE 7. (Left) Base of the cranium of a Paleo-Aleut. The relative narrowness of this cranium and the long occipital area are characteristic of the earlier Aleutian population. (Right) Base of the cranium of a Neo-Aleut. The great breadth of this cranium and the short occipital area are characteristic of individuals of this more recent population.

Bering Sea areas. One site in particular is comparable to Chaluka; this is the great Kukulik mound of St. Lawrence Island, which shows continuous occupation from Old Bering Sea II times (about A.D. 300) to 1884. Walrus hunting, sealing, and whaling have been of continuing importance and, interestingly, the artifacts used in these activities show only a slow change in style and a gradual loss of the art of engraving over 2000 years. As Giddings comments (*10*), "No basic change appears abruptly in the pattern of subsistence, and only a few exotic elements were introduced before the coming of Europeans." The significance of this continuity and stability in these three Bering Strait areas for studies of evolution lies in the indication that there has been little real migration of groups. It may be that many of the later physical variations are due, rather, to internal changes, with gene flow resulting from exchange of mates across the boundaries of isolate groups making a relatively small contribution.

Important to an understanding of the early interconnections between Mongoloids in the Eskimo-Aleut area as a whole is recognition that early cultural traditions were more widespread than the relatively localized cultures of the last several hundred years. Of critical im-

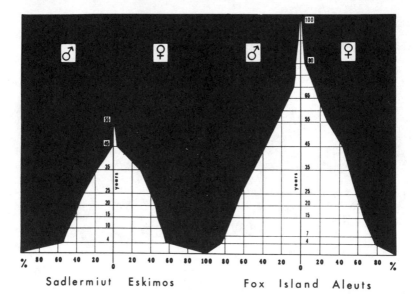

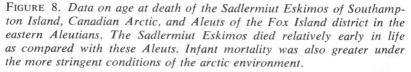

Sadlermiut   Eskimos   Fox   Island   Aleuts

FIGURE 8. *Data on age at death of the Sadlermiut Eskimos of Southampton Island, Canadian Arctic, and Aleuts of the Fox Island district in the eastern Aleutians. The Sadlermiut Eskimos died relatively early in life as compared with these Aleuts. Infant mortality was also greater under the more stringent conditions of the arctic environment.*

portance is the Arctic small-tool tradition, defined by Irving, which provided roots for the development of the pre-Dorset and Dorset cultures of the eastern Canadian Arctic and Greenland (*11, 12, 21*). This tradition, which includes the Denbigh Flint complex, is characterized by large numbers of microblades struck from conical polyhedral cores and by burins, retouched burin spalls (also used as engraving tools), small bifacially retouched blades for insertion in the sides of harpoon heads, and medium-sized (4 to 10 cm) biface points and knife blades (*11*). This tradition appeared in Alaska and Siberia as early as 6000 years ago, and reflections of it reached the Canadian Arctic and Greenland very early. Collins, who initiated the early work on St. Lawrence Island and continued his investigations across the Arctic, points out that the Arctic small-tool tradition is "pre-Eskimo" but that the prefix *pre* in this case connotes "predisposed" or "leading up to" (*12*). Thus, the evidence, though meager, indicates that the people of the Dorset culture were Eskimo in their morphology (*22*).

In general, the more northern cultures used the toggle-head harpoon more often than the harpoon with a simple detachable head that is used in southern Alaska. Toggle-heads presumably turn inside the animal with tension on the harpoon line. (Much the same effect is produced with multi-barbed, detachable harpoon heads, especially those that are asymmetrical.) These harpoon heads are indispensable time markers, just as pottery is in the southewestern United States. They are more closely related to the way of life than pottery is, but there is still by no means a one-to-one correspondence. Other general characteristics of the northern cultures are their greater use of the umiak and their custom of hunting on the ice, with the sled drawn by dogs. Kayaks were inevitably more important in the south, where there is more open water. Hunting from kayaks has many advantages: kayaks provide speed and a means of rapidly scanning complex coastlines. Moreover—and this is extremely important—the kayak does not have to be fed! The Aleuts and Koniags developed the kayak to a higher degree than any other members of this stock, and much of the material culture reflects the elaboration of open-sea hunting of mammals.

Adaptation to Cold and Glare

A common misconception about Eskimos is that they are fat or chubby. Measurement of the thickness of skin folds confirms the observation that they are in fact lean. Though muscular, with heavy bones, they have little fat even at advanced ages. They are medium-

TABLE 1. *Preliminary Summary of Data for Excavated Bones, Chaluka, 1962. [L. Lippold, G. Streveler, and R. Wallen]*

BONES (%)

LAYER	BONES (NO.)	BIRD	FISH	PINNIPED	SEA OTTER	CETACEAN
Upper I	3,626	27.8	44.2	20.4	6.8	2.0
Upper II	5,906	15.2	50.6	25.8	5.8	2.2
Upper III	10,858	19.6	7.3	47.0	25.3	0.1
Lower IV	1,127	29.8	13.3	39.8	16.6	.4

to-short in stature, with long trunks and short legs. The lower leg is particularly short. Their heads are large, and their hands are small-to-average in size. When they are fully clothed for protection against dry cold, only a portion of the face is exposed. Possibly the large face with broad jaws and the bulky clothing have contributed to the notion that they are fat.

Thermoregulation in the Eskimo is characterized by basal metabolism that is higher than clinical standards for normal metabolism and high in view of the lean body mass. When the Eskimos are fully clothed they are living in a tropical microclimate in which sweating accounts for most dissipation of the excess metabolic heat. F. Milan has found that Eskimos maintain their warmth even while lying on the winter ice, hunting seal. They probably have more sweat glands than members of other races, but too few counts have been made to confirm this. Blood flow to the hands and legs is greater when the limbs are cooled in water than it is in normal white controls. The perception of pain resulting from cold appears to be less acute in both children and adults than it is in other races, and the Eskimos have higher finger temperatures during cooling in cold air (32).

Equally important in the adaptation to cold have been the material culture of the Eskimos and the Aleuts and the child-training practices. The ordinary clothing includes undergarments, pants, boots, mittens, and parka with ruff. Where hunting is done from kayaks, the clothing is made of waterproof materials, such as the esophagus of hair seal or sea lion and the intestines of various mammals, such as whales, walrus, or seals. Parkas made of the skins of birds—cormorants, puffins, and auklets in particular—are used in all areas. Insulative materials such as dried grass and caribou skin are worn inside boots.

Glare from water, ice, or snow is minimized by the use of slit goggles or visors. In the Aleutian Islands and in southern Greenland, kayakers habitually wore visors or shades for protection against spray and glare. Eskimos who use sleds wear slit goggles instead of visors. Selection for cold-adapted individuals has probably been extensive in the southern area, where there is greatest use of the sea. Heat loss is so greatly accelerated in cold water that a victim who has been immersed for a few minutes often cannot be saved even by rapid rewarming techniques. Ability to withstand wet cold for even a few additional minutes has often meant rescue by another hunter. On land, by contrast, a fully clothed person can survive many days of extreme cold. No studies on the heritability of resistance to cold have been made. There is no experimental evidence to suggest that the Mongoloid face, the long trunk, and the short legs are characteristics that have developed as a result of the climate.

Longevity

A critical variable, about which reliable information is slowly being accumulated, is that of age at death. In this respect there are large contrasts between isolates, with ascertainable genetic and cultural consequences. In general, it appears that the people who lived in the more harsh arctic environments died earlier. Those who inhabited ecologically richer areas—subarctic and more ice-free areas—lived much longer. A sharp contrast, for which the cultural context is known, is that of the extinct Sadlermiut Eskimos of Southampton Island (Northwest Territories), in the northern part of Hudson Bay, who died at a much earlier age than their Aleut counterparts in the eastern Aleutians. The Sadlermiut numbered about 57 at the time they became extinct, in 1903. The Unalaska Aleuts (from the Fox Island district), already decimated by disease and massacre, numbered some 1500 between the years 1825 and 1835. Their chronicler, I. Veniaminoff, reported age at death for 491 Aleuts (24). These ages are therefore directly comparable with ages at death estimated from the skeletal remains of the Sadlermiut. As Fig. 8 shows, the maximum age at death among the Sadlermiut was between 50 and 55 years. In marked contrast, the maximum age at death among the Aleuts was between 90 and 100.

Age at death affects not only such things as disease patterns but the genetic composition and cultural complexity of the group as well. There is more wastage in the group in which a higher percentage of the offspring die before the age of reproduction, and each generation is a less adequate sample of the preceding generation. Age at death is closely correlated with population size, and this in turn is correlated with the ecological base and the technological system.

The cultural consequences and the biological consequences may be considered separately for purposes of analysis. The greater overlap between generations associated with greater longevity provides more time for transfer of information. The experience of older people is stored in accessible form for a longer period in more "storage cells." The florescence of medical and anatomical knowledge among the Aleutian Islanders indicates a specific form of feedback. Difficult deliveries could be successfully managed because of the presence of old and skilled individuals (25), and treatment of serious injuries enabled the injured individual to participate in group life, if not in active hunting, on his recovery. Artistic expression and the larger number of public ceremonials and myths are among the correlative benefits of greater longevity and greater population.

Various patterns of pathology are characteristic of the Eskimos and Aleuts, and in some of these conditions there is probably a high element of heritability. Spondylolysis of the lumbar vertebrae is especially common (26). Developmental anomalies such as premature or irregular closure of cranial sutures are also common. Arthritis occurs frequently, and there is an interesting sex difference: in arthritis of the elbow, arthritic lesions occur much more frequently on the capitellar surface of the humerus in males and on the trochlear surface in females.

Blood-Group Evidence of Origins

The blood-group data, in addition to their value in studies of population genetics of small isolates, throw much light on Eskimo-Aleut affinities and origins. They show that the members of this stock are clearly distinguished from American Indians and more similar to Asiatic Mongoloids. The percentage of blood type B in Eskimo-Aleut isolates ranges from 2 to 26, whereas in American Indians it is zero. The percentages in Asiatic Mongoloids are the highest in the world; those for the Chukchi (the lowest in the Asiatic Mongoloid group) are a little higher than the average for the Eskimos (27). Indians who live in contiguous areas—the Tlingit, Athabascan, and Algonkin—have no gene for blood group B. The percentage of group B is especially low among the Eskimos of the central Canadian Arctic. Chown and Lewis (28) have suggested that this indicates a Dorset-culture residuum. Traces of earlier peoples should show through more frequently in areas of low population density, or in areas where the earlier population made a large contribution to the newer population, as in the western Aleutians. North American Indians have genes for blood groups A and O, and as in all Eskimos and Asiatic Mongoloids, the A is of subdivision A_1. Though Alaskan Athabascan Indians are low in group A, the highest frequencies of group A in the world are found among the Blood and Blackfoot Indians of Alberta and Montana.

An interesting cline shows the distribution of the frequencies of blood type MNSs. Chown and Lewis found the occurrence of type MS higher in the Copper Eskimos of the central Canadian Arctic and lower as one proceeds to the southeast. Significantly, as the Eskimos approached the Indians geographically they became genetically more dissimilar (*29*).

Eskimos lack the Diego factor, which is found in highest frequency in Venezuela and reappears in Asia. All Eskimos secrete blood-group substance in their saliva, but many are nontasters of phenylthiocarbamide (PTC), in contrast to Indians, among whom tasters of PTC are fairly numerous. The Rh chromosomes R_1 and R_2 are common, and similarities between Aleuts and Greenlandic Eskimos are marked (*30*). Both differ from Indians in having low rates of excretion of β-aminoisobutyric acid and a low incidence of haptoglobin type 1-1 (*31*).

Discontinuous Variation

The component isolates and populations of the Eskimo-Aleut stock are self-defining in that they are breeding isolates. They generally choose their mates within their own groups. Eastern Aleuts mate with eastern Aleuts and Polar Eskimos mate with Polar Eskimos, through preference and because of proximity. These groupings exist, regardless of whether we choose to recognize or classify them. The Polar Eskimos are a classic example of a geographically isolated breeding isolate. When they were discovered, in 1818, they thought they were the only people in the world. In addition to cultural and geographic barriers to mating—that is, to gene flow across isolate boundaries—the factor of relative population size has played an important role in minimizing the effects of mixture between Eskimos and Indians. The size and density of the Eskimo populations provided genetic insulation against the smaller groups of contiguous Indians. The physical traits which characterize isolates may be divided into those which vary continuously (stature, intermembral proportions, size of the ascending portion of the mandible) and those which are discontinuous or not present in all the people (particular blood groups, fissural patterns on the teeth, various foramina and sutures) (see Fig. 9).

Among the continuous traits in Eskimos and Aleuts are the very large cranium, the large flat face, the broad mandible with unusually broad ascending ramus (the mandible is broader in Eskimos and Aleuts than it was in Neanderthal man), and the medium-to-narrow nose. Earlier Aleuts and Eskimos had heads that were narrow in proportion to their length (head breadth is usually less than 75 percent of the length, in cranial series). The greatest head breadth occurs on Kodiak Island, where, among the living, the head breadths are some 86 percent of the head lengths. This value, the cephalic index, decreases both to the west and to the north. Trunks are long and legs are short, though the total height varies. Eskimos in the interior of northern Alaska and Canada are taller than those along the coast (*32*). Interestingly, Eskimos and Aleuts grow over a longer period of time than people of other stocks (*33*).

Although all Greenlandic Eskimos can be characterized as a single group, it is more profitable, in research at the microevolutionary level, to recognize and compare the constituent isolates within Greenland. Findings on variation between breeding groups can then be used for the study of traits as such, for inferring the direction of migration, and for estimating rates of change. Blood type B is rare among the

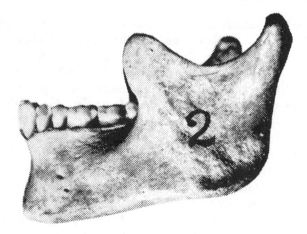

FIGURE 9. *Mandible of a man of the Okhotsk culture, Hokkaido, Japan, about A.D. 1000. The enormously broad ascending ramus is characteristic of many Mongoloid groups. The breadth of this feature in Eskimos and Aleuts exceeds the breadth in Neanderthal man. There are multiple mental foramina in the region of the chin. (Specimen courtesy of Kohei Mitshuhaski, Sapporo Medical College)*

Polar Eskimos, more frequent along the west coast, and most frequent among the Angmagssalik Eskimos of the southeast coast. No blood-group comparison with Eskimos of northeast Greenland is possible, for those Eskimos are extinct. However, in studies based on discrete traits of the skull they can be included, and thus it is possible to draw comparisons among peoples whose migrations were limited to coastal areas because of inland ice. The Greenland Eskimos could migrate only clockwise and counterclockwise, or in both these directions, from a single area of entry, and no mating between isolates on opposite sides

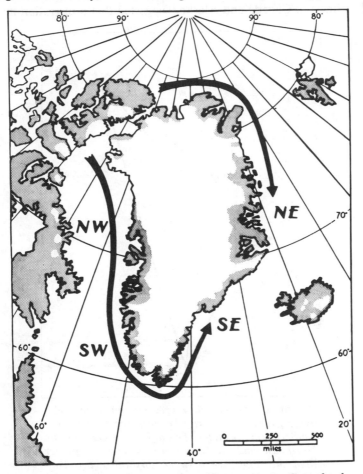

FIGURE 10. *Migration of the Eskimos about Greenland. The migration was confined to the coasts because of the inland ice. It moved in two directions, with the result that the terminal isolates (the Northeast and the Southeast), separated for the longest period, show the greatest morphological differences.*

of Greenland was possible (see Figs. 10 and 11). If they moved in both directions, the terminal isolates should display the greatest differences (Table 2). Studying eight discontinuous traits observed in some 600 skulls representing four isolates, Jorgensen and I found that the northeast series and the southeast series did in fact show the greatest differences. We inferred, therefore, that the Eskimos migrated in two directions around the coasts of Greenland (*34*). This conclusion is supported by ethnological and archaeological evidence. As early as 1909, Boas (*35*), on the basis of similarities between artifacts found in Greenland and artifacts in Canada and Alaska, suggested that a migration move-

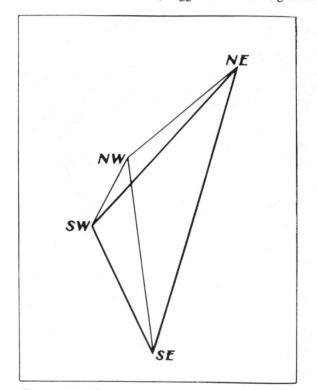

FIGURE 11. *Geometric representation of the relative degrees of similarity between the four Greenlandic Eskimo isolates. The difference between the Northeast and the Southeast isolates is greater than the difference between any other two contiguous isolates. Thought geographically as far apart as the Northeast and Southeast isolates, the Northwest and Southwest isolates exchanged mates more frequently and are much more similar to each other. [Courtesy of L. S. Penrose (43)]*

TABLE 2. *Frequency (in percentages) of discontinuous cranial traits in Greenlandic Eskimo isolates. The percentages, based on a total series of 293 male skulls that J. B. Jorgensen and I studied in the Laboratory of Anthropology, University of Copenhagen, provide the basis for estimating similiarity, as illustrated in Fig. 11.*

TRAIT	NORTHWEST	SOUTHWEST	SOUTHEAST	NORTHEAST
Dehiscences	26	32	19	26
Parietal notch bone	22	21	17	14
Supraorbital foramina	60	58	59	48
Mandibular torus	69	65	44	90
Palatine torus	36	32	24	9

ment north around Greenland had taken place. Through measurement of continuous traits, the northeast and southeast series have been identified as the terminal isolates. Measurements for the northeast series are the largest in Greenland, and those for the southeast series are the smallest. The cranial samples represent migrations after A.D. 1000 and roughly indicate the extent of differences which may occur between isolates in some 800 years. The southern Norse colony on the southwest coast of Greenland was raided by Eskimos in A.D. 1379, and it disappeared about A.D. 1500. Eskimos who had come from the west coast had been living in southeast Greenland no more than 400 years when they were discovered in 1884.

Differences between more distantly related peoples are larger, as would be expected (Table 3). The mandibular torus (Fig. 12) occurs most often in Mongoloids. It also occurs in American Indians and in Europeans. Among the latter groups, however, the proportion of palatine tori is greater. This suggests a different mode of inheritance (*36*).

Sinanthropus and Modern Mongoloids

The time depth for contemporary Mongoloid types is short, perhaps on the order of 10,000 to 15,000 years. The record of changes within the last several hundred years is considerable. Therefore, the finding that Middle Pleistocene *Sinanthropus pekinensis* displays traits that recur in Mongoloid and related populations, such as American Indians and Polynesians, is of major importance.

It has not been definitely established that any of the fossil men of China are Mongoloids. The most frequently mentioned as being so are three skulls from the Upper Cave of Chou Kou Tien, in north China. They are thought to be late Pleistocene, but they are probably

TABLE 3. *Frequencies (in percentages) of discontinuous traits in distantly related races. The relatively large differences between (i) Norse and (ii) Eskimos and Indians and the smaller differences between Eskimos and Indians parallel the anthropometric and serological differences. Caucasoids and American Indians both have an excess of palatine tori over mandibular tori, in contrast to the Mongoloid Eskimos. (No submedium or ambiguous tori are included in these series.)*

	MEDIEVAL NORSE IN GREENLAND		ARIKARA INDIANS OF SOUTH DAKOTA		ESKIMOS OF GREENLAND	
	♂ ($N = 38$)	♀ ($N = 43$)	♂ ($n = 60$)	♀ ($n = 40$)	♂ ($N = 293$)	♀ ($N = 291$)
Dehiscences	6	1	29	43	27	36
Parietal notch bone	15	17	10	12	21	15
Supraorbital foramina	16	38	50	59	59	62
Mandibular torus	37	41	0	0	67	47
Palatine torus	59	58	29	44	32	36

no older than early American Indian remains such as the "Midland Woman," to which a date earlier than 8000 B.C., and possibly as early as 18,500 B.C., has been assigned. These three skulls are quite different from each other and have been individually compared to skulls of Melanesians, Europeans, and Eskimos. The best appraisal that can be made is that they resemble "unmigrated American Indians" (*37*). Other fossil men of China do not look like Mongoloids of the last 5000 years. The evidence from China indicates that modern Mongoloids are a relatively recent development. (*38*).

Japan offers no early materials that can be categorized as Mongoloid. The Pleistocene remains are fragmentary. Ushikawa Man has been assigned a date in the Upper Middle-Pleistocene, but the fossil consists only of a portion of the left humerus. The Mikkabi skull fragments are Upper Pleistocene, but no racial assignment is possible (*39*). The earliest definitely Mongoloid remains in Japan are from the last few thousand years.

Weidenreich observed that *Sinanthropus pekinensis* displayed 12 traits found in Mongoloids, in which category he included Polynesians and American Indians. Three of the 12 fit into the category of traits that may or may not occur in Mongoloids—the mandibular torus, shovel-shaped incisors, and the Inca bone. (Fig. 13). Two other traits

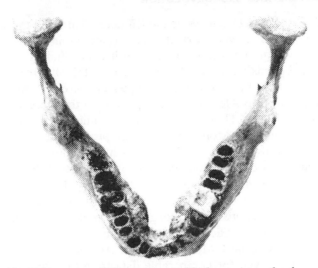

FIGURE 12. *Eskimo mandible with mandibular torus—the bony mound on the lingual surface. A form of this torus is found in Sinanthropus pekinensis. In Eskimos and Aleuts the number of mandibular tori exceeds the number of palatine tori; the converse obtains in American Indians and Europeans.*

FIGURE 13. *Inca bone in the occipital bone of the cranium of a Neo-Aleut. A horizontal suture separates the upper portion of the occipital into a triangular portion. This is found in Sinanthropus pekinensis, Mongoloids, and American Indians in varying but often high frequencies.*

of the 12 are also relevant. Weidenreich noted that in all the temporal bones there was a well-marked notch (parietal incisure). This is common in modern Mongoloids, though it is not limited to them. In many of the fossils a separate bone is found at this site; these separate bones can simply be considered examples of extremely well marked notches. [In a Paleo-Aleut skull (not pictured)] there are slits in both tympanic plates. . . . These slits occur in the same area as the tympanic dehiscence of modern Mongoloids and are probably related to it. The auditory exostoses described by Wiedenreich occur most often in American Indians; they do not occur in Eskimos or Aleuts. When we review these traits in *Sinanthropus* and in modern Mongoloids, keeping their general morphology in mind, we cannot consider them grounds for regarding *Sinanthropus* as a Mongoloid. On the other hand, these traits are additional evidence of similarity between *Sinanthropus* and modern man, especially Mongoloids and American Indians. Further evaluation must wait for comparable data from the other representatives of the erectus stage in Java, Africa, and Europe. In discussing the nomenclature and classification of *Sinanthropus*, Weidenreich remarked (40): "It would be best to call it '*Homo sapiens erectus pekinensis*'. Otherwise it would appear as a proper 'species', different from '*Homo sapiens*' which remains doubtful, to say the least."

Recent Changes

There is good evidence from Japan, Alaska, and Greenland that appreciable changes in morphology have taken place within a relatively short period. Suzuki has documented differences between proto-historic times (the 4th to 8th centuries A.D.) and modern times (41). The ancient Japanese had long heads, broad faces, and wide, flat nasal roots, and they were prognathic. The later Japanese had rounder heads, narrower faces, and narrower and higher nasal roots, and they were less prognathic. The possibility that there was admixture with other races is slight. By the 7th century the Japanese people numbered 6 million; this density of population would, of itself, have been an effective barrier against the effects of mixture with immigrants.

The mean cranial index for Paleo-Aleut males is 74, and the mean cephalic index for Aleuts now living in the same area is 85. Subtracting 2 index units from the latter value (a step that is necessary in comparing cephalic indexes of the living with cranial indexes), we find a difference of 9 index units, representing a large change in the ratio of length to breadth. The cranial index for early male Koniags of Kodiak Island is 77, in marked contrast to the index of 86 for later Koniags. A similar but smaller change has taken place in east

Greenland, where there can be no question of admixture (*19*). Similar changes, and also an increase in stature, are reported for many series of American Indians (*42*). Local migrations may explain the change in particular places but cannot explain the change for all the areas involved. The question of local evolutionary changes must be given more attention.

Summary

The emerging picture for the immediate origin of New World Mongoloids, the Eskimos and Aleuts, is that of a Bering platform inhabited by contiguous isolates stretching from Hokkaido around to what is now Umnak Island, probably some 10,000 to 15,000 years ago. The lithic similarities between Anangula and Hokkaido and the similarities in human morphology suggest this. The probable linguistic relationship between Eskimo and Aleut on the one hand and Chukchi, Koryak, and Kamchadal on the other is in general agreement with this picture and raises the possibility that the Yupik-speaking Eskimos of Siberia and St. Lawrence Island may be derived from populations that formerly lived on the Bering Platform and withdrew toward their present locations as the platform was inundated. Diffusion of traits, both genetic and cultural, from the center in southwestern Alaska became of increasing importance as the population differential between south and north became greater. Once Bering Strait became a channel, major migrations ended; successional continuity is indicated wherever deep stratified sites are found. Paleo-Indians (proto-Mongoloids or semi-Mongoloids) were clearly established in South and Central America before 10,000 B.C. Their separation from ancestral Eskimo-Aleut-Chukchi Mongoloids was probably insured by differences in economic adaptation and therefore by differences in their routes of migration into the New World. The land bridge that connected Siberia and Alaska during early Wisconsin time, as early as 35,000 years ago and as late as 11,000 years ago, was more than 1000 miles wide. The ancestral Indians, with their land-based economy, could have crossed often, following big game, without coming in contact with the Mongoloids, who worked their way along the coastal edge of the reduced Bering Sea.

Upon reaching the end of the Bering Platform, the Umnak Island of today, the Mongoloids flourished, owing to the richness of the marine fauna. As deglaciation proceeded from west to east, they spread in two directions, following the retreating ice and setting out in boats toward the western Aleutian Islands. The earliest known Aleut skeleton is some 4000 years old. Early Kodiak Eskimo skeletons slightly less old are easily distinguishable from the Aleut skeleton. The populations have not become demonstrably more similar, but they have undergone some parallel changes.

As a distinctive group in their present form, Mongoloids represent a recent evolutionary development that has occurred within the past 15,000 years. They do share more discontinuous traits with middle-Pleistocene *Sinanthropus* than members of any other living racial divisions, though *Sinanthropus* is clearly different from a modern Mongoloid. Inferences concerning long-term connections must remain tentative in view of the small number of fossil remains, the great time spans, and the deficiencies, in our knowledge of the modes of inheritance of many traits. However, when we find that significant differences have developed, over a short time span, between closely related and contiguous peoples, as in Alaska and Greenland, and when we consider the vast differences that exist between remote groups such as Eskimos and Bushmen, who are known to belong within the single species of *Homo sapiens*, it seems justifiable to conclude that *Sinanthropus* belongs within this same diverse species.

References

1. E. Sapir, *Can. Dept. Mines Geol. Surv. Mem. 90, Anthropol. Ser. 13(1916)*, 76 (1916).

2. G. Marsh and M. Swadesh, *Intern. J. Am. Linguistics 17*, 209 (1951).

3. M. Swadesh, in *Proc. Intern. Congr. Americanists, 32nd, Copenhagen* (1958), pp. 671–674.

4. ———, *Am. Anthropologist 64*, 1262 (1962).

5. L. L. Hammerich, in *Proc. Intern. Congr. Americanists, 32nd, Copenhagen* (1958), pp. 640–644; C. F. Voegelin, *Univ. Ariz. Bull. 29*, 47 (1958).

6. A. L. Kroeber, *Univ. Calif. (Berkeley) Publ. Am. Archaeol. Ethnol. No. 38* (1939).

7. W. S. Laughlin, *Anthropol. Papers Univ. Alaska 1*, 25 (1952); *ibid. 6*, 5 (1957).

8. ——— and G. H. Marsh, *Am. Antiquity 20*, 27 (1954).

9. ———, *Anthropol. Papers Univ. Alaska 5*, 5 (1956).

10. J. L. Giddings, *Current Anthropol. 1*, 121 (1960).

11. W. N. Irving, *Arctic Institute of North America Technical Paper 11* (1962), pp. 55–68.

12. H. B. Collins, *ibid.*, pp. 126–139.

13. W. S. Laughlin and W. G. Reeder, *Science 137*, 856 (1962).

14. V. B. Scheffer, *Seals, Sea Lions, and Walruses* (Stanford Univ. Press, Stanford, Calif., 1958).

15. A. Hrdlicka, *The Aleutian and Commander Islands* (Wistar Institute, Philadelphia, 1945).

16. W. S. Laughlin and G. H. Marsh, *Arctic 4*, 74 (1951).

17. C. F. A. Moorrees, *The Aleut Dentition* (Harvard Univ. Press, Cambridge, Mass., 1957); A. A. Dahlberg, *Arctic Anthropol. 1*, 115 (1962).

18. W. S. Laughlin, in *The Physical Anthropology of the American Indian*, W. S. Laughlin, Ed. (Viking Fund, New York, 1951).

19. ———, in *Proc. Intern. Congr. Americanists, 32nd, Copenhagen* (1958), pp. 516–530.

20. A. Hrdlicka, *The Anthropology of Kodiak Island* (Wistar Institute, Philadelphia, 1944).

21. W. E. Taylor, *Anthropologica 1*, 24 (1959).

22. W. S. Laughlin and W. E. Taylor, *National Museum of Canada Bull. 167* (1960), pp. 1–28.

23. F. A. Milan, thesis, University of Wisconsin (1963); L. K. Miller and L. Irving, *J. Appl. Physiol. 17*, 449 (1962); B. G. Covino, *Federation Proc. 20*, 209 (1961); K. Rodahl and D. Rennie, *Arctic Aeromedical Laboratory Technical Rept. 8–7951* (1957); G. M. Brown and J. Page, *J. Appl. Physiol. 5*, 221 (1952); G. M. Brown, J. D. Hatcher, J. Page, *ibid. 5*, 410 (1953); J. P. Meehan, A. Stoll, J. D. Hardy, *ibid. 6*, 397 (1954).

24. I. Veniaminov, *Notes on the Islands of the Unalaska Division* (St. Petersburg, 1840).

25. G. H. Marsh and W. S. Laughlin, *Southwestern J. Anthropol. 12*, 38 (1956); W. S. Laughlin, in "Man's Image in Medicine and Anthropology," I. Galdstone, Ed. (in press).

26. C. F. Merbs and W. H. Wilson, *National Museum of Canada Bull. 180* (1962), pp. 154–180; T. D. Stewart, *J. Bone Joint Surg. 35A*, 937 (1953); ———, *Clin. Orthopaed. 8*, 44 (1956).

27. M. G. Levin, *Sov. Ethnografiya 1958*, No. 5, 8 (1958) (in Russian); ———, *ibid. 1959*, No. 3, 98 (1959) (in Russian); W. C. Boyd, *Science 140*, 1057 (1963).

28. B. Chown and M. Lewis, *National Museum of Canada Bull. 167* (1960), pp. 66–79.

29. ———, *Am. J. Phys. Anthropol. 17*, 13 (1959).

30. W. S. Laughlin, *Cold Spring Harbor Symp. Quant. Biol. 15(1950)*, 165 (1950); A. E. Mourant, *The Distribution of the Human Blood Groups* (Blackwell, Oxford, 1954).

31. A. C. Allison, B. S. Blumberg, S. M. Gartler, *Nature 183*, 118 (1959); B. S. Blumberg, A. C. Allison, B. Garry, *Ann. Human Genet. 23*, 349 (1959).

32. R. GESSAIN, *Medd. Gronland 161*, No. 4 (1960).

33. J. B. JORGENSEN and W. S. LAUGHLIN, *Folk 5*, 199 (1963).

34. W. S. LAUGHLIN and J. B. JORGENSEN, *Acta Genet. Statist. Med. 6*, 3 (1956).

35. F. BOAS, *Science 30*, 535 (1909).

36. C. F. A. MOORREES, R. H. OSBORNE, E. WILDE, *Am. J. Phys. Anthropol. 10*, 319 (1952).

37. W. HOWELLS, *Mankind in the Making* (Doubleday, New York, 1959), p. 300.

38. K. CHANG, *Science 136*, 749 (1962).

39. H. SUZUKI, in *Actes du 6ᵉ Congrès International des Sciences Anthropologiques et Ethnologiques* (Paris, 1960), vol. 1; *Zinruigaku Zassi 70*, 1 (1962).

40. F. WEIDENREICH, *Palaeontol. Sinica 1943*, No. 10, 127, 246, 256 (1943).

41. H. SUZUKI, in *Selected Papers of the Fifth International Congress of Anthropology and Ethnological Sciences* (Philadelphia, 1956), pp. 717–724.

42. M. T. NEWMAN, *Am. Anthropologist 64*, 237 (1963).

43. Professor Penrose adjusted his coefficient of divergence to accommodate discrete traits, made the original three-dimensional model, and provided a photograph from which the figure was drawn.

Catawba Indians:
Morphology, Genetics, and History*

WILLIAM S. POLLITZER, DAVID S. PHELPS,
ROBERT E. WAGGONER, AND WEBSTER C. LEYSHON

(*Editor's Note*) This article deals with the problem of how a particular living population arrived at its current genetic and phenotypic constitution. For a solution the investigators have considered evidence from prehistoric, historic, and modern sources, using analytic techniques from archaeology, social anthropology, biometry, and genetics. Unlike a genetically isolated population in a peripheral geographic area, the Catawba inhabit an area which has always been ethnologically complex and characterized by persistent and extensive culture change. Nevertheless, through the use of multivariate statistical techniques and modern computational methods, Pollitzer and coworkers have been able to utilize manifold types of data for the solution of a complex problem.

O UTSIDE the city of Rock Hill, South Carolina, live the remnants of a once flourishing tribe of Siouan-speaking Indians, the Catawba. In 1962 their reservation came to an end at their own request, and these wards of the government became private citizens. An investigation of the physical anthropology of the population was initiated concurrently with a study of culture change. A rare blood type (Solomon *et al.*, '65) in one of the Indian families had just come to the attention of the American Red Cross, who participated in the collection and typing of blood samples. Physical measurements, observations and pedigree data were obtained on the same individuals.

Archaeological investigations in the Carolinas and just across the line in Virginia have revealed skeletal remains, as well as many cultural artefacts, of Indians most of whom are related to the Catawba.

From American Journal of Physical Anthropology, vol. 26, January, 1967, pages 5–14. By permission of the authors and the publisher.

Measurements are available from these ancient bones, and ABO typings have been made on some of them.

The present inquiry seeks to answer these questions: How do the Catawba Indians compare in their morphology and serology with other populations? What is the contribution of probable ancestral populations to this isolate? How do they compare with ancient Indian populations of the region? And what cultural factors have determined their composition?

Historical

In 1858 Lieber published a brief vocabulary of the Catawba language. Morgan (1870) noted strong similarities between Catawban and Dakotan dialects, and Hale (1883) found that the language of the related Tutelo showed evidence of being older than the Siouan language of the Plains. Gatchet's ('00) first-hand study of Catawba speech confirmed it as a dialect of the Eastern division of the Siouan family. Voegelin ('41) considered it one of four major groups within the Siouan; and Siebert ('45) stated that Catawban has been carried further along in a drift toward inflection than any other Siouan language.

Largely on linguistic evidence the Indians of Virginia and the Carolinas fall into three great groups. The Cherokees of the mountains and the Tuscaroras along the Neuse River are representatives of the Iroquois language. The many tribes of the coastal plain are Algonkin. The remaining tribes of the Piedmont are Siouan: Tutelo, Saponi, Occaneechi, and other Virginia tribes who moved North and Catawba, Keyauwee, Sara, Eno, and other tribes of the Carolinas who moved south after 1700.

The recorded history of the Catawba begins with Juan Prado's visit in 1567; Lawson gave descriptions of their populous villages in North Carolina which he visited in 1701. During the English expansion of the eighteenth century, the Catawba absorbed remnants of many neighboring and related tribes. Throughout the Colonial period they were allied with the English against the Cherokee, the Tuscaroras and the Iroquois. Following the Revolution they were friendly with the Americans and prospered as middlemen in the trade between coastal South Carolina and Virginia. This close rapport with the Whites proved a two-edged sword for they were ravaged by smallpox in 1738 and again in 1759. In 1763 South Carolina granted the Catawba Indians a reservation 15 miles square in the present York and Lancaster counties. In 1826 nearly the whole reservation was leased to Whites, and in 1841 the Indians sold to the state all except one square mile. In the 1840's many Catawbas went to live among the Cherokees but nearly all of them soon returned (Mooney, 1894).

Throughout the nineteenth and early twentieth centuries the Indians eked out a living from fishing, berrypicking, woodcutting, and the sale of pottery which they have continued to produce to the present day in the style of their ancestors. A "New Reservation" begun in 1940 under the administration of the Federal Government and the "Old Reservation" under the State were terminated in 1962.

Speck's ('38) study of the social anthropology of the Catawba revealed no trace of matrilineal descent. While the Catawba Indians of today are similar to surrounding Whites, one facet of their culture stands out. In the closing years of the nineteenth century, they became converted to the Mormon religion, evidently the only time a whole tribe has joined that faith.

Swanton's ('53) estimate of population at different times shows wide variations from 1600 on, as follows:

1600	5000	1784	250
1682	4600	1822	450
1728	1400	1826	110
1752	1000	1881	120
1757	700	1910	124
1775	400	1930	166
1780	490		

According to the U. S. Census, 202 Indians lived in York County in 1940, 246 in 1950, and 362 in 1960.

Materials and Methods

The living subjects appear to be a representative sample of the population; 104 were blood typed, 69 were observed for skin color, and 47 adults, 17 males and 30 females, were measured for stature, head length, head breadth, total morphological face length, bizygomatic face width, nose length, and nose width. Cephalic, facial, and nasal indices were calculated. Observations were made on hair form, size of nasal angle, and size of ear lobes. Skin color was read on the medial surface of the arm using Reflectometer Model 610 with amber tristimulus filter and with the grey enamel standard set at 23.

Bloods were typed at the American Red Cross (REW) and the National Institutes of Health (WCL) in Washington, D. C., and at

Chapel Hill, N. C. (WSP) for ABO group, subgroup, Ulex, Rh (anti D-C-E-c-e), MNSsU, P, Kell (K, k, Kp^a and Kp^b), Duffy, Kidd, Vel, Henshaw, Diego, and Biles. Gene frequencies were calculated from phenotype frequencies.

From the archaeological sites along the Yadkin River, occupied by the Tutelo in the sixteenth century, Phelps has measured 17 male and seven female skulls for cranial, facial, and nasal dimensions, and estimated stature from long bones (manuscript in preparation).

Skeletal remains from Keyauwee site, representative of the Catawba around 1700, have been studied by Neumann ('47). Measurements on remains from the Tolliferro and Clarksville sites in Virginia (Hoyme and Bass, '62), from Mecklenburg County, Virginia (Sigmon, '63), and from Alamance County, North Carolina, representing Indian populations between 1500 and the early 1700's, and those from Indian Knoll, Kentucky (Snow, '48), are available for comparison.

Bones of individuals from the Yadkin River sites were typed for ABO blood group by the inhibition method of Candela ('40) in which cancellous bone is mixed with anti-A, anti-B and anti-H serum, and the titre of such absorbed sera against appropriate cells is then compared with unabsorbed sera. A second, and sometimes a third, absorption was necessary in order to demonstrate differential blood group activity. While questions of the validity of typing ancient bones have been raised, the apparent reasonableness of results obtained and the absence of blood group activity in the soil near the bones justify their presentation as tentative findings.

Results

The physical appearance of the mixed Catawba Indians varies widely, from those with straight black hair, wide cheeks, and coppery skin color to those who are indistinguishable from the Caucasian population around them. A predominantly Caucasoid appearance, but great phenotypic variation, is fairly typical of the population. Of 30 adults who estimated their degree of Indian ancestry only one said "full-blood"; six indicated more than three-fourths Indian; eight were three-fourth, seven were one-half, six were one-quarter, and two were White. These fractions average to approximately one-half.

Physical measurements and indices, summarized in Table 1, show that the population is tall, mesocephalic, mesoprosopic, and mesorrhine. Skin color values recorded by the photometer in the high 30's may be compared with Negroes who range in the teens and Whites in the 40's. The lighter skin color among females is a phenomenon previously noted among Indian and Negro populations. Age differences are not as clear, the mean for 21 children being 36.4 compared with 38.0 for all adults. Of 48 adults noted, hair was straight in 40, wavy in seven, and curly in one. Of 47 adults observed, 19 had a shallow nasal angle, 24 were medium, and only four were deep.

TABLE 1.   *Summary of Morphology in Catawba Indians.*

	MALES			FEMALES		
	MEAN	RANGE	S.D.	MEAN	RANGE	S.D.
Stature	1715.8	1594–1858	65.2	1612.4	1455–1695	54.0
Head length	192.0	182–205	6.6	183.6	74–191	4.6
Head breadth	152.8	142–165	6.6	146.2	136–157	5.4
Cephalic index	79.6	72–84	3.1	79.7	71–86	3.6
Face length	127.9	115–143	8.2	116.7	108–131	5.6
Face breadth	144.6	134–160	7.2	137.4	127–148	6.5
Facial index	88.5	81–97	4.8	85.0	79–95	3.4
Nose length	56.0	44–62	4.1	51.3	45–57	3.4
Nose width	41.0	36–47	2.8	36.2	32–44	2.9
Nasal index	73.4	63–84	5.5	70.8	61–82	5.1
Skin color	35.7	26–43	4.2	39.3	27–50	4.5

Sample size for males is 17 (18 for skin color); sample size for females is 30 (28 for stature). All measurements are in millimeters. Skin color is the reading on the photometer (Photovolt Corporation Reflectometer Model 610) with amber tristimulus filter, and with gray enamel standard set at 23.

Results of the blood typing are presented in Table 2. Almost half of the sample are in Group O, but the frequency of A and of B are more in line with Caucasoid values. Rh_1 and Rh_2 are common; Rh_z is distinctive; Rh_o, like U, Diego and Henshaw, is noticeably absent. Phenotypes with M are far more common than those with N; and s is more common than S.

Kinship data permit the calculation of gene frequencies in three ways: by population formulas that assume random mating, by a family method that utilizes knowledge of parents, sibs, and offspring to detect heterozygotes, and by the procedure of Ceppellini *et al.* ('55) that counts the genes only in those "original parents" from whom others in the pedigree are descended. Table 3 shows that population and family method values are essentially in agreement. Figures marked with superscript were used in the subsequent analyses.

Gene frequencies from three populations similar to the probable ancestors of the Catawba are presented in Table 4: English White (Race and Sanger, '62), Charleston Negro (Pollitzer, '58), and Cherokee Indian "full-bloods" (Pollitzer *et al.*, '62). It is noteworthy that all of the Catawba Indian gene frequencies fall within the range of these three parental populations. Of 260 Sioux Indians of South Dakota typed by Matson ('41) 68% were O, 29% A, and 3% B, yielding gene frequencies of 0.8257, 0.1588, and 0.0155 respectively.

Roberts has kindly analyzed by his method (Roberts and Hiorns, '62) the contribution of the three presumed ancestral groups to the

TABLE 2.   *Summary of Blood Factors in Catawba Indians.*

FACTOR	NUMBER	FREQUENCY
O	49	0.4712
A	39	0.3750
B	15	0.1442
AB	1	0.0096
Total	104	1.0000
Rh_1Rh_1	17	0.1635
$Rh_1/$	15	0.1442
"Rh_1Rh_2"	30	0.2885
Rh_2Rh_2	8	0.0769
$Rh_2/$	11	0.1058
Rh_zRh_1	11	0.1058
Rh_zRh_2	3	0.0288
Rh_zRh_z	2	0.0192
rhrh	7	0.0673
Total	104	1.0000
MSS	3	0.0291
MSs	31	0.3010
Mss	15	0.1456
MNSS	9	0.0874
MNSs	24	0.2330
MNss	16	0.1553
NSs	4	0.0388
Nss	1	0.0097
Total	103	0.9999
Fy^a+	74	0.7115
Total	104	
KK	3	0.0288
Kk	17	0.1635
kk	84	0.8077
Total	104	1.0000
P^1+	91	0.8835
Total	103	
Jk^b+	63	0.6632
Total	95	

All bloods tested were positive for Kp^b and Vel, and negative for Kp^a, Di^a, He, and Bi.

TABLE 3. *Summary of Gene Frequencies in Catawba Indians by Three Methods.*

GENE	POPULATION	FAMILY	ORIGINAL PARENTS
O	0.7017	0.7163*	0.6282
A	0.2174	0.2063*	0.3455
B	0.0808	0.0774*	0.0263
R^1	0.3885	0.4231*	0.4309
R^2	0.2442	0.2788*	0.2467
R^z	0.1403	0.0961*	0.1842
r	0.2268	0.2019*	0.1382
MS	0.2818	0.2864	0.3009
Ms	0.4318	0.4272	0.4097
NS	0.1211	0.1165	0.0411
Ns	0.1653	0.1699	0.2483
M	0.7136*	0.7136	0.7106
S	0.4029*	0.4029	0.3420
Fy^a	0.4629*	0.4805	0.5453
K	0.1105*	0.1105	0.0526
P^1	0.6587*	0.7460	0.8139
Jh^a*	0.5803	0.5625	0.4259

*These gene frequencies were utilized in the computation of parental contribution to the hybrid. Jk^a gene frequency used was 0.5486.

TABLE 4. *Gene Frequencies in Parental Populations.*

GENE	ENGLISH WHITE	CHARLESTON NEGRO	CHEROKEE INDIAN
O	0.683	0.710	0.973
A	0.257	0.137	0.018
B	0.060	0.153	0.009
R^0	0.026	0.551	0.000
R^1	0.420	0.100	0.615
R^2	0.141	0.073	0.288
r	0.389	0.253	0.038
Other	0.024	0.023	0.059
M	0.532	0.509	0.801
S	0.327	0.266	0.449
Fy^a	0.414	0.016	0.547
K	0.046	0.013	0.006
P^1	0.548	0.776	0.592
Jk^a	0.520	0.650	0.469

TABLE 5. *Morphology in Living Populations.*

	MALES				FEMALES			
	SEMINOLE INDIANS[1]	SIOUX INDIANS[2]	WHITE AMERICANS[3]	AMERICAN NEGROES[4]	SEMINOLE INDIANS	SIOUX INDIANS	WHITE AMERICANS	AMERICAN NEGROES
Stature	1676	1724	1744	1705	1560	1600	1618	1586
Head length	188	195	198	196	183	187	186	187
Head breadth	156	155	155	151	150	151	148	145
Cephalic index		79.6	78.0	77.1		80.5	79.4	77.8
Face length	125	125	119	123	117	117	111	114
Face breadth	149	149	139	139	138	143	130	132
Facial index		83.6	86.1			82.3	85.3	
Nose length	57	58	54	53	53	55	49	51
Nose width	41	40	36	41	38	37	32	37
Nasal index		68.8	67.4			68.0	66.0	
Sample size	93	540	247–727	534–961	142	157	211	759–928

[1]Pollitzer *et al.* (in preparation).
[2]Sullivan, '20.
[3]Hrdlicka, '25.
[4]Herskovits, '30.

Catawba Indian hybrid. Utilizing 11 alleles (R°, Fy^a, R¹, r, M, O, A, R², S, P¹, Jk^a) he computes 55% White, 6% Negro, and 39% Indian admixture. If only those six alleles which yield the best discrimination are used, Roberts finds approximately 50% Indian and 50% White. Elston (Personal communication) with his modified maximum likelihood method for all alleles finds 59% White and 41% Indian admixture in the Catawba. Thus, genetic analyses confirm the subjects' own statements and the impression from their appearance that the remnant of the Catawba Indians today are about equally White and Indian in ancestry.

The Catawba may be compared with certain living populations for whom the same physical measurements are available on large samples of both sexes: Seminole Indians of Florida (manuscript in preparation), "Pure" Sioux and closely related Indian tribes of the Plains measured by Sullivan ('20), Hrdlicka's ('25) Old White Americans of English derivation, and the American Negro measured by Herskovits ('30). Stature, head, face, and nose dimensions, and indices, are shown in Table 5. In stature and head length the Catawba are most similar to the Sioux; in face dimensions they are very close to both Seminoles and Sioux; in nose dimensions they are similar to the Negro and to both Indian populations. Mahalonobis et al. ('49) have devised a measurement of "generalized distance" or D^2, the degree of dissimilarity between populations, utilizing correlations between traits as well as the difference in the means of those traits but no indices. The correlations he found among the peoples of India, being complete and fundamentally similar to those in other populations studied, are used here. The results of this analysis, comparing Catawba Indians with Seminole Indians, Sioux Indians, Old White Americans, and American Negroes, are shown in Table 6. The smaller numbers imply a closer similarity of the Catawba to Seminole and Sioux Indians and to American Negroes than to the Old White Americans, a conclusion not completely in line with that from their serology or appearance.

TABLE 6. *Summary of Distance Between Catawba Indians and Other Living Populations Based on Seven Measurements*.

	MALES	FEMALES	AVERAGE
Seminole Indians	3.00	3.21	3.10
Sioux Indians	3.00	4.26	3.63
White Americans	11.78	7.69	9.74
American Negroes	3.69	2.78	3.24

*Stature, head length, head breadth, face length, face breadth, nose length, nose width.

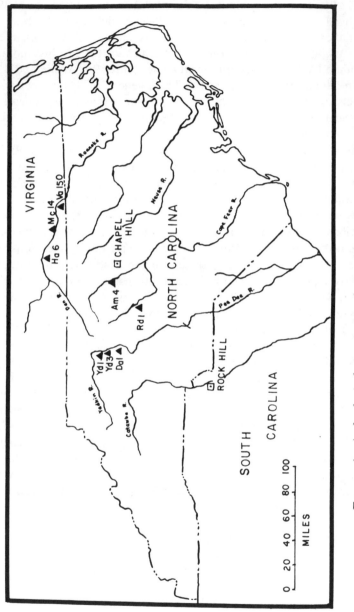

FIGURE 1. *Archeological sites in North Carolina and southern Virginia.*

Ancient Indian sites with skeletal remains are shown on the map, Figure 1. Ha6 is the Tolliferro site in Virginia probably occupied by Occaneechi from 1500–1600 A.D. Yd1 along the banks of the Yadkin River in North Carolina was occupied in a similar period by Tutelo. Mc14, the Clarksville site in Virginia, is Occaneechi dated 1600–1675. Am4 in Alamance County, North Carolina, was probably occupied by Occaneechi for a similar time space. Rd1 is the Keyauwee site, occupied from 1650 to 1725 by this tribe who are closely affiliated with the Catawba. Va150, a Virginia site dating from this same period, is non-Siouan and shows signs of non-Indian admixture and of spyhilis.

Physical measurements possible on the remains from these sites, and indices calculated therefrom, plus those from the Shell Mound people who lived in Indian Knoll, Kentucky, around 3000 B.C., are presented in Table 7. The measurements are used in the subsequent D^2 analysis. Shown in the right hand column are measurements on the living Catawba, corrected for skin thickness based on Krogman's ('62) summary: 10 mm subtracted from head length, head breadth, and face breadth; 6 mm subtracted from face length; and nose width estimated as three fifths that in the living. Stature and nose length are uncorrected. Both the Ha6 and Yd1 materials show similarity to the ancient Indian Knoll population. The corrected living Catawba show resemblance to these Shell Mound people and to the remains at the Yadkin and Clarksville sites. The Yadkin, Clarksville, and Tolliferro people also show shallow nasion depression, like the living Catawba.

"Distance" was computed between the corrected Catawba and those populations with adequate skeletal remains. The results of this analysis shown in Table 8, confirm the morphological similarity of the Catawba to the Yadkin people. Ha6 and Mc14 remains are not too far removed, especially if males only are considered, and the Shell Mound people appear in a similar position.

Of bones of 26 individuals for whom adequate ABO blood typing was possible, all appear to be in Group O, except two which suggest appreciable Group A activity. Negative results from the typing of soil samples in the area of the bones are significant. The apparent absence of Group B and the preponderance of Group O are in line with blood group frequencies of most living Indian populations.

Discussion and Conclusions

The current study suggests that, despite wide fluctuations in population size of the Catawba throughout their recorded history, the serological genes provide a good indication of the degree of admixture of

TABLE 7. *Morphology in Ancient Populations.*

Males

	Oh2 INDIAN KNOLL, KY. 3000-5000 BC SHELL MOUND	Yd1 YADKIN, N. C. 1500-1600 AD TUTELO	Ha6 TOLLIFERRO, VA. 1500-1600 AD OCCANEECHI	Mc14 CLARKSVILLE, VA. 1600-1675 AD OCCANEECHI	Am4 ALAMANCE, N. C. 1600-1675 AD OCCANEECHI	Rd1 KEYAUWEE, N. C. 1650-1725 AD CATAWBAN	Va150 MECKLENBURG, VA. 1650-1725 AD MIXED	LIVING CATAWBA*
Stature	1648	1622	1680	1730			1741	1716
Cranial length	179	182	182	182		183	182	182
Cranial width	135	137	137	143		135	132	143
Cranial index	75.8	76.2	75.9	80.1		73.8	73.3	
Face length	119	115	117	118			121	122
Face breadth	136	136	135	143			137	135
Facial index	86.9	83.6	86.8	82.4			89.2	
Nose length	51	50	50	54			52	56
Nose width	24	26	24	26			28	25
Nasal index	48.0	51.9	49.0	47.3			52.2	
Sample size	260	17	10	11		1	5	17

TABLE 7. *Morphology in Ancient Populations* (Continued).

	Oh2 INDIAN KNOLL, N. C. 3000-5000 BC SHELL MOUND	Yd1 YADKIN, N. C. 1500-1600 AD TUTELO	Ha6 TOLLIFERRO, VA. 1500-1600 AD OCCANEECHI	Mc14 CLARKSVILLE, VA. 1600-1675 AD OCCANEECHI	Am4 ALAMANCE, N. C. 1600-1675 AD OCCANEECHI	Rd1 KEYAUWEE, N. C. 1650-1725 AD CATAWBAN	Va150 MECKLENBERG, VA. 1650-1725 AD MIXED	LIVING CATAWBA*
Females								
Stature	1550	1561	1600	1600	1477	1524	1726	1612
Cranial length	172	172	180	175	162		174	174
Cranial width	132	131	130	136	144		132	136
Cranial index	76.3	75.9	72.5	77.7	88.8		75.9	
Face length	110	107	106	106	103		112	111
Face breadth	127	123	124	127	133		130	127
Facial index	87.0	90.7		83.4	79.2		86.8	
Nose length	48	48	50	49	50		50	51
Nose width	24	22	25	26	24		29	28
Nasal index	50.2	46.5	50.3	53.1	47.0		58.0	
Sample size	211	7	5	10	2	1	5	30

*Appropriate mm have been subtracted from the measurements of the living Catawba of the present study to approximate bone measurements. See text.

(All measurements, but not indices, were used in the computation of D^2 or generalized distance.)

441

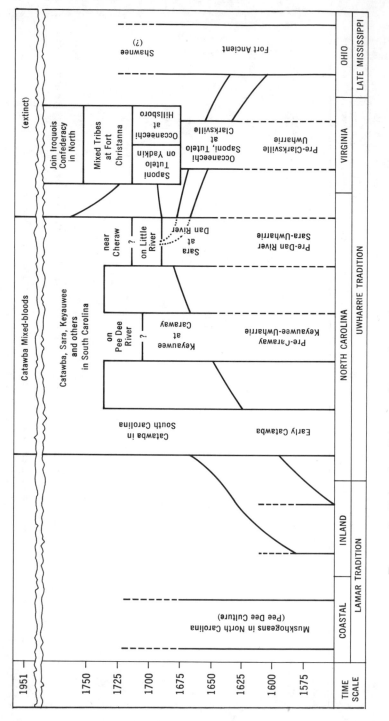

FIGURE 2. *Cultural traditions and interrelationships in the eastern Siouan area.*

442

the Indians with others, namely about 50% White. Opportunities for Indian-White unions existed from Colonial days. The conversion of the Indians to the Mormon religion in the nineteenth century affected their social status. Neighboring Whites, at first opposed to Mormonism, were impressed with its emphasis on work, abstinence, and moral respectability. The Mormon view that Indians, while lower in status than Whites, are above Negroes and will someday become "a white and delightsome people," appealed to the Indians, reinforced traditional Southern racial attitudes, and probably increased Indian-White marriages (Hicks, '64).

TABLE 8. *Summary of Distance Between Catawba Indians and Skeletal Populations based on Seven Measurements**.

	MALES	FEMALES	AVERAGE
Oh2, Indian Knoll, Ky.	8.01	6.35	7.18
Yd1, Yadkin, N. C.	8.78	2.52	5.65
Ha6, Tolliferro, Va.	5.60	10.86	8.23
Mc14, Clarksville, Va.	5.73	8.90	7.32
Va150, Mecklenburg, Va.	14.99	28.18	21.59

*Stature, head length, head breadth, face length, face breadth, nose length, nose width.

Analysis of metrical data does not appear to bear out Indian-White admixture; if other traits, such as hair form and skin color, were also used in the computation, the estimate would no doubt be improved. The "parental populations" chosen are not identical for the two methods. While the living Catawba show similarity to protohistoric tribes in physical measurements, they are taller than most of the populations. This increase in stature, and possibly the slight increase in nose length, may reflect changes in nutrition. It is quite possible that despite linguistic similarities, the Sioux of the Plains are not closely related to those of the Southeast. Although Mooney (1894) suggested that the Western Sioux had originally come from the Southeast, and Swanton ('36) thought that both Eastern and Western Sioux had migrated in recent centuries from an Ohio Valley homeland such as that represented by the Fort Ancient people, Neumann ('52) maintains on skeletal evidence that the Siouan language was taken over in the northern Plains by Prairids of mixed origin from the more ancient Iswanid people of the East. The Catawba are probably as closely related to the Seminoles of Florida as they are to any living Indian tribe.

Coe ('52), who has dug most deeply into the archeology of North Carolina, classifies the cultural sequence of the Piedmont into three stages. Formative before clay vessels goes back 10,000 years; Developmental is characterized by pottery and agriculture extending from the 500's to the 1500's A.D.; and Climactic lasts from 1550 to 1750. At the beginning of the Developmental, the people of the Badin Focus, physically similar to those of Indian Knoll, are probably the direct ancestors of the Siouan. During the late Archaic there was also a high degree of similarity between the cultures of the Southern Piedmont and those of Indian Knoll. The bearers of the later Uwharrie Focus, beginning about 1200, are definitely ancestral to the Siouan.

Ceramic traditions in the Eastern Siouan area, taken from the thesis of Lewis ('51) are shown in Figure 2. He suggests that the Catawba lost their Uwharrie ceramic traits to a Lamar influence from Georgia in the early sixteenth century. While Fort Ancient people had trade relations with the Siouan people of the Carolinas, they could not have been ancestral to the Catawbas. If Siouan tribes migrated from the Ohio Valley it must have been millenia ago. The present study is consistent with kinship between the Shell Mound people, the Tutelo on the Yadkin, and Occaneechi as found at Clarksville, and the mixed Catawba who have persisted to the present day.

References

CANDELA, P. B. 1940. Reliability of blood group tests on human bones. Am. J. Phys. Anthrop., *27:* 365–381.

CEPPELLINI, R., M. SINISCALCO and C. A. B. SMITH. 1955. The estimation of gene frequencies in a random-mating population. Am. J. Hum. Genet., *20:* 97–115.

COE, J. L. 1952. The cultural sequence of the Carolina Piedmont. In: Archeology of Eastern United States. J. B. Griffin, editor, Univ. of Chicago.

ELSTON, R. 1966. Personal Communication.

GATSCHET, A. S. 1900. Grammatic sketch of the Catawba language. Amer. Anthrop., *2:* 527–549.

HALE, H. 1883. The Tutelo tribe and language. Proc. Amer. Phil. Soc., *XXI:* 114.

HICKS, G. L. 1964. Catawba acculturation and the ideology of race. Symposium on new approaches to the study of religion. M. Spiro, editor, Proc. of Amer. Ethnol. Soc., 116–124.

HOYME, L. E., and W. M. BASS. 1962. Human skeletal remains from the Tolliferro (Ha6) and Clarksville (Mc14) sites, John H. Kerr Reservoir Basin, Va., River Basin Surveys Papers no. 25, Bureau of American Ethnology, Bulletin 182.

HERSKOVITS, M. J. 1930. The Anthropometry of the American Negro. Columbia Univ. Press, New York.

HRDLICKA, A. 1925. The old Americans. Williams and Wilkins, Baltimore.

KROGMAN, W. M. 1962. The Human skeleton in forensic medicine. Charles C Thomas, Springfield.

LEWIS, E. 1951. The Sara Indians, 1540–1768; an ethno-archeological study. Unpublished thesis. Chapel Hill, N. C.

LIEBER, OSCAR M. 1858. Vocabulary of the Catawba language. Collections of the South Carolina Historical Society, *II:* 327–342.

MAHALONOBIS, P. C., D. N. MAJUMDAR and C. R. RAO. 1949. Anthropometric survey of the United Provinces, 1941: a statistical study. Sankya, *9:* 89–324.

MATSON, G. A. 1941. Distribution of blood groups among the Sioux, Omaha and Winnebago Indians. Am. J. Phys. Anthrop., *28:* 313–318.

MOONEY, J. 1894. The Siouan tribes of the East. Bureau of American Ethnology, Bulletin, *22:* 1–101.

MORGAN, L. H. 1870. Indian migration. The North American Review, *110:* 33–82.

NEUMANN, G. K. 1947. Skeletal remains from Keyauwee. Manuscript. Research Laboratories of Anthropology. University of North Carolina.
———. 1952. Archeology and race in the American Indian. In: Archeology of Eastern United States. J. B. Griffin, ed., Univ. of Chicago.

POLLITZER, W. S. 1958. The Negroes of Charleston (S. C.); a study of hemoglobin types, serology, and morphology. Am. J. Phys. Anthrop., *16:* 241–263.

POLLITZER, W. S., R. C. HARTMAN, H. MOORE, R. E. ROSENFIELD, H. SMITH, S. HAKIM, P. J. SCHMIDT and W. C. LEYSHON. 1962. Blood types of the Cherokee Indians. Am. J. Phys. Anthrop., *20:* 33–43.

RACE, R. R., and R. SANGER. 1962. Blood Groups in Man. Fourth Edition. F. A. Davis Co., Philadelphia.

ROBERTS, D. F., and R. W. HIORNS. 1962. The dynamics of racial intermixture. Amer. J. Human Genetics, *14:* 261–277.

SIEBERT, F. T. 1945. Linguistic classification of Catawba: Part I. International J. of Amer. Linguistics, *11:* 100–104.

SIGMON, B. A. 1963. A preliminary investigation of the skeletal material from six Roanoke River Basin sites. Unpublished honor's thesis. Chapel Hill, N. C.

SNOW, C. E. 1948. Indian Knoll skeletons of Site Oh2, Ohio Co., Ky. Univ. of Ky. Reports in Anthrop. and Arch. Vol. 4, no. 3, pt. 2: 371–555.

SOLOMON, J. M., R. WAGGONER and W. C. LEYSHON. 1965. A quantitative immunogenic study of gene suppression involving A_1 and H antigens of the erythrocyte without affecting secreted blood group substances. The ABH phenotypes A^h_m and O^h_m Blood, *XXV:* 470–485.

SPECK, F. P. 1938. The question of matrilineal descent in the Southeastern Siouan area. Amer. Anthrop., *40:* 1–12.

SULLIVAN, LOUIS R. 1920. Anthropometry of the Siouan tribes. In: Anthrop. Papers of the Amer. Mus. of Nat. History, *XXIII:* 81–174.

SWANTON, J. R. 1936. Early history of the Eastern Siouan tribes. In: Essays in anthropology presented to A. L. Kroeber, Univ. of Cal. Press, Berkeley.

———. 1953. The Indian tribes of North America. Bureau of Amer. Ethnology. Bulletin, *145:* 90–92.

UNITED STATES BUREAU OF THE CENSUS. Reports of 1940, 1950 and 1960.

VOEGELIN, C. F. 1941. Internal relationships of Siouan languages. Amer. Anthrop., *43:* 246–249.

INDEX